UNPUBLISHED STORIES

STORIES

EDITED BY BRIAN HERBERT
AND KEVIN J. ANDERSON

D1600523

UNPUBLISHED STORIES

EDITED BY BRIAN HERBERT
AND KEVIN J. ANDERSON

FRANK HERBERT

AUTHOR OF DUNE

WordFire Press
Colorado Springs, Colorado

ISBN: 978-1-61475-408-4

Cover design by Janet McDonald

Art Director Kevin J. Anderson

Cover artwork images by Dollar Photo Club

Book Design by RuneWright, LLC
www.RuneWright.com

Published by
WordFire Press, an imprint of
WordFire, Inc.
PO Box 1840
Monument CO 80132

Kevin J. Anderson & Rebecca Moesta, Publishers

WordFire Press Trade Paperback Edition May 2016
Printed in the USA
wordfirepress.com

Contents

BURIED TREASURE

THE UNPUBLISHED SHORT STORIES OF FRANK HERBERT

Even the author of *Dune*—the best-selling science fiction novel of all time—had trouble getting published. At first. Frank Herbert wanted to be a writer, and though today his name is practically synonymous with worldbuilding and epic science fiction, Herbert didn't start out with a particular genre in mind. He wrote mainstream stories, mysteries, thrillers, mens' adventure pieces, humorous slice-of-life tales, and, yes, some science fiction.

In his early years, Herbert faced many rejections. His submissions came close-but-not-quite at magazine after magazine. Frank Herbert was an inspired writer with an unpredictable muse. He wrote what he wanted to write, about the characters and the situations that struck his fancy, paying very little attention to the market or the requirements of the magazines to which he submitted.

As a result, his stories were often the wrong length—too short to be released as a novel but too long for traditional periodicals. Magazines liked his work but could not use it. His agent also had a frustrating time finding a home for Herbert's work.

And yet he kept writing.

Finally, in 1956, he found success, placing his novel *The Dragon in the Sea* with Doubleday, which received wide critical acclaim and made him a writer to watch.

So Herbert wrote another novel … which he couldn't get published. And another novel, and more short stories, and other novels. He kept trying, with his subjects wandering all over the map, until finally he wrote *Dune*, which was possibly the most unpublishable SF novel of all, rejected more than twenty times before it was finally released by a house that specialized in auto repair manuals.

And eventually, that novel made him a world-famous author.

In Frank Herbert's files, we found the completed and polished manuscripts for four novels—*High Opp*, *Angels' Fall*, *A Game of Authors*, and *A Thorn in the Bush*—all of which have been released, as Herbert wrote them, from WordFire Press.

We also found the submission manuscripts for thirteen completed short stories, all of which failed to find a home in the magazines of the day. This volume collects all those previously unpublished stories, including the mystery/thrillers "The Yellow Coat," "The Heat's On," "The Wrong Cat," and "The Little Window"; humorous mainstream stories "The Illegitimate Stage," "Wilfred," and "The Iron Maiden"; serious mainstream stories "The Cage" and "A Lesson in History"; South Sea adventure stories "Paul's Friend" and "The Waters of Kan-E"; and science fiction tales "Public Hearing" and "The Daddy Box."

Readers can now appreciate the writing of one of the field's masters in a kaleidoscope of stories that have not previously seen print. Enjoy.

—Brian Herbert and Kevin J. Anderson

MAINSTREAM

THE CAGE

Davis straightened the diagonal fold in the blanket at the foot of his hospital bed, smoothing the U.S.N. initials. He knew the corpsman, Blackie, was standing behind him, and Davis wondered if he'd be able to take it as he'd seen some of the others do. He'd seen it coming in the corpsman's small, close-set eyes—the way they watched out of the corners—and the sadistic twist of the mouth that smiled without showing teeth. Davis knew he was lucky to have stayed in the ward three days without getting it sooner. "Seventeen" was notorious: Igor Blackston ran it on fear, and he seemed to have a sixth sense to tell him which of the "observation cases" would not rebel at his treatment.

Out of the corner of his eye, Davis watched the corpsman's feet advancing, and the fear began to rise. Blackie leaned over to examine the bed. That was the way it always started. Criss-crossed shadows from the barred window at the head of the bed framed one eye in the corpsman's square face. This man was all dark corners, Davis thought.

"A lousy job!" Blackie said. He ripped the blankets off the bed. "Do it again—right this time."

Turning, he placed a heel on Davis' slippered left foot, grinding it deliberately. Davis screamed. Blackie lifted his foot and turned back. He put his right hand to his chin as though pondering some question. "Oh, did I step on your foot? I'm sorry." The right hand described a short arc and cracked against

Davis' jaw, staggering him back onto the bed.

"Don't scream," Blackie said. "It gives people the wrong idea. Only crazy people scream."

Davis clenched his fist and started to push himself off the bed. Out of the corner of his eye he saw two others, the red-haired corpsman and the stocky one they called Shorty, moving down the passage between the beds. Suddenly Davis realized they were afraid of Blackie, too. But Blackie was in charge here.

"Don't get tough," Blackie said. "We'd have to restrain you."

Davis waited, and the others paused.

"If the bed isn't made when the chow cart comes through, you don't eat," the corpsman said, and turned away.

Lifting the covers off the floor, Davis shook the spread free and placed it over the back of his chair. He took a blanket and threw it over the bed. As he smoothed it, he saw the occupant of the next bed standing at the foot.

"Just take it," the other said. "It's easier that way."

The chow cart banged against the outside bars as Davis finished. He looked up. The corpsmen gathered at the head desk apparently weren't paying any attention to him. He stepped to the foot of the bed and waited his turn. The cart was pushed through the doors, and Blackie took up the ladle. That was a bad sign. The head corpsman didn't have to do the menial work. When the cart came up, Davis took a spoon, picked a bowl, and held it out. Blackie dipped a small portion of mush into the ladle and upended it into the bowl, poured a few drops of milk over it, and moved on. Davis compressed his lips and remained silent. He knew better than to reach for a cup of coffee or one of the halved grapefruits. He'd seen the young marine across the ward try it yesterday. Blackie'd sent the boy out back to the loony ward last night.

Blackie pushed the cart on up the line, stopping at each bed to give the others a complete breakfast. Davis, watching the corpsman, noticed that Blackie never turned his back on any of the patients, and when he stopped to serve the big Negro at the head of the ward, he stayed on the opposite side of the cart. "Blackie's afraid," he thought.

After breakfast, Davis moved over and took his place in the line at the shaving stand. The clang of the inner door brought his head around. A corpsman stood outside the bars with a sheaf of papers. Blackie opened the door and took the papers.

A cuff on his arm brought Davis around. Shorty was holding out a razor and one of the tiny shaving cream tubes. Automatically, Davis took the razor and tube. He stepped into the washroom and found an unoccupied bowl and mirror. The day's growth of beard made his cheeks appear hollow. "More of their program to lower morale," he thought: "let you shave only every other day." His eyes were bloodshot under their thin brows. He put a hand to his head where the cargo hatch had hit him. It still felt tender after all these weeks. Funny they'd stick him in a place like this just because he was hit on the head ... take all his clothes, censor his mail, even light his cigarettes for him because he couldn't have matches.

Looking sideways, Davis saw the eyes of the man beside him staring back from the mirror. Their wild light suddenly made him glad the corpsman was watching from the door. He opened his shaving cream tube and began to lather his face.

After returning the razor, Davis headed for the magazine rack. If he could read for a while, maybe he could forget these sadistic bastards. He debated whether or not it would be wise to try to talk to the doctor. Then he wondered why no one else had ever talked. The white walls of the ward seemed too close to him. He shook his head.

"Davis!"

Blackie was sitting at the desk by the inner door. "Come here," he said.

Davis walked up to the desk and stood before it, pulling his bathrobe tighter around him.

"You're up for X-ray today," the corpsman said. "Be ready at ten thirty."

Nodding his head, Davis turned away.

"When I'm through talking to you, I'll let you know." Blackie's voice was low. Davis turned back and saw that the corpsman was standing.

"I just wanted to warn you against telling any funny stories while you're outside. It'd be easy for me to turn in a report that you have a persecution complex. Know what that means?"

Davis remained silent.

"That means you'd be diagnosed as a paranoid. They'd send you up the river to Bethesda and a nice, quiet padded cell. You'd think this cage was heaven." He paused. "Don't forget it. That's all." He waved the back of his hand toward Davis to signify that he was finished.

At ten thirty, Shorty came down the bed line with a sheaf of papers. "Emlot, Davis, Granowski, Parker, come with me."

Davis took his place with the others and followed the corpsman outside. They went up the disinfectant smelling hall, climbed some stairs, down another hall, and sat on a bench outside a door marked "X-ray Lab." Davis went in after Emlot. The impersonal technician ordered him up nude on a bare table and set his head for the picture.

In the chill of the room, with his skin against the cold slab, Davis felt as if this was the way he'd appear on a morgue slab. He pushed the thought out of his mind. Those sons of bitches had him thinking like a crazy man.

When the X-rays were completed, the corpsman led them downstairs again and rapped for the outer door of the cage to be opened. He held Davis' arm and allowed the others to pass through.

"You gotta see Doctor Knauffer," he said.

They went down another hallway and through the fracture ward. Davis wondered if the patients in here knew he was from Seventeen. They didn't seem to be paying any particular attention. At the end of the ward was an office with a lettered board across the door: "R.J. Knauffer, Lieut. Comdr., MC, U.S.N." The corpsman rapped twice.

"Come in," a voice said.

Davis entered and sat down on a chair opposite the tailored neatness of the doctor. He felt out of place in the bathrobe.

A full-toothed smile passed across Doctor Knauffer's tanned face. He raised his manicured hands and steepled them before him, elbows resting on the desk.

"Do people pick on you or talk about you behind your back?" he asked.

Davis felt his body grow chill. What had that son of a bitch Blackie said?

"No ... no, sir."

Doctor Knauffer glanced down at a paper between his elbows.

Was that the ward report?

The doctor looked up. "Have you ever been hit on the head before?"

"A couple of times, sir. When I was a kid I was hit with a baseball. And a girl beaned me with her books once."

Doctor Knauffer smiled. "Well, you see, what bothers us is that you fainted after being discharged from sickbay and sent back to duty. I went to school with Doctor Logan and have every confidence in his diagnosis. There really was no reason for you to faint unless ..." The doctor lowered his hands and picked up the papers. "Are you certain you fainted? After all, the navy does get tiresome at times, and a good rest in a hospital ..."

Davis felt the fear tightening his throat, constricting his chest. What were they trying to do to him? He hadn't asked to come here. "I ... I guess I really fainted, sir."

"You guess you fainted, but you're not certain. Is that it?"

"Sir, I passed out."

"Have you ever spent much time in a hospital before?"

"No, sir."

"I find from the report here that you were in sick bay on the *Ajax* for three days after you were hit by the hatch."

"That isn't very long, sir."

The doctor's face hardened. "No, it isn't. Well, you go back to your ward, and we'll wait until we see the pictures. They'll be down shortly."

Davis stood up. "Uh, doctor ..."

"Yes." Doctor Knauffer already was going on to other papers.

"I wonder if it would be possible for me to get transferred to another ward?"

The doctor looked up sharply. "Why do you want to be transferred?"

"Why, I ... uh ..."

"Are you certain no one is picking on you—the corpsmen, for instance?"

"Oh, no, sir. They're very good to me."

"I see. Well, why do you want a transfer?"

"It's just that I don't like the atmosphere in there, sir … all of the …"

"I'm sorry, but you'll have to stand that atmosphere for at least a week. We have to make a thorough check on you."

Back in the ward, Blackie caught his arm as he came through the door. "And what did we tell the doctor this morning?" he asked.

Davis was pleased to notice the fear in Blackie's eyes. He stifled the urge to give a flip answer. "I didn't tell him anything."

Blackie brought up his knee and caught Davis in the groin. Davis collapsed on the floor with his leg doubled under him.

"See that you don't," the corpsman said.

Rolling over, Davis started to rise. Through the bars he saw Doctor Knauffer turn the corner down the hall and come striding toward the cage. Davis stood up and hobbled toward his bed.

Doctor Knauffer rapped on the bars and the corpsman in the middle cage pushed the buzzer for the outer door. The doctor paused at the head desk a moment, talking to Blackie, then made his way down the aisle to Davis' bed.

"I saw you on the floor as I came down the hall," he said. "What happened?"

Davis looked up and saw Blackie's eyes on him. Did he dare tell the doctor the truth? Blackie's eyes were unwavering.

"I tripped, sir."

"Tripped? On what?"

"On my slippers, sir."

"Oh? Blackston said you seemed to fall down in a faint, but that you got right back up, so he didn't assist you. Has there ever been any epilepsy in your family?"

Again Davis felt the chill. Why wouldn't they leave him alone and send him back to duty? A fellow could take that out there, but not this.

"I asked you if there's ever been any epilepsy in your family," the doctor repeated.

"Huh? Oh. I don't know, sir."

"Well, I came over to have another chat with you, son. The pictures came down right after you left. They show no fracture.

Frankly, I'm afraid we may have to send you up to Bethesda for further examination unless we can get some ready explanation of your case."

Davis turned his head and looked out the barred window to the other barred windows across the courtyard. "This ... this epilepsy—you think I have it, sir?"

"No, but you could have a mild form—*petit mal.*"

"Is that bad, sir?"

"Well, not too bad. But of course we'd have to discharge you from the service. You understand that such a condition would endanger your shipmates. You might pass out sometime when it was important."

Davis looked up the ward at Blackie. The corpsman was still watching him. "Why not?" he asked himself. "Why not? It'd get me away from these bastards."

"I had a cousin once with epilepsy," he said.

The doctor pounced. "I thought so. Did you ever have these fainting spells before?"

"Off and on, sir."

"Uh-huh. Just as I thought. You know, of course, that you should have told your recruiting officer about this."

Davis nodded.

"Well, I'll have you sent to an out ward tomorrow morning. You'll have to wait several weeks to come up before the board, and then you can go home."

The first thing Davis noticed about the out ward was that it had no bars on the windows. *Maybe the lie was worth it,* he thought. It was good to get out of the bathrobe and into his uniform again, too. The corpsman in the office at the end of the ward smiled at him. "Take lower eight," he said. "You're in the port watch—cleaning detail every other day. You start tomorrow. The bulletin board is right around that corner. Your name will be posted the day before your survey date."

Davis went down the ward, found bunk eight, and hung his sea bag from the headpost. He sat down on the bunk and tried the springs. Then he thought of the "No sitting on beds" order in Seventeen. He looked around. Men were sitting on their bunks all up and down the ward. He felt like crying.

The following morning when he returned from the chow hall, Davis found the bulletin board and examined the mimeographed sheet with the names of the men who would come up before the survey board the next day. The names were in purple ink in long, even rows. For ten days he studied the sheet every morning. On the tenth day, a Friday, he found his name fourth from the top in the middle row: "Davis, Charles, S1c." He went back to his bunk and began putting his sea bag in order.

There was no elation in Davis when he awoke the next morning. He was nervous. What if there'd been a slip? What if they'd written his folks and gotten some wrong answers? He walked over to the main building a half hour early and joined the group waiting on a bench outside the board room. The others appeared nervous, too. "This is it," someone said. There was a ripple of tight laughter.

Davis hoped he wouldn't see Blackie. This was in the same wing as Seventeen, but maybe he'd be lucky. Then his name was called, and he stepped through the mahogany door. Blackie sat at a desk just inside the door. Five doctors were in a circle around a table in the center of the room. Doctor Knauffer was in the middle on the far side of the table.

Stepping forward, Davis stood at attention.

"Have you any objection to being discharged?" Doctor Knauffer asked.

"No, sir." He hoped his voice wouldn't crack.

"Then please sign the papers the corpsman has over there," the doctor said.

Davis remained standing before the table. There should be more to it than this.

"That's all." The doctor gestured with the back of his hand.

Davis turned and stepped over to the table.

Blackie held out a pen and pointed to a line on a paper. Davis signed. Blackie pointed to another line. Again Davis signed. He looked up and his eyes met Blackie's. The corpsman smiled and pointed down to the paper. Davis followed the finger to a single word: "Epilepsy."

O O O

Waiting in the station for the train to take him home, Davis knotted and unknotted the rope on his sea bag. "Well, I'm outta that," he told himself. "I oughta feel great. That's the way I oughta feel."

The dispatcher's loudspeaker came to life: "Chicago passengers! Chicago passengers! Through gate five!"

Davis arose, picked up his sea bag, and joined the crowd jostling and pushing one another across the depot and through the tall, barred gates.

THE ILLEGITIMATE STAGE

From the outside, it was a peaceful scene—six green-and-white houseboats moored along the east bank of the Wallan River in the shadow of a steel bridge. The houseboats nestled against a weathered gray boardwalk. Between the boardwalk and the riverbank grew cattails and marsh grasses.

The jade-colored curtains on the first houseboat's riverside windows snapped back. The dark face of a young man appeared at the window, scowling out at the morning sunlight. Without turning his head, he spoke to the slim blonde woman seated at the kitchen table behind him.

"It was your crazy idea in the first place!"

The woman turned her narrow, sensitive features toward the man's back, drawing her brows down.

"Roger Corot, you stop acting like that! I'm not a child. I just said it for a joke, and you took it up and made everybody believe it."

The man half turned from the window, raised his palms up, and looked toward the ceiling.

"That's right," he said. "It's all my fault. When I'm fired and we're reduced to begging on the street, you can tell your friends, 'Roger did this to me!'"

"Now you're going to be dramatic," she said. "You know you're the one who wants to keep up this Bohemian atmosphere." She gestured around her at the houseboat, an array of bamboo furniture in pastel greens and oranges, a grass mat rug.

Roger hurled himself into a chair opposite the woman, buried his head in his hands. He raised his head, looked across the table. His dark eyes were opened wide; his black hair was disarrayed, curled slightly at the forehead; his voice was deep.

"Pepina!" he said. "Don't destroy me! You know I can't create in a flat. I have to have the soothing atmosphere of life—like the great current of a river around me. Don't do this to me."

"Very poetic," she said. "Now, what about—"

He raised a restraining hand. "Please. If you'd only explain to me why you told everyone we're not married ... Well, perhaps I could understand. If you could only explain it to me."

The woman brought her hands from her lap—long, thin hands on thin wrists. She put her hands over her face, lowered them. In the depths of her green eyes there was a bemused twinkle.

"Roger, for the nine thousand, nine hundred and ninety-ninth time, I was just making a joke. If I had suspected for a moment that you would take me up and make it a great dramatic production—we artists together—I'd have kept my big trap shut, as my father used to say."

She stood up, an emerald housecoat falling gently into place around her. "Now be a good boy and get off to the college. You'll have a whole class full of French students wondering where their instructor is."

Roger stood up, took an English tweed topcoat from the back of an adjacent chair, and draped it over his left arm.

"Yes. And as soon as this story gets back to President Coleman, they'll know where I am—fired!" He leaned across the table. "Why didn't you think of that? You knew the president of the college was the chairman of the Wallan County Anti-Vice League."

Her voice was flat as she replied: "So did you, Roger; so did you."

He shook his head. "Why? Why? Why?"

"Roger!" Pepina stamped her foot. "I've got a *why* for you. You've had two whole years to scotch this story. But no! You have to keep adding to it. You have to brag about it! You haven't explained *that* to my satisfaction."

Roger slumped back into the chair he had vacated, draped the coat over his knees. "I've told you. It's this play."

"Oh, Roger. You know that doesn't make sense."

"Yes, it does. You don't understand this authoress. I will explain it in words of one syllable. This is Mrs. Abelarde Gruntey. She is the widow of Amos Gruntey, who endowed Gruntey Hall. She has written this play. She calls it *Rhythm of Life*. That should tell you enough about it."

Pepina sighed and sat down in her chair. She took an electric coffee pot from the corner of the table, poured herself a fresh cup.

"I've read the play. I know. But I don't understand what all this has to do with your sudden attack of respectability."

"Pepina," he said, drawing out the syllables, "President Coleman wants a new gymnasium from this woman. He ordered me to produce her play. I have to do it. And when we get into production, this female behemoth will be at mine elbow."

He raised his voice. "And sure as fate, one of those dunderhead dramatics students of mine will let it slip to her that we're a pair of sinners, and she'll take it straight to Coleman. I tell you, the jig is up!"

Pepina shrugged her shoulders. "So take him our marriage license and make a fool out of her."

Roger's voice became low and charged with feeling. "But Pepina! I'd never be able to face them again. Never! The … the shine would be all gone off our relationship. This way it's dramatic. It inspires them. When I tell them how to act, they leap to obey. They know I'm right. I have the … the Continental touch."

"Yes," Pepina said, "and a couple of these starry-eyed students will try to follow our supposed example one of these days, and then the fat will really be in the fire."

"Everywhere I turn I see a blank wall," Roger said. "It's fate creeping up on me. I feel like one of those psychological cats in a puzzle box. There's no door out."

"We'll talk about it tonight," Pepina said. She looked up at the Bavarian cuckoo clock above Roger's head. "You're already five minutes late. I love you. All is lost. Scram!"

Roger leaped to his feet. "You have no soul. I love you anyway. Here, kiss me."

He bent down, kissed her lips. As he pulled away, Pepina patted his cheek. "Life is but a series of excursions and alarms," she said. "Now hurry."

Roger stood up, shrugged. "C'est la vie!" He turned, hurried from the houseboat.

Pepina walked after him, stopped at the door, watching. A soft look filled her eyes.

Roger strode briskly up the boardwalk, shrugging into his topcoat.

Under her breath, Pepina said, "You ham!"

From the reeds at the riverbank there came the rumbling basso of a bullfrog.

"Mr. Amonto," Pepina said. "I haven't fed you this morning."

She went into the houseboat, returned in a moment with a handful of bacon scraps. She tossed a piece of bacon toward the muddy bank. There was a splash. A wide green shape with two up-bulging eyes swam majestically out, engulfed the bacon. The frog floated upward until only the eyes protruded from the water. Pepina tossed the rest of the bacon in front of the frog. Mr. Amonto gave a brief kick with his hind legs, caught the first piece, moved on to another.

Pepina returned to the houseboat.

O O O

At east Comity College, President Clinton Coleman was having an early morning conference with Mrs. Gruntey. He sat at his wide mahogany desk in a leather-upholstered swivel chair, now and then turning it from side to side.

On the wall behind the president, a linen sampler hung in a dark oak frame: a little red-and-green house with smoke curling from a chimney. Doves and ivy crowded each other in the top corners. Worked in blue cross-stitch across the center was a motto: "If one ferrets out sin wherever it appears, this will be a better world in which to live."

The remarkable thing about the motto was that President Coleman *did* resemble a ferret. He had beady eyes set close above a long, hooked nose. A thin mouth poised over a long, outjutting chin, ready to pour out vitriol.

Mrs. Gruntey, a contrast in fat, sat clothed in satins and silks, a sable stole over her shoulders. She looked the German housefrau suddenly come into money. Her face was oval. The eyes had avoided the pinch of fat cheeks and now stared out with a round blue clarity at the world. Mrs. Gruntey was telling President Coleman how she had come to write *Rhythm of Life*.

President Coleman, his mind adding up the cost of gymnasium flooring, bleachers, and equipment, nodded from time to time as words buzzed somnolently around him.

"I was in Portland," Mrs. Gruntey said, her voice taking on a dreamy, distant note. "A woman friend just insisted I go with her to see the road show performance of an Italian movie. I didn't want to go. When I think how close I came to not going, I just shudder. I had Lincoln drive me right home afterward. I was so excited I couldn't sleep. Finally, I got up and took out Amos's old typewriter and began my play."

Her voice took on a flat, explanatory tone. "It's an Oliver, you know," she said. "The typewriter. Very old."

The dreamy note crept back into her voice. "I had the title in my mind before I wrote the first word. *The Rhythm of Life*." Her voice lilted over the words; she repeated them. "*The Rhythm of Life*. It has ..." She looked down at her fleshy hands clasped in her lap, brought her hands to her mounded bosom. "It has such vibrations."

President Coleman nodded. "Indeed it has. I never dreamed you were so talented." He kept his eyes raised to the level of Mrs. Gruntey's dyed hair. ("Just a little chestnut tint to bring out the highlights.")

"Your Mr. Corot is so talented," Mrs. Gruntey said. "He knows exactly how it should be staged. I'm certain it's going to be the hit of the Fall Fiesta. The vibrations of my play so fit the mood of the Fiesta."

President Coleman pursed his lips. "It is a proper play, of course."

"It's life," Mrs. Gruntey said. "It has reality; it vibrates with living. You know that place in the third set where ..."

President Coleman coughed. "Well, I've not read that far yet. The responsibilities of my position ... seeing the architects ... You know how it is."

"You really are such a busy man, Mr. Coleman. It's unkind of me to take up so much of your time. I must be running along."

She stood up.

President Coleman arose with her. "Oh, my dear Mrs. Gruntey. Every minute with you is a pleasure. Really. We must get together for tea sometime this week. I want to talk about the new gymnasium."

"I'll check my calendar and call you," Mrs. Gruntey said. "Au revoir!" She raised one fleshy hand. The jeweled fingers flashed and twinkled. The reflected beam from a large diamond flickered into President Coleman's eyes and seemed to lodge there.

Mrs. Gruntey went out the door.

President Coleman sank back into his chair, opened the bottom right-hand drawer of his desk. He extracted Mrs. Gruntey's manuscript from where he had placed it, unopened, the day she had presented it to him. He put the manuscript neatly in the center of the green desk blotter, opened to the first page, made a crease down the fold where he had opened it. He began to read:

"Melissa Corday is a beautiful girl of twenty-two whose mother came over from the old country and has raised her daughter by doing housework for the rich. Melissa is actually the illegitimate daughter of a famous count, but her mother has kept this fact hidden from her daughter for fear it would taint the young mind. For a year before our play opens ..."

"Mustn't taint young minds," he thought.

President Coleman's telephone rang. He put down the play, picked up the telephone. It was the architect for the new gymnasium. The architect wanted to see President Coleman at the gymnasium. President Coleman said he would be there. He stood up, took the manuscript, and carried it out to his secretary.

"Miss James," he said to the spinsterish woman in the outer office. "Read this through and write me a two-page report giving the highlights of it." He put the manuscript on the corner of her desk.

"Yes, Mr. Coleman."

Mr. Coleman turned, marched out of his office, going over in his mind sample ways of presenting to Mrs. Gruntey the fact that there was a twenty-eight thousand dollar deficiency in the gymnasium building fund.

O O O

For Roger, the day passed in a frenzy of French, a dollop of drama, and a stale slab of meat loaf he ate in the Commons for lunch. The meat loaf sat undigested in his stomach all afternoon.

"Mother would have known what to do," he thought. "Pepina is being unreasonable."

Roger's mother had been the wife of a diplomatic attaché. She had guided her son's life toward a career in the ballet. When he was two years old, she had enrolled him with special instructors in Paris. She had nurtured his tantrums, clothed his ego, guarded him from the world and, when he was fifteen, had died. This act of maternal desertion had thrown Roger into his first real contact with a father who was a stranger. The father had solved the problem with a Swiss boarding school. The headmaster's daughter, Pepina, a girl two years Roger's junior, turned out to have such a close physical resemblance to Roger's mother that Roger had substituted love for his grief and resentment.

A result of Roger's ballet training was that he was a graceful man. He walked with the balance of a panther.

As he joined the evening crowds on East Comity's Center Street in his walk toward the houseboat, Roger added an unconscious dance rhythm to the flow of pedestrian traffic. He deposited a coin in a newsboy's hand, accepted a paper without pausing more than a half beat, danced aside to avoid a hurrying woman whose arms were loaded with packages. In the same rhythm, he stepped off the curb, crossed toward Lyttle Street. On the opposite walk, he opened his copy of Mrs. Gruntey's manuscript to the second act, began to read as he walked:

"Melissa takes the baby home to …"

With a thump which sent the manuscript fluttering to the street, Roger collided with a short man who was reading a newspaper.

"So sorry," Roger muttered. "Wasn't looking." He stooped, collected the manuscript.

"Hrrrrmph," the short man said, and walked around Roger.

Roger folded the manuscript under his arm, stood up.

"Boors," he muttered, and strode toward the houseboat.

Pepina, wearing a red peasant skirt and halter and tan ballet slippers, was improvising a ballet to the music of "Death and Transfiguration" when Roger burst into the living room. A tall girl, she reflected the Swiss-Italian beauty of her mother and the blondness of her American father. Her eyes were large, nose slightly overlong, lips full, chin gently rounded.

Seeing Roger, she whirled once, did a deep curtsey.

Roger threw his papers and the play onto a couch, leaped into the center of the room. As Pepina picked up her cue, they executed a pas de deux to the closing strains of the music. The record ended. Roger completed the steps of the dance in such a fashion as to bend over the record player, lift the needle, and shut off the machine all in one fluid motion.

"I perish of hunger," he said, collapsing onto the couch. "Give me your lips and then sweetbreads, perhaps."

Pepina rose to her tiptoes, bent low over Roger, and brushed his lips with hers. Pulling back, she said, "Fish, m'love."

"Fish!" Roger made a face, slid farther down on the couch. "You caught it yourself?"

"At Mulganey's Market," Pepina said.

Roger's outstretched hand touched the manuscript of Mrs. Gruntey's play. He picked it up and leafed through it.

"Don't try to change the subject. We both know there never has been and never will be a person named Mulganey. That is the name of a stew which is fed to starving peasants."

Pepina folded her arms on her breast, lowered her head, said, "My lord knows best."

Without warning she leaped at him, landed in his lap, knocking the copy of the play behind the couch. Their mood dissolved in laughter.

"Was that Mrs. Gruntey's play you were reading?" Pepina rested her head in the curve of Roger's neck.

Roger pushed her away, shuddered.

"Don't mention it before I've eaten. It's hideous. That woman has more money than brains. Unfortunately, her money and the deficiency in the gymnasium building fund appear to have come to some blinding focus in Coleman's pinhead."

Pepina blinked her eyes at him. "You're just tired and hungry."

"And I have to produce the abominable thing."

"The deficiency?" Pepina asked.

"Cease, woman; I shall bite you. President Coleman's command performance must go on!"

Pepina's voice took on a pensive tone. "You know, Roger, I've read the play and …"

"Food!" Roger pushed her off his lap onto the floor. "Come, naiad! Produce the finny brothers you have bewitched from the depths."

"Mulganey's," Pepina said. She stood up.

O O O

After dinner, Roger put on swimming trunks, took a swim in the river from the front porch, and returned to the living room. He sat down, making a damp spot on the straw carpet, and wrapped a towel around his shoulders.

Pepina was on the couch with the play in her hands. Tears of laughter rolled down her cheeks. When she could control herself, she turned to Roger.

"Darling, I'm just reading over some of this thing. This is the most wonderful farce since *Uncle Tom's Cabin*."

"*Uncle Tom's Cabin* wasn't a farce; it was a serious play."

Pepina nodded, a blonde curl falling across her forehead. She puffed out her lower lip and blew it back. "I know. But sometimes seriousness is the most farcical thing in the world, and you must admit *Uncle Tom* is now a delightful farce."

Roger ran a hand through his wet hair and shook the water at Pepina.

"Stop that!" she said.

"If we lampooned that play, the Lady Gruntey would dissolve in the smoke from a burning deficiency." Roger stretched out on the carpet. "Besides, I'm too lazy."

"What're you going to do?" Pepina asked.

"Produce the play. All the time I shall be quaking in my slippers that some egghead doesn't convey your *little joke* to her. Pah!"

"Ro-ger ..." Pepina's voice drew out the name with an ominous tone.

Roger ignored her. "After I have produced this disaster, I shall drink a glass of Chablis and walk quietly off the end of the dock."

"Reciting Shakespeare in a hoarse whisper," Pepina said. "Besides, you couldn't walk quietly off the end of the dock. You'd splash." She leaned toward Roger. "Dear Heart, have you thought of the fact that if you produce this play at all, it'll get nothing but guffaws? It's a caricature of life."

"Mrs. Gruntey is a caricature of life," Roger said. "You remember her. You saw her at last year's faculty tea." He sat upright in a graceful arc. "She speaks of vibrations, and most appropriately. Her whole front vibrates like two bowls of jelly." Again he reclined on the floor.

Pepina slid off the couch, stretched out beside him.

"You'll get wet," Roger said.

"Mmmmmmm," Pepina nibbled at his ear. "Does my own Machiavelli wish a word of advice?" She slid a hand along his cheek and jaw line.

"What?"

"When the audience laughs, watch your authoress and join her. She may want credit for having produced a hit ... intentionally."

Roger jerked to a sitting position. "That thing? A hit?"

He leaned across Pepina and retrieved the play from the couch. "This needs another look."

O O O

The casting of *Rhythm of Life* began the following Friday in an English Department classroom. A temporary stage was created at the end of the room by stretching a length of clothesline across at the level of the window tops and hanging drop cloths at each end.

Roger, Pepina and Mrs. Gruntey—each with a copy of the play—sat in three adjoining chairs about ten feet from the improvised stage. The room lights were turned off. A spotlight set on a table illuminated a junior coed reading Melissa's part.

Mrs. Gruntey leaned her wide bosom across Pepina toward Roger. "She doesn't have the correct rhythms for the part."

"I'm inclined to agree with you," Roger said. "She's too skinny. No chest."

"That dark girl over in the corner," Mrs. Gruntey said. "I like her emanations."

Roger's gaze followed her direction. "Yes, she does have excellent … uh, emanations. She was a supporting player in last year's play. Not quite so nubile then." Roger stood up. "Okay. Okay." He waved the girl into the wings. He turned to the girl in the corner. "Shirley. Take it from where she says, 'Mother, daaaarling.' Skip the stage directions. Just read the part."

The dark girl walked to the stage, taking a copy of the play from the wings.

"Well-developed wench," Pepina said.

"Good emanations," Roger said.

The dark girl began reading in a husky contralto.

Mrs. Gruntey leaned toward the stage. "Excellent! Oh, perfect!"

Roger whispered out of the corner of his mouth to Pepina: "Our methods of selection are different, but we are in surprising accord." He turned to the girl on the stage. "That's it, Shirley. Start learning the part." Turning back to Pepina, he said, "Now we'll pick Leopold. I like Carl Boler, that tall fellow who was talking to Shirley. Remember him from *Macbeth*?" Roger lowered his voice. "Let's hope his rhythms are right."

To the tall, blond student leaning against a wall by a side window, Roger said: "Carl, turn to page nine. Take Leopold from where he says, 'Suppose the brat *is* mine?'"

Mrs. Gruntey turned to Roger, a look of exaltation on her face. "He doesn't have to say a word. I could have chosen him for the part from a crowd of ten thousand. His emanations are positively indecent."

Pepina leaned close to Roger's ear. "Your authoress has an observing eye. Carl must be in a rut."

Carl began reading the part, walking forward of the curtain line.

Mrs. Gruntey again leaned across to Roger. "I know just the costuming he needs," she whispered. "Black tights and a frock coat. A gold chain around his neck to signify that he's rich, and right in the middle of his chest, hanging from the chain, a big gold starburst. I have just the thing on an evening gown."

"A sort of stallion medallion," Roger said. "Good idea."

Pepina giggled.

"For the girl—a red, floor-length gown," Mrs. Gruntey persisted. "And over the bosom, two hands painted on the gown the color of ashes. At the bottom of the gown a rough edge of gray to signify more ashes. A soul burning ..."

Again Pepina whispered in Roger's ear: "Mrs. G. is past her prime, but she has advanced ideas. Me, I'm beginning to think you've misjudged her. I like her."

"Going over to the enemy," Roger whispered.

"I'll see my dressmaker tomorrow," Mrs. Gruntey said. "I believe I have a red gown that could be made over to fit that girl."

"I hope her feelings won't be hurt when they laugh at her play," Pepina whispered. "Invite her down to the houseboat when this is over. I wish to know more of the Lady Gruntey."

O O O

It was past ten o'clock when the chosen cast of *Rhythm of Life*, accompanied by the authoress and Roger and Pepina, descended the steps to the houseboat. At the top of the steps, Mrs. Gruntey's Cadillac and Chinese chauffeur waited in a darkness broken only by a single unshaded streetlight on a telephone pole. Two more unshaded lights strung on thin uprights illuminated the steps.

Mrs. Gruntey held carefully to the handrail as she descended.

"You live in one of those lovely houseboats," she said. "I've seen them so often … from the bridge. So Bohemian looking."

The bottom step creaked in protest as she eased her weight onto it.

At the houseboat, Pepina switched on the lights, swung open the door, stood aside. Mrs. Gruntey stopped in the doorway, halting the procession behind her.

"Just as I had imagined it," she murmured. "Oh, you people don't know how lucky you are. Young … married to someone you love …"

In the background, a member of the cast giggled.

"Married yet!"

Roger drew in a breath sharply, glanced at Pepina. She leaned over and kissed him on the cheek.

"Courage," Pepina whispered.

Mrs. Gruntey moved forward into the houseboat. The others followed.

"Where's some chow?" someone asked. "Pepina, make some sandwiches. We brought the beer."

Roger pulled back a corner of the straw carpet and lifted a trapdoor, which exposed a screened box sunken in the river. "Put the beer in here. There's some down there already cold. We can drink that."

In a corner of the room, a girl put a record on the player. The music of Ravel's "Sacred and Profane Dances" filled the room.

From the kitchen, Pepina shouted, "Turn that thing down. It would wake the dead."

"They should be awake," Roger said. "This is their hour."

Mrs. Gruntey had carefully seated herself on the brilliant orange couch. She looked from one person to another, smiling.

Suddenly, she turned to Roger. "I've never really lived before. I know you …"

The front door of the houseboat burst open. Three of the four independent college students who occupied the next houseboat walked in. They wore bathrobes, slippers, and swimming trunks.

"Sounds like a party," the one in the lead said. "Where's the beer?"

An opened bottle of beer was thrust into his hand. He took a deep drink, wandered over, and sat down beside Mrs. Gruntey.

Mrs. Gruntey beamed upon him. "This is a celebration. We've just completed casting my play."

"You wrote a play?" the student asked. "What's it about?"

"The vibrations of life," Mrs. Gruntey said.

The student looked at her out of the corners of his eyes. "You kidding me?"

Roger had seated himself on the floor beside the couch. He leaned across to Mrs. Gruntey. "It's bad luck to talk about a play to outsiders before it's had its first rehearsal." He turned to the student. "Clam up, weasel!"

Pepina entered with a platter of sandwiches, dodged two students dancing past the kitchen doorway, and in a graceful sweeping motion, put the plate on the floor in the middle of the room.

Roger stretched out on the floor, took two sandwiches from the plate, and handed one to Mrs. Gruntey. Carl, an expression of disdain on his narrow face, came from the corner where he had been talking to two coeds. He sat down beside the trapdoor and began lifting bottles of beer from the box, opening them with an opener tied to a string on the trapdoor. The student beside Mrs. Gruntey took one of the bottles, handed it to her. He clinked bottles with her, spilling foam on her bosom.

"Here's to the success of your vibrations."

"Oh, I know it will be," Mrs. Gruntey said. She tipped up the bottle and drained it in a single swallow.

Roger's eyes bulged. He watched the beer pour down Mrs. Gruntey's throat. Mrs. Gruntey blinked her eyes, held the bottle away from her, and stared at the label, pursing her lips. "Oh, you shouldn't be drinking this," she said. She turned toward the young people in the center of the room. "Would one of you lovely children run up to the top of the steps and tell my chauffeur to get a case of beer from my cellar and bring it down to us?"

One of the students in bathrobe and swimming trunks stood up. "I'll go." He ran out the door.

Mrs. Gruntey turned to Roger. "I like American beer," she said. "Amos had his beer imported from Munich like yours there.

But I can't stomach German beer. I was raised in the Midwest. Amos was my husband, God rest him. May I have another sandwich?"

"We learned to drink German beer in Switzerland," Roger said. He found another sandwich, handed it to Mrs. Gruntey. He stood up, excused himself, and went into the kitchen, where Pepina was making more sandwiches and talking to Shirley. The dark girl had a knife in her tanned hand and was slicing French bread.

"This is terrible," Roger said. "She's turning out to be a human being. And I sneered at her. I feel like the lowest heel of creation."

"Darling, you're drunk," Pepina said.

"Swacked," Shirley said. "Excuse me while I get some more bread."

"No." Roger shook his head. "I've had only one beer." He frowned in concern. "I think I should tell her about her play."

Pepina whirled on him. "And destroy her happiness? I wouldn't let you."

"But ..."

"No!" Pepina stamped her foot.

Roger shook his head from side to side. "There's another thing. She's drinking beer. What if she asks to go to the bathroom?"

"Well...?"

"Your murals."

Pepina grinned at him. "So they're reminiscent of the walls of Pompeii. There are people in this town we don't even know who have bragged about using that bathroom!"

"The test of fame," Roger said. "But she's bound to have some kind of a bad reaction. She couldn't be a pal of old Coldman's without being an anti-vicer."

"Roger, will you stop figuring out things to worry about? You're beginning to make me nervous."

Roger shrugged his shoulders. "One lives; one must expect problems, eh?"

"That's the spirit," Pepina said. "Now go back in there and entertain our guest."

Roger walked back into the living room. The record player blared Boris Godunov. Alexander Kipnis' baritone voice filled the room.

Mrs. Gruntey raised herself from the couch, avoided a dancing couple, and walked over to Roger.

"Pardon me, Mr. Corot," she said. "Where is your washroom?"

Roger stiffened.

A student near the kitchen door heard Mrs. Gruntey. "Whoops!" he said. "Prepare for christening!"

Roger glared at the speaker.

Mrs. Gruntey took no notice. "Your washroom?"

Roger swiveled slowly to the left, pointed. "Down that hallway. First door on your left."

"Thank you."

Mrs. Gruntey entered the shadows of the hall and disappeared from sight, humming "Once Upon a Time in the City of Kazan."

Without looking down, Roger reached out with his left hand, found the arm of an unoccupied chair, and slumped into it. He put his head in his hands.

"Ohhhhhhh," he moaned.

It seemed less than a minute before Mrs. Gruntey reappeared. As she emerged from the hallway, a student took a yellow paper lei from a hook beside the door and looped it over her neck.

"Welcome, oh fellow explorer into the depths of Pepina's washroom," he said. "You win the lei of success for surviving the ordeal."

Everyone in the room except Roger laughed. Roger kept his face in his hands. Pepina appeared in the kitchen doorway, remained silent.

Mrs. Gruntey blushed. She turned to Roger, her eyes wide. "Who did those magnificent murals?"

"Huh?" Roger raised his head.

"Those murals?" Mrs. Gruntey asked.

"Mrs. Gruntey, I ..."

Her words penetrated his consciousness. He fell silent.

"I did them," Pepina said. "They're copies of a Pompeian frieze."

Mrs. Gruntey descended to the chair opposite Roger. "They're so primitive. When Amos and I were on our honeymoon, we visited India. There's a palace ruin beside the Mogul desert. Perhaps you've heard of it—the carvings on its walls ... fertility symbols."

Roger continued to stare at Mrs. Gruntey, his eyes large, his face expressionless.

Pepina sat down on the arm of Roger's chair. "Oh, I've seen them. I visited India with my father. It was the funniest thing. He tried to leave me behind. I was only twelve. I hired my own guide, and he explained everything in great detail. Poor daddy. He was so disturbed when I started asking questions."

"Well, some people call them indecent," Mrs. Gruntey said. She smiled at Pepina. "Somehow I couldn't quite accept that. After all, what is art?"

Pepina nodded.

"I took photographs of the Mogul carvings," Mrs. Gruntey said. "Perhaps you'd like to see them sometime." A reminiscent smile touched her lips. "I had to hide the photographs from Amos. He was a little prudish about some things." Again she looked at Pepina. "But you have such surpassing talent," she said. "Those ..."

She was interrupted by the entrance of the Chinese chauffeur, who was carrying a large box.

As he came through the door, the chauffeur filled it from side to side. He was a squarish man with a face set in the same pattern, broken only by the upslanted eyes. He paused inside the door; his eyes swept around, fastened on Mrs. Gruntey.

"Ah, Lincoln, put it right there in the floor," she said. "Is it cold?"

"Right out of the cellar, madam."

"This is my chauffeur, Abraham Lincoln Li," Mrs. Gruntey said. "I call him Lincoln. He's a great practical humanitarian." She smiled. "Open the case, will you, Lincoln?"

The front door of the houseboat banged open. The student who had taken Mrs. Gruntey's message to the chauffeur entered. He carried a cardboard box.

"Whooof!" he said, putting it down on the floor.

"What in heaven's name is that?" Mrs. Gruntey asked.

"I went along for the ride," the student said. "I noticed a load of grub in your cupboard, so I brought it back. Beer's no good without something to eat."

"You are absolutely right," Mrs. Gruntey said. "Take it out in the kitchen."

Pepina stood up from the arm of the chair. "Here, I'll clear a place for it." She went into the kitchen.

Carl Boler, a copy of Mrs. Gruntey's play in his hands, slouched over beside Roger, taking Pepina's place on the arm.

"Roger, this business in the second act where ..."

"No more shop tonight," Roger said. "Learn the part first." He slumped into the chair.

Mrs. Gruntey turned to Roger. "Your wife has real talent as an artist. How long have you been married?"

Carl laughed. "They're not married. They've got an open agreement, subject to change if either ever wants it. Wonderful thing."

Roger's indrawn breath was like a gasp of shock. He sat, unmoving, in the chair.

Lincoln, having opened the case of beer, stood up and walked to the door. "Will that be all, madam?" he asked.

"Uh ..." Mrs. Gruntey's gaze remained on Roger. "Oh, yes, Lincoln. That will be all for now."

Lincoln gave a silent bow. "Thank you, madam." He reached for the door knob.

The student who had accompanied Lincoln stood up from the beer case with a bottle in his hand. "Hey!" he shouted. "You're not sending him away from the party?"

Mrs. Gruntey tore her gaze away from Roger. A look of agitation crossed her face, was quickly erased. "Of course not. This is a celebration." She looked at Lincoln. "But mind you, Lincoln; you stay sober enough to drive us all home."

Lincoln nodded his dark head toward her. "Of a certainty, madam," he said. "*Chung lun yu tai hyung oh yau hoy*. It is written that a good wheel may do evil."

"Lincoln is a philosopher, too," Mrs. Gruntey said.

Lincoln turned to the student who was holding the bottle of beer. "Here. You have to be careful how you open these. They open like champagne." He put both thumbs to the cap, flipped it off with a loud pop. Foam surged over the top of the bottle. "Shaken up a bit bringing it over," he said. He put the bottle in his mouth and upended it.

"Hey!" the student said. "That's quite a trick. How do you do that with just your fingers?"

Lincoln lowered the bottle and displayed a thumb. "Calluses," he said, and put the bottle back in his mouth.

Mrs. Gruntey looked at Roger.

"You're not married? I could have sworn you were married."

Roger nodded his head.

Pepina returned from the kitchen, slipped an arm under Roger's. "Marriage is for people who aren't in love. We don't need a contract."

Mrs. Gruntey nodded. Her eyes were large, expressionless. "Not married." She looked around at the room full of students.

"They're all over twenty-one," Pepina said.

Mrs. Gruntey looked back at Pepina. "Of course."

From the darkness outside the houseboat, Mr. Amonto, the bullfrog, gave one basso rumble and subsided.

"Good heavens, what was that?" Mrs. Gruntey asked.

"That was Mr. Amonto, our pet bullfrog," Pepina said.

"A pet bullfrog," Mrs. Gruntey murmured. "How delightful." Her voice lacked vitality.

A speedboat roared past in the river close to the houseboats. The houseboat rocked gently. Mrs. Gruntey stood up, walked over to the far side of the room. She stood there, watching the lights of the speedboat as it rushed under the bridge.

Roger looked at Pepina. "Now you've done it," he muttered.

"What's wrong?" Carl asked.

"If she doesn't take that story straight to Coleman, then I'm a monkey's uncle," Roger said. He lowered his head to his hands. "Get me the want ads. Gotta start looking for a job."

Mrs. Gruntey turned from the window, came back to Roger. "It's getting late," she said.

"Is it?" Roger asked.

Pepina walked to the couch and sat down. "Party's over," she said. "Roger, ring the bell."

Roger stood up and disappeared into the back of the house. Soon, a ship's bell echoed over the dark waters. "Lincoln, we'll take anyone home who needs a ride," Mrs. Gruntey said. "See that they're all in the car." She turned to Pepina. "It's been a lovely evening. Thank you so much."

Pepina stood up, shook hands with Mrs. Gruntey. "Certainly."

When all the guests were gone, Pepina wandered back to the couch and sank into it. She stretched out, stared up at the ceiling.

Roger came into the room, sat in a chair near her. Pepina turned her face away. One tear rolled down her cheek. She tasted salt in her mouth. She didn't hear Roger stand up and walk over to the couch.

"Pepina! You're crying! What's wrong?"

Pepina rubbed her eyes dry. "I am not."

He sat down on the couch and put his arm around her. "What's wrong?" he demanded.

"I-I-I l-like that lady."

Roger stared at her. "And that's why you're crying?"

"I'm sorry, Roger. I'm just being silly. But I feel sort of dirty ... oh ... I don't know, not quite respectable or something."

"Oh, darling." Roger kissed her on the ear. "*I* did it. *I* made you cry." He tried to hug her, but she pulled away. "And now I've made you hate me." His voice was melodramatic.

She took his hand. "It's just that, well ... There's something else you don't know ..."

He was alarmed. "What?"

"Oh, never mind. It's just that I'm worried about Coleman and I *do* like Mrs. Gruntey. I hate to have her feel that way about us."

Roger looked away from her, studied the toe of one shoe. Neither spoke.

Suddenly Roger stood up and hit one fist into the palm of the other hand. "I've had enough of it," he said. "I'm going to tell them all we're married. I'll take our marriage license and frame it and hang it on the door."

Pepina sat up on the couch and looked at him. "I won't let you."

Roger started pacing up and down on the straw carpet. "I won't have them talking about my wife," he muttered. "I'll tell all."

Pepina stamped her foot. "You will not! You're just doing it for me; and all you'll do is prove yourself pretty silly. I absolutely won't allow it."

Roger raised himself to his full height. "Nothing you say will stop me!"

Pepina glared back at him. "I won't be married to a fool. If you dare tell ... I'll leave you."

Roger's face crumpled. "Darling, you wouldn't!"

"I would. I won't have you showing yourself up like that and ruining everything for yourself. You will not tell anyone."

Roger turned away from her. He shrugged. "If you put it that way, what can I say?"

Pepina persisted. "Do you promise you won't tell?"

Roger's voice was low and unhappy. "I promise."

O O O

It was the fifth week of rehearsals for *Rhythm of Life*. Life had settled into an uneasy equilibrium. Roger wondered when Mrs. Gruntey was going to President Coleman with the scandal. He decided she was waiting until her play had been produced.

"She's using me," he thought. "I wish I could hate her."

Roger, Pepina, and Mrs. Gruntey were in the first section seats of the campus's Little Theater, where the rehearsals had been moved to give the cast the feel of the stage. It was a musty structure; the seats were hard. If one listened, one could hear the floorboards on the stage creak as the actors walked across them.

The theater was darkened. On stage, the dark-haired Shirley, playing Melissa, and Carl Boler, doing Leopold, were going through a scene for the ninth time. There was a wooden uncertainty about their motions, as though they were afraid to move in a way that had previously aroused Roger's scorn. The actual lighting of the finished scene was being used, although the actors were not in costume. Shirley was wearing slacks and a white blouse. Carl wore dungarees and a blue shirt. The footlights were red, and a purple spotlight was on Shirley. The resultant blend gave a Faustian cast to the setting.

The scene was a boudoir. Props consisted of a settee, dressing table, and chair. Melissa sat at the dressing table. Carl reclined on the settee, jangling his chain and medallion.

In the middle of the scene, Roger leaped to his feet. "Break it!" he screamed.

Shirley stopped in mid-sentence.

Roger sat down, held his head in his hands. After a long pause, he looked up at the silent stage. "The trouble with you, Shirley, is you don't know how to be a bitch."

The dark girl flushed. She jumped up from the chair, upsetting it with a clatter, stalked to the front of the stage. Putting both hands, fists clenched, on her hips, she glared down at Roger. "The trouble with you, Roger Corot, is that you *do* know how to be a bitch!"

Roger leaned back, sighed. "Exactly. *That* is the tone I want in this scene." He leaned forward. "Shirley, does Melissa get the necklace?"

The girl on the stage thought a moment. "No. Of course not."

Roger nodded. "And in this scene she knows she's not going to get it. But she tries anyway. She is angry but tries to hide it." Roger pivoted his head toward Carl, who still reclined on the settee. "And you, you big lump of clay. You're not supposed to be bored. You're amused. You don't want this woman anymore. You're playing with her—cat with mouse." Roger leaned back. "Now roll through it once more, and this time wrap it up. Take it from where Melissa says, 'My neck looks so bare.'"

On stage, the scene began to unfold anew. Roger leaned back, closed his eyes. Suddenly, he sighed, relaxed.

Pepina leaned close to him, whispered in his ear. "All right, darling. I give up."

Roger opened his left eye and looked at her. "Yes?"

"I have been trying for five weeks to figure out something," Pepina said. "You work on a scene and then you seem to listen; but you don't listen to the actors. I can tell. I want to know what it is you hear."

Roger glanced at Mrs. Gruntey, who was bent forward, staring at the stage. He put his mouth close to Pepina's ear, whispered so low, Pepina had to strain to hear. "It's Lincoln. He hasn't missed a rehearsal. He's back there in the rear. I listen for his laugh. When he laughs, the scene's ready."

"How do you know?"

"He's my sample audience."

Pepina listened. From the darkened rear of the theater there came a barely suppressed snicker. Pepina nodded her head, smiled, and slid farther down in her seat.

"You are a faker, my only."

"A successful one," Roger whispered.

Pepina's eyes glistened. She looked at Roger, sighed, and put her head on his shoulder. Roger put a hand up, smoothed her hair.

On stage, the scene ended. Mrs. Gruntey sat back in her seat.

"At last. Roger, you are a genius. I thought that scene would never come right. And it was the last one we really had to work on."

"A matter of finding the correct tone," Roger said.

"Yes, vibrations," Mrs. Gruntey said.

"All we need now are the bumps and grinds," Pepina whispered.

"Did you say something, my dear?" Mrs. Gruntey asked.

Pepina took her head from Roger's shoulder and sat up. "I said we've ground through all the bumps in this one."

"Yes, haven't we?" Mrs. Gruntey said. "Roger, we have only four more nights until we open. I'm so excited I can't sleep at night."

Roger slapped his palms against his knees. "That's it. I think we're all too finely pitched. I'm going to give the cast a two-day rest. We'll have dress rehearsal Thursday and open Friday." He stood up, cupped both hands beside his mouth. "Everybody on stage!"

The cast trouped onto the stage. A switch clicked backstage; the theater lights came to life.

"Well, you're not perfect, but I think you'll do. This is all we're going to do until Thursday-night dress rehearsal. I don't want you going stale before we open. We'll start the final run at six thirty. Be here on time."

Mrs. Gruntey arose, resting her fleshy hands on the back of the seat ahead of her. "I want to have a party Thursday after the rehearsal." She turned to Roger. "May we use the houseboat?"

Roger hesitated. Through his mind raced a cloud of questions: *Why does she want to come to the houseboat? Last time she walked out on us. What is that woman going to do to us now that the play is ready to go?*

On the tip of Roger's tongue was an excuse to avoid the party. Pepina forestalled him.

"Certainly," Pepina said. "The houseboat is the perfect place."

In Roger's mind was the question: "Place for *what?*"

"I'll phone my caterer in the morning," Mrs. Gruntey said. "Don't you worry about a thing. Leave all the arrangements to me."

Roger shuddered.

A student on stage blew Mrs. Gruntey a kiss.

Pepina tugged at Roger's sleeve. Roger whirled and looked down. Pepina was half turned around in her seat, staring at the rear of the theater.

"Who was that?"

Roger looked toward the exit, saw the back of a woman who was walking through the curtained arch at the end of the aisle.

"She was writing in a notebook when I saw her," Pepina said. "She was sitting back there by the end of the aisle. When she looked up, she glared at me and then got up and left."

"It was a rather broad derriere," Roger said. "But I confess it was unfamiliar."

Pepina put a hand to her breast. "I have a premonition." Her voice quavered.

Mrs. Gruntey moved up beside Roger. "Nonsense!"

Roger's face was set in tense lines, nostrils quivering, eyes large. "You don't know Pepina's premonitions. The last time she had a premonition we packed up and left Vienna in exactly twenty-seven minutes. The next day, the *Anschluss*, and Hitler's stormtroopers were rounding up all our friends. We were in Switzerland by that time." Roger shivered. He looked down at Pepina. "It isn't a very big premonition, is it, darling?"

Pepina's eyes were wide and fearful. "Yes. Worse than Vienna."

Roger gasped. "I shall buy some cyanide immediately! They say it is quick."

"Good heavens!" Mrs. Gruntey said.

"I'm fey," Pepina said. "All of the women of my family have been fey."

Mrs. Gruntey's nose quivered. She appeared to be smelling the air around her.

"The vibrations do feel a bit uneasy. I shall call my astrologer immediately when I get home. These things always leave me fluttery until I find out what's going to happen."

"We could make a pact—go out together," Roger said.

"You know, I've seen her face before," Pepina said. She brought the tips of the fingers of her left hand to her forehead and closed her eyes, thinking.

"Off the bridge into the river," Roger said. "A quick death in the depths. Whose face?"

"That woman's face," Pepina said. "They are painting the bridge."

Mrs. Gruntey looked from Roger to Pepina and back to Roger. "Must we give up hope?" she asked.

"You don't know Pepina's premonitions," Roger said. "She had her first when she was thirteen. She kept her father from going to the village of Apari in Switzerland. The next day, an avalanche. Sixty killed. The village destroyed."

"My word!" Mrs. Gruntey stared at Pepina. Suddenly, she squared her shoulders. "Whatever happens, don't give up. That's what Amos always said. If you're at the bottom, there's no place to go but up."

"Like on a roller coaster," Pepina said, brightening.

"Exactly," Mrs. Gruntey said.

"I had a friend killed on a roller coaster once," Roger muttered. "Come, Pepina, let us go home and prepare for the end."

"I can't let you go like this," Mrs. Gruntey said.

Roger turned away from her, walked out to the aisle. Pepina followed. Mrs. Gruntey brought up the rear, wringing her hands. Several of the students, seeing the discussion, had come down from the stage.

"What's wrong?" one asked.

"Pepina just had a premonition."

"Ohhhhhhhh."

They had heard about Pepina's premonitions.

"Please, Roger," Mrs. Gruntey said. "At least wait until I've consulted my astrologer."

Roger turned back and stared at her, his eyes seeming to look through her. Mrs. Gruntey shivered.

"Please," she repeated.

"If you must," Roger said. He turned and strode up the aisle, followed by Pepina and Mrs. Gruntey. Several students trailed behind.

At the curtains, Roger turned. The procession behind him stopped.

"Life is but a walking shadow," Roger said. He turned and strode through the curtains, and they fell in place behind him.

O O O

A listless crescent moon dangled over the hills east of the river at eleven o'clock that night. Below the bridge, the lights along the boardwalk illuminated the houseboats. The lapping of water against the float logs, the occasional splash of a jumping fish, and the despondent croaking of Mr. Amonto the bullfrog dominated the night.

The lights of a car came up Lyttle Street above the houseboat. They illuminated the trees on the far bank of the river. The car stopped; its motor was turned off, its lights extinguished. A car door slammed. The wooden clatter of feet hurried down the steps to the houseboats. A rapping sounded at the Corot's door.

Inside the houseboat, a man screamed.

"They've come for us! Run! Hide!" The voice was Roger's.

"Hush, darling," Pepina said. "You're having a nightmare. It's only somebody at the door."

"Storm troopers!" Roger screamed.

"We're in East Comity," Pepina said. "There are no storm troopers. Now be quiet while I answer the door."

Bedsprings creaked. A light came on; feet pattered across the floor. Pepina opened the front door with one hand as she finished buttoning her housecoat with the other. Mrs. Gruntey stood on the porch, Lincoln a dark shadow behind her.

"The worst has happened," Mrs. Gruntey said, and shouldered her way through the door.

Pepina stepped aside, one slender hand at her mouth, her eyes wide.

Lincoln followed, his visored hat held in his hand. "*Juh bun shoo shiah yooi swei bin.* It is in the book that rain follows its own convenience."

"Lincoln is so comforting at times like this," Mrs. Gruntey said.

"Now, perhaps, we can have a little action," Lincoln said.

Roger appeared in the hallway, belting a cerise bathrobe around him. "What is it?"

"The worst has happened," Pepina said. "I knew it. My premonition."

Roger looked at Mrs. Gruntey, who was seating herself in a chair. She looked suddenly old and sad. He thought, *She has found out that her play is a farce. She has come to tell us that Coleman knows all.*

"We are the outcasts of East Comity," Roger said.

Mrs. Gruntey nodded, looked up at Pepina. "It's uncanny … your premonition. They were waiting on my front porch when I arrived home after the rehearsal."

Pepina's mind swayed back to Roger's nightmare.

"Did they have guns?" she asked, leaning forward.

Roger nodded.

Mrs. Gruntey opened her mouth, but no words came out. She looked at Lincoln. "*Wau yeh-shur juh-mah shiahng,*" he said. "My thought follows your thought."

Mrs. Gruntey looked at Roger. Again he nodded. She looked at Pepina. "Guns?" she asked.

"The storm troo …" Pepina said. "Oh, goodness! What am I thinking of?"

"It was a deputation from the Anti-Vice League," Mrs. Gruntey said, drawing down the corners of her mouth with each succeeding word.

Roger staggered, clutched at the door.

Pepina gasped. "That woman! Now I know where I saw her. She's the one who made the college buy the expurgated edition of Spenser's *Faerie Queene.*"

"Mrs. Ellis Trelawney, president of the Women's Puritan League," Mrs. Gruntey said. "Her husband is vice-chairman of the Anti-Vice League. They were both on my porch." Her lips quivered.

"What did they say?" Pepina asked.

"They had an outline of my play. They said they got it from President Coleman. They said such nasty things: 'illegitimacy, sin, children of the devil.' Ohhhhh … they called it indecent."

"I feel faint," Pepina said. "Roger, get me some water." She slumped onto the couch.

Roger slowly turned his head toward Pepina, looked down his nose at her. "With the cyanide?"

"Of course not," Pepina said. She fanned at her face with one hand. "It's so warm."

Roger vanished into the kitchen, then reappeared in a moment with a glass of water, which he held to Pepina's lips. He supported the back of her head with his hand. Pepina looked up at him, a question in her eyes.

"It's just water," Roger said.

Pepina took several sips and relaxed on the couch.

Mrs. Gruntey stood up. Her mouth was drawn into a thin line. Her face was flushed.

"I have ordered President Coleman to meet me here." She stamped her foot. "After all, I do have some influence in this community. We are going to produce my play."

Roger looked forlornly at the glass of water in his hand. "It's just water," he said.

Lincoln, standing by the door, turned and opened it. "I hear somebody coming. Sounds like two people."

Roger walked to the door, looked over Lincoln's shoulder. Into the light of the open door came President Coleman, his thin ferret face grim. He was followed by a wide-bodied, wide-faced man with sagging jowls. They stomped onto the houseboat's porch.

"Good evening," Roger said.

The two paused. They did not answer.

"Won't you come in?" Roger asked.

He stepped aside. Lincoln opened the door wider.

The two men entered the living room. Lincoln glanced around the room, said, "Excuse me." He stepped through the door, closed it behind him. Mrs. Gruntey strode to the center of the room. She nodded to the wide-faced man beside President Coleman.

"Good evening, Mr. Trelawney. We meet again."

"Hrrrrmmmph!" the man said.

From the darkness outside came an echoing rumble by Mr. Amonto.

Pepina stifled a laugh.

"What's wrong with you?" Roger whispered.

Pepina indicated Mr. Trelawney with her eyes. "He sounds just like Mr. Amonto, our bullfrog," she whispered.

Mr. Trelawney's face crimsoned. "Hrrrrmmmmph! What are you two whispering about?"

Again Mr. Amonto echoed his "Hrrrrmmmmph!"

Pepina rolled over on the couch, no longer able to suppress the laughter. The motion dislodged the corner of her robe, revealing a long expanse of tan thigh. The two men in the middle of the room quickly averted their gaze.

"Well, President Coleman," Mrs. Gruntey said.

President Coleman cleared his throat.

Pepina's laughter subsided. She straightened her robe and sat up.

"Mr. Trelawney tells me I can't put on my play," Mrs. Gruntey said.

President Coleman raised a placating hand. "Perhaps with a few revisions."

"The other day, when we had tea, you assured me you'd read my play and thought it was wonderful."

President Coleman blushed. "Yes, yes. But perhaps I was a bit hasty. I was so concerned with the problems of the new gymnasium."

"For which I kicked in twenty-eight thousand dollars," Mrs. Gruntey said. "I've a notion to stop the check."

"Just minor revisions," President Coleman said, his voice pleading.

"Not so much as a word!" Mrs. Gruntey said.

Pepina clapped her hands.

Mr. Trelawney placed a hand on President Coleman's arm.

"Clinton, I'm afraid you don't know all of the facts. I've been saving something to show you just how depraved these people are." He looked gloatingly at Mrs. Gruntey. "As for the deficiency in the gymnasium building fund ... I'm sure the League could raise it easily."

President Coleman looked from Mrs. Gruntey to Mr. Trelawney. "What have you been saving?"

Mr. Trelawney pointed at Roger and then at Pepina.

"These ... defiers of the commandments—they're not married. They're living together in sin!"

Mrs. Gruntey raised a hand, started to speak, then hesitated.

President Coleman paled, swayed. "My French teacher, not ... Oh, no!" He shook his head. "Ellis, are you sure?"

"As sure as sure! My wife overheard two students talking. They've known it for years. They've been hiding it from you."

President Coleman put a hand to his chest. His face flushed, then became pale. "My heart! I must take my medicine." He looked around him, eyes darting. "Where ... where's the bathroom?"

Mrs. Gruntey stepped forward, took his arm. "Be calm. The bathroom is right down here." She led him across the room, steered him into the hallway. "First door on your left. Will you be all right?"

Mr. Trelawney stepped between them. "I'll help him. Here, Clinton, old man. Calm's the word. Right down here." They went down the hallway.

Mrs. Gruntey turned around, started back toward Roger and Pepina. Both were standing in the middle of the room. Suddenly, Mrs. Gruntey remembered the murals in Pepina's bathroom. She stopped, put a hand to her mouth, started to turn back, then thought better of it. She looked at Roger.

Roger shrugged his shoulders. "C'est le guerre. Some use guns, some use knives, some use words, and some use copies of the walls of Pompeii." Again he shrugged. "If they ..."

He was interrupted by a bellow from the rear of the houseboat. President Coleman charged out of the hallway, his face crimson. He was followed by Mr. Trelawney, jowls jiggling as he walked. Roger, who had stepped to the hallway entrance at the first bellow, caught up the yellow paper lei from its hook beside the door. He looped it around President Coleman's neck as the latter emerged.

"Must maintain tradition," he said.

President Coleman glared at Roger, wrenched the lei from his neck and flung it to the floor.

"You!" He pointed a finger at Roger. "You're fired. I'll see that the board of trustees acts on it tomorrow."

Mr. Trelawney, already at the door, opened it and stepped outside. "Come, Clinton. We're not too soon shut of this sinkhole." President Coleman thrust his head forward and strode through the door, slammed it after him.

The slam of the door was followed almost immediately by a splashing noise from outside. This was accompanied by howls and screams. Roger, Pepina, and Mrs. Gruntey wrenched open the door, dashed onto the porch. President Coleman and Mr. Trelawney were floundering in the water at the end of the houseboat.

"Good heavens!" Mrs. Gruntey screamed. "They'll drown."

"Not if they put their feet on the bottom," Roger said. "It's only about four feet deep there."

Their attention was attracted by a motion on the boardwalk. In the shadows, they could make out Lincoln's square form leaning against the rail. Lincoln waved at them.

"Somebody took away the plank that goes up to this boardwalk," he said. "These gentlemen did not watch where they walked." He paused. "*Sheng yo yen shau cho loo chun chun choo yooi, oh yen ming kwahn ten.* It was once said that the great unwashed pray much for rain, but a man's life is in the care of heaven."

"You!" President Coleman screamed, shaking spray at Lincoln.

"You there," Lincoln said. He pointed to his left with his left hand. "If you will but walk over there between the houseboats, you will find the ladder meant for swimmers."

"I'll sue," President Coleman shouted.

"I'll sue," Mr. Trelawney shouted.

The two men splashed to the ladder, clambered up to the boardwalk.

Behind them, they left the tumultuous sound of laughter.

When Roger could find his voice, he turned to Pepina. "Oh, that was ..." he stopped; his face sobered. "I've been fired!" He shrugged. "Darling, have we hit the bottom of the roller coaster yet?"

Pepina shook her head negatively. "No. I still have the premonition. In fact, I feel very faint."

Roger's face blanched. "If it's worse than this, there's no hope for us."

"You mustn't ..." Pepina began and stopped. "Ooooh," she moaned, and collapsed into Roger's arms.

Roger looked around wildly at Mrs. Gruntey. "I knew it!" He lowered Pepina to the floor. "Oh, Pepina, my darling. What's wrong?"

There was no answer from the motionless Pepina.

Roger looked at Mrs. Gruntey. "The worst is here. She's dead."

Mrs. Gruntey squared her shoulders. "Take her inside. Put her on the couch." She whirled toward Lincoln. "Lincoln, get a doctor! And put that fool plank back."

Lincoln dropped the board in place, then dashed off toward the steps, pushing aside the dripping forms of Mr. Trelawney and President Coleman.

"We'll sue," they shouted after him.

Roger picked up Pepina's limp form, took her inside, and stretched her on the couch. There was a look of deepest concern on his face.

"My dear," he murmured, bending over her.

Mrs. Gruntey shouldered him aside, began rubbing Pepina's wrists. "Get a damp cloth," Mrs. Gruntey said. "Do you have any spirits of ammonia?"

"I don't know," Roger went into the kitchen, returned with a damp cloth.

Mrs. Gruntey applied the cloth to Pepina's forehead. Pepina moaned. Immediately, Roger was at her side. "What is it, my darling?"

"Ooooooooh," Pepina moaned.

Tears came to Roger's eyes. Mrs. Gruntey sniffled.

"Can I get you anything?" Roger asked.

Pepina opened her eyes. "No gardenias. No flowers."

She closed her eyes and became silent.

"Ooooooooh," Roger said. He bowed his head.

Several minutes passed, broken only by the gentle rising and falling of Pepina's breast. Footsteps sounded on the boardwalk. Roger leaped to his feet, dashed to the door and flung it open.

"Hurry!" he shouted. "She's dying!"

The footsteps came faster. Lights popped on in the next houseboat. Into the light of Roger's doorway came a small, fat man carrying a black bag. He was followed by Lincoln. The small man had his trousers pulled on over pajamas and was wearing shoes without stockings.

"I'm Doctor Steffens. Where's the patient?"

"There." Roger pointed toward the couch, averted his face.

The doctor walked over to the couch, gently eased Mrs. Gruntey aside, and bent over Pepina. He placed the black bag on the floor, opened it, and extracted a stethoscope. He put the stethoscope to his ears, began examining Pepina.

"Hmmmmmmm," he said. "Hmmmmmmm."

He rolled back an eyelid, looked at Pepina's eye. Pepina opened both eyes.

"Ouch," she said. "That hurts."

"Dizzy spell?" the doctor asked.

Pepina nodded.

"How long have you been feeling these dizzy spells?"

"Several weeks now." Her voice was faint.

The doctor leaned over and whispered in Pepina's ear.

Pepina nodded.

He whispered another question.

Again she nodded.

"What is it?" Roger screamed.

The doctor stood up and smiled. He folded his stethoscope in one hand, looked at Roger out of the corners of his eyes.

"Well, I wouldn't be surprised, but you're going to be a father."

Roger's mouth made a small "O." Without a sound, he toppled backward. Mrs. Gruntey caught him.

Pepina sat up.

"I suspected it, but I was afraid to tell him. I knew this would happen."

O O O

One day passed. Sunset gilded the river. Mr. Amonto croaked a tired soliloquy from his lodgings in the reeds.

The cast of *Rhythm of Life* sprawled in random positions on the couch, chairs, and straw carpet of the Corots' houseboat. In a new rocking chair by the kitchen door sat Pepina. Roger bent over her, attempting to tuck a blanket around her feet.

Pepina kicked at the blanket.

"Roger, will you take away that fool blanket? It's the middle of summer."

"But darling, you have to be careful."

Carl, lounging in the corner by the record player, looked up from an album of records. "When's the little illegitimate going to be born?"

Roger's face darkened. He turned around. "The *baby* will be born in about six months. I will thank you to—"

The front door of the houseboat banged open, and Mrs. Gruntey entered. Lincoln followed, carrying a case of beer.

"There's food up in the car," Mrs. Gruntey said. "A couple of you young men make yourselves useful." She looked around at the long faces. "Let's liven up this wake."

The students by the door stood up, went outside.

Carl looked at Roger. "What're you going to call the little illegitimate?" he persisted.

Mrs. Gruntey glanced at Carl. "Young man, you ..." She paused, turning back to Roger. "Don't you think this has gone far enough?"

"What do you mean?"

Mrs. Gruntey fumbled in her handbag and produced a yellow cablegram, handed it to Roger. Roger opened the paper. It crackled under his fingers. It was from Paris, addressed to Mrs. Gruntey.

He read:

"Roger Corot and Pepina Lawrence married at City Hall, Lausanne, Switzerland, August 29, 1938. Father gave away the bride. Eugene Dessereux, European director Ballet Russe, best man. Amelie Basat, daughter of Swiss president, maid of honor."

The cablegram was signed: "Emile Vudon, Investigations Discrete."

Roger handed the cablegram to Pepina. She read it and smiled. "I'll never forget that day as long as I live. You forgot all of your dress shirts at Basel and had to wear one of Papa's." She giggled.

"The neck was too small."

"What is this?" Carl asked.

Roger took the cablegram from Pepina, handed it Carl.

"The joke's gone on long enough," he said.

Carl read the cablegram. "Well, I'll be a double-dyed dog." He passed the cablegram along. Students clustered around, reading it.

"It was just a joke," Roger said. "We hated to hurt your feelings. You all seemed so … so dependent upon us."

Mrs. Gruntey suppressed a grin. "This calls for a celebration."

Roger started to smile, then stopped. His shoulders sagged. "Sure. Big celebration. Pepina's going to have a baby. I've been fired. Your play won't go on. Trelawney and Coleman are going to sue me." Roger curled his lip. "Sure. Big celebration."

Mrs. Gruntey looked up at the ceiling. "About the play. You remember that old barn of a movie theater out on Center Street that went broke during the depression?"

Pepina showed signs of interest.

"The one where the East Comity Players put on their show last year?" Roger asked.

Mrs. Gruntey nodded.

"What about it?" Roger asked.

Mrs. Gruntey looked at Pepina. "Your charming wife"—she put the sound of doves around the word— "telephoned me last night and suggested I rent it for the play."

"I'm the brazen one," Pepina said.

"I've bought the theater," Mrs. Gruntey said. "I detest fooling with leases. There's an army of workmen in there right now, cleaning up the place. The tickets for our play went on sale at one o'clock today."

Everyone in the room began to show interest.

"Tickets?" Roger asked.

"I had them printed this morning," Mrs. Gruntey said.

"How're they going?" Pepina asked.

"Like hotcakes," Mrs. Gruntey said. "I once heard there was nothing like being banned in Boston to make a bestseller out of a poor book." She looked around the room, smiling. "Well, the word is around town that the Anti-Vice League pushed us off the campus."

"But I've been fired," Roger said.

"And I've hired you," Mrs. Gruntey said. "I can afford it."

Roger shook his head from side to side. "And every cent I make, those two vultures, Trelawney and Coleman, will take away from me. You heard them say they were going to sue."

"Oh, now," Mrs. Gruntey said. "About that. I forgot to mention that I went up to Coleman's office with my attorney this morning. It seems those two vultures, as you call them, went around telling everybody you and Pepina weren't married. My attorney asked them how they'd like a slander suit."

Mrs. Gruntey thrust her head forward belligerently.

"One peep out of the League *or* Coleman, and I said you'd sue them until they'd have to mortgage the college to pay you off. President Coleman even went so far as to offer you back your job. I said you might consider it, if the salary was right. The president and Mr. Trelawney weren't speaking to each other when we left."

Roger frowned and looked down at the floor. "Mrs. Gruntey ..." He blushed. "You've been wonderful to us, and we don't deserve it." He looked up. "I have a confession to make. It's about your play. You see ..."

Mrs. Gruntey raised a hand. "You mean about its being so funny?

Roger nodded. "Yes ... and ..." He paused.

How I've misjudged this woman, he thought.

"I know," Mrs. Gruntey said. "Lincoln told me. I guess it hurt my feelings for a while; then I remembered something Amos always said. He said the best thing in the world a person could do is to make other people laugh."

Mrs. Gruntey smiled around at the room.

Pepina stood up from her rocking chair.

"Roger, my premonition is gone."

"How can it be?" Roger asked. "Nothing has happened. I mean, the baby hasn't ..."

"Silly," Pepina said. "It wasn't a real premonition. It was just the baby. I've never been pregnant before. I didn't know how it felt to be an expectant mother." She smiled. "It's just like a premonition."

Mrs. Gruntey walked over and put an arm around Pepina's shoulder. "This really calls for a celebration. Lincoln, what is a good saying for this moment?"

Lincoln, who had been opening the case of beer, stood up. He cocked his head on one side, thought for a moment.

"Toi hoy nun lei hoi." He flashed white teeth in a grin. "Sin is a difficult thing with which to part."

A Lesson in History

Rome's morning clamor penetrated a fifth-floor room of the Hotel Serfilia, awakened Charles Howorth. He got out of bed, closed the windows. This muted the outside noises enough that he became conscious of water hissing in the shower and the sound of Katherine slapping her skin as she bathed. He glanced at her bed. It had a neat, pulled-together look, *almost* as though there had been an attempt to conceal its use. Beyond it, on the folding stand, her large suitcase stood open like a giant brown toad waiting for a fly. Charles yawned, turned back to the view. This room was two floors higher than the one he'd had during the war. Up here, he saw tiled tiers of roofs instead of other walls. And up the river, he could make out a curve of the round stone shadow that was Castel Sant'Angelo, Hadrian's tomb.

Twelve years ago, he thought. It made him feel old, vacant … like one of those echoing grocery warehouses leased by the Howorth Chain Stores where nothing ever happened but the trundling in and out of food. Endless passage of food. But a quickened pulse told him that those seventeen weeks of wartime Rome still hovered in his memory. Something different *had* happened. He frowned, crossed to the dresser, and began brushing his hair. The bristles dug into his scalp. A narrow, golf-tanned face and ice-blue eyes stared back at him from the mirror: a stranger's face because the repressions of twelve years separated it from the memories pressing out through his eyes. He could see behind him in the mirror the metallic ivory décor of the room, his own rumpled bed.

"Dora Pucetti," he whispered. Immediately, he felt foolish, soiled.

Early in his life, High Church and wealthy parents had stretched polite distance between the *self* of Charles Howorth and the brute nature of his body. He had carried that balancing tension within him for thirty-two years.

Until the seventeen weeks with carnal, erotic Dora Pucetti.

But the war had moved on, taking Major Charles Howorth with it. He'd rebuilt his inner defenses. The memory of Dora had become encysted to keep it from disturbing the polite balance.

And the war had ended, and he had gone home.

Katherine noted, in time, that something not of guns and fighting had happened to Charles overseas. Mention of Rome brought a clouding of his eyes, a straying attention. The marriage bed had become more of a service to an animal—a frenzied animal that appeared to be hunting something lost. The slow patience of a wife with too much leisure—and an accumulation of probing observations—had finally revealed the encysted memory of Dora as surely as if it had been a physical tumor.

Rome ... another woman. That was the shape of the thing in Charles.

Katherine had pushed through this vacation over all his objections. "Everybody's going to Italy this year, Charles," she'd said.

"The more reason to go somewhere else!"

"We have to go somewhere, you know."

"Why?"

Katherine had won mainly because Charles had become tired of arguing. (Besides, Lorna Philpott had been there last year, and the Philpotts were going again this year. "And what will Lorna and I *talk* about if I don't go?") When she'd started using *those damn bores*, the Philpotts, for an argument, Charles had thrown up his hands. But once the decision had been made, he'd been filled with a remorse he couldn't explain.

So the Howorths had come to Rome, a tourist-crowded city. And a mix-up in reservations had forced them to take rooms in the hotel where Charles had lived for seventeen weeks during the war. It was the kind of coincidence that alerted all of Charles' religious fears. For three days he'd managed to crowd his time with tourism—ruins, bars, dinners, shopping. But last night he'd dreamed of cannon fire the way it had sounded at Lacata. And this morning, the street noises had set him off. The clock of memory he'd thought safely broken and thrown away had begun its precarious ticking. It persisted while he dressed.

Right down below us two floors—309—that's where I was the night they threw Dora into my room and nailed the door shut.

He'd been wide awake in his bed, smoking in the dark, his mind filled with fatalistic musings. The door had slammed open with an eruption of light from the hall. A dark figure had been thrust into the room—all shadow against the glare. Then the door had been closed—the pounding, the drunken laughter. And in the dark room, a voluptuous female voice saying, "They geev you to me!" He'd snapped on the bedlight and, in its dull yellowness, had seen Dora wearing nothing but a pair of black lace panties. She'd swayed drunkenly, advanced on the bed.

And Charles remembered her eyes: black holes, undrunk in that gorgeous drunken body.

It had been surprising how easily civilization, High Church, everything had just peeled away, leaving only a man and a woman.

And Charles remembered the things she'd asked for: coffee, chocolate, cigarettes. These had been easy to get for a major in the quartermaster corps.

Now that he was wallowing in the memory—letting his body dress itself—Charles recalled tiny details about Dora: the wild hair that grew beneath her left ear, the white scar on her thigh. Bur her eyes intruded in every memory: the lithe body might be abandoned to passion, but the eyes still measured things, weighed values.

Coffee, chocolate, cigarettes. And once, ten pounds of powdered milk and a case of spam.

Katherine called from the bathroom, interrupted his reverie: "You awake, Charles?"

It took him a moment to come up through the mists that separated past and present. "Yes, I'm awake." He finished buttoning his shirt.

"Do you want the shower?"

"I took one last night."

Katherine came out of the bathroom fully dressed. Her round face with its frame of careful blonde hair was blank behind its mask of makeup: the face of a dove, the mouth arranged to say *coo*. She wore one of her knitted suits—the pale blue one—rigid as armor over the foundation garment.

"Did you sleep well?" she asked.

He stood before the mirror, plugging in his electric razor. "Certainly. Always sleep well."

She raised her voice above the razor's buzzing: "You tossed around so much last night, I thought you might've had a nightmare."

He saw her eyes in the mirror, weighing him. No sympathy. *That* occurred only in her voice while the eyes abstained. Again, he thought of Dora's eyes: *never soft*. She'd loved with her body but not with her eyes. Charles put away the razor, knotted his tie.

"All ready?" asked Katherine.

He slipped into his coat, touched his hair once more with the brush, then replaced the brush in its leather case.

"All ready."

"I'm glad we're getting an early start," she said.

He took his homburg and the camera from the dresser as they left, closed the door with a solid thump. There was yellow light in the hall: gently blending, gently unexciting. They made polished walking movements down the dull carpet footing. He wore the hat (it felt light in front, lacking the military eagle) slanted at a sculptured angle across his forehead. Underneath the brim: the ice-blue eyes without pardon, the golf-tanned face. Hands dark and leashed. (And the rest of him beneath the refined tailoring: a sun-shunning powder white.)

Polished, polished movements.

"This seems to be a very nice hotel," said Katherine.

"They've been making money here since the war," he said.

"Oh? You know this hotel?"

"It was our BOQ."

"What a fascinating coincidence! Why didn't you say something before?"

"Didn't think it was important."

"Charles, *everything* you did here was important."

He cleared his throat. "Crrhummmph."

The end of the hall opened into a skylighted space with potted green plants and elaborate iron scrollwork across the elevator well. Charles pressed the ivory button. Presently, something clanked below them. There came a grinding humming. He cast a seeking glance around, objecting to what he saw without finding a specific object of objection.

Katherine watched him: waiting, unsympathetic eyes—eyes of a dove intent upon its morsel.

"This place must be full of memories for you," she said.

"Just another hotel," he said.

"But you'd just liberated Rome, and the people must've been so grateful. I'll bet you did lots of fascinating things."

Again he cleared his throat. "We fought a war."

"But not all the time. Not every minute."

He turned, stared at her, encountered the probing eyes. "Sometimes we ate, and sometimes we slept." And he thought: *We should've gone someplace else ... back to France. Rome belongs to a time better forgotten.*

"Does the hotel look the same?" she asked.

"All redecorated." Again he studied his surroundings. "You can bet they did it with dollars." He became aware that the elevator sounds had stopped, and he pressed the buttons.

"So many tourists," she said. (*Sweet moist pressing voice!*) "But I'm so glad we finally came. Your stories about the war made me so curious."

He darted a sidelong glance at her. *I never mentioned Rome ... except to say that we came through here.*

She said: "Anyway, I'm tired of France."

There's no way she could possibly know about Dora, he thought. And he said: "It was quite a bit different here during the war."

"One would imagine," she said.

A feeling of bitter distaste for this place welled up in Charles. He fought down an involuntary shudder.

"You look tired," said Katherine. "Are you sure you want to go out today? Perhaps you should just rest in ..."

"Of course I want to go out! Not tired. Just hungry. Where's that damned elevator?" He leaned his thumb against the ivory button.

Remorse at the outburst came over him. *She's just trying to be kind. I must learn to control my temper. I must be kinder to Katherine and put Dora out of my mind. Katherine is soft, sweet, tender sympathy. She never smells of sex and sweat. I must be kinder.*

Now the elevator resumed its sounds: a humming, mechanical awareness. The cage arose out of the depths, operated by a gnome-faced little man in a blue uniform. The Howorths entered, relaxed in the iron well.

Breakfast in the hotel dining room: silver sugar service, Roman eagles on the cups and plates. Wide reaches of round white tablecloths, spotting of dark heads. Sleepy gliding of help.

A murmurous, expensive clinking.

"This damn coffee tastes of licorice!" said Charles. "They always use too many spices! And they've put some hot stuff on my eggs."

"That's too bad," said Katherine.

"You'd think they could understand a simple order! I told him I wanted *plain* fried eggs."

"They do things so differently here," she said.

"Huh! Things have sure as hell changed since the war! Krauts took everything with 'em. Even cleaned out the food. We had to feed everybody!"

"It must've been hard for you. Helping so many hungry people." Watching eyes. "But weren't they grateful?"

Hah! Grateful! Stealing everything they could lay their hands on! Begging! He began to feel drunk with anger. An image of Dora arose in his mind. *Whatever happened to her?* He wiped his mouth with the napkin, pushed the image aside. *By now—if she's still alive—she'll be a fat slattern surrounded by squalling brats.*

"But it must've been interesting here during the war," said Katherine.

Charles took a deep breath, stared around the room, seeking an object to catch his attention. *The balcony.* "Our flag hung right over there from that balcony."

"I find it hard to picture you here during the war," she said. "What did you do with your spare time?"

He waved a hand. "Nothing."

A woman walked past under the balcony. The proud swinging motion of her young body caught his eye, and against his will, the image of Dora returned. *She walked like that. And she used to say, "What's a woman without a man?" That's one thing about these Italians: their women know how to treat a man.* He cleared his throat. *These are thoughts I must not think!* And he became aware that Katherine had spoken.

"I asked you about these tables, dear," she said.

"Eh?"

"Did you have these same tables here during the war?"

"These?" He nudged the table. A dollop of water spilled from his glass. *Damn waiter keeps them too full!* "No. These are new. We had stuff we liberated from some fascist's palace."

Katherine moved her gaze around the room. "The women are beautiful here," she said. "Don't you think so?"

He shrugged.

"Rome is famous for its beautiful women," she said. "Did you meet any beautiful women during the war?"

"Too busy," he said. "Didn't notice."

He shot a glance at her, looked away. *Could she know? Nonsense! No way for her to know.*

Katherine stirred more cream into her coffee. "Did you have anything in particular in mind for today?"

"Nothing special. I want to get some more pictures at the Forum before we go on up to Florence. Never had a camera with me during the war."

And a good thing I didn't have a camera, he thought. *I'd probably have taken pictures of Dora, maybe saved one.* He passed a hand in front of his eyes, looking at the marks in his palm. *God! How she used to tread the bed like it was a trampoline! Bouncing! Not a stitch on! Hair flying! Jumping up and down on the bed like it was a trampoline. And laughing. "You like to see me like this. Yes you do."*

"Perhaps we could look at antiques this morning," said Katherine. "I heard about a little shop off the Via Magdalena."

His eyes shorted across sudden attention. "Antiques? Oh, now, I ..."

"Just to look. I feel like browsing."

"Katherine, I am remembering the carpets from Brussels."

Little *S*'s beside her mouth. "You know I didn't get cheated *very* much."

He stared at her armor-tortured bustline. "Cheated, though."

Kinder, he thought. *This is not being kinder.*

"We could go for a little while this morning," he said. "They tell me afternoon light's best in the Forum."

And he thought: *It's not much she's asking.*

"Sometimes you're very sweet, Charles," she said.

"Huh!" Yet he smiled a sad, heavy smile.

Some cars filled Charles with metal dread. This astonishing taxi made his skin crawl. It was old, high, neck-jerking—driven by a gawky, leather-skinned creature with a great Franz Josef mustache. But it had been the only taxi at the stand outside the hotel.

We should've waited for another one. Rice on the seats. A wedding? Do they have that custom here? I never learned.

Poplars lined the Via Magdalena. Whiz-chop of little squirtdarting cars. Gas stink. Bicycles. Upcraned necks.

"We must get the correct intersection," said Katherine. "I'm told it's hard to find."

He glanced at her neck, saw little powdered creases infolding above the dress collar. So neat. So prim. They opened like mouths when she leaned forward to peer.

Paper-bag anger popped in his chest.

"Here!" he barked. "We get off here!"

The taxi jerked to a stop at the curb.

"But ..." said Katherine, her dove face blank while the eyes measured his mood.

"You said it was in the Torrenta Alley just off the Via! We can walk from here."

Weak laughter in her pale, powdered throat. "Of course. You still know the city from when you were here before."

He was impatiently polite with the driver, positive of the overcharge, letting the bastard know his game was so damned transparent. *The money isn't important, you little bastard. I make more in a day than you make in a year! It's the principle of the thing. To hell with your ... No, Signore! No, Signore! To hell with it!*

And the minute the taxi had pulled away in its cloud of oil stink, he felt remorse overtake him. *The man probably has a big family to support. Needs every cent he can get. For all I know, he could be married to Dora. I'll wait until I see him again outside the hotel, send him a tip.* Charles tried to imagine Dora living with the taxi driver and failed. *No. She was the kind who'd catch on to a petty official, a clerk in some ministry. Once her beauty started to go.*

Katherine spoke from the walk behind him: "Are we going?"

"Uh … yes."

Now the Torrenta Alley. There had been a whorehouse at the end of it, and his men had gotten into a fight there. But now the neighborhood was changed. Little outpulled drawer balconies on new buildings. The hotel clerk had said the rough districts moved farther out.

Out of the Via's sunlight into a dark, broom-swept, twisting, narrow grotto effect: cool after the glare on the avenue. Charles had an abrupt jolt-bounce thought of all the people who'd witnessed these yellow-ochre bricks. Ancient. A lesson in history. It was as though a heavy cape had been pulled away, flickering, and he saw down the years: Centurion, Barbarian, Christian knight, Blackshirt, the Second Hun, and the Citizen Army—the brawling Citizen Army—and himself coming to get Sergeant Brady's platoon away from the MPs.

But it was not the same now. Too clean. And the smells were different. Drier.

"This must be it," said Katherine. "Number eight."

Thin, in-shadow doorway. He allowed himself to be guided by her movements through into a green-washed gloom. A deep-sea stillness, scent of camphor. His eyes adjusted to the dim light. A room of controlled patience: crowded with dutiful furniture that waited on fat legs, on slim legs. Only to obey. The placidity of the place filled him with a latent rage.

"It's beautiful," said Katherine. "Simply beautiful. All these lovely antiques."

Provoked, he said, "All this damned dust stinking crap full of worm holes!"

A little silence. Again she watched him: the undove eyes in the dove face. "Suppose I just buy one piece," she said.

"Suppose you just look and don't buy anything."

"Darling, could I come back this afternoon, or tomorrow? I mean, while you go take your pictures of the Forum or whatever?"

"Let you come here alone? I'd as soon let you loose in an arena full of hungry lions!"

"Darling!" she hissed. "They probably speak English here!"

"Good."

This silence was longer.

She sighed, said, "I wish you could understand the simple pleasure I get out of ..."

"Simple!" He thumped onto the word with both feet.

In the back of the shop, green curtains parted with a sound of scratching vellum. The shopkeeper glided out of the gloom—a pale, wizened man with conundrum lines between his eyes, a dry sprinkling of somberness over small features. But the eyes clashed with the rest of him—as though they were the man's only weapons, and he had learned out of necessity to slash and parry with them.

"May I be of assistance?" he asked, and his English hopped along on a tired accent. A pill-sounding voice. Bitter medicine.

Katherine put on her public poise. "I'm interested in something for our upstairs sitting room, something to suit a Renaissance décor."

"I'm warning you," said Charles. "We're not plundering the Continent this time." And there was the sourness of pen scratching in his tone.

"My husband likes his little joke," she said, one gloved hand outstretched like a particular exclamation point.

"You are my guests," said the shopkeeper. Hopping of dry accent. An eye-concealing nod.

And Charles thought, *Thus spoke Caesar to his victims!* "The dollar," he said. "The world's most welcome guest."

She pencil-lined her mouth, no sweetness. "Darling! Must you?"

Must I what? Be a bore? Such a bore? Boor, perhaps? Why'd I let her talk me into this? I've never been so bored in my whole life. Or maybe I'm just bored!

He startled her by chuckling.

"I fail to see the humor," she said.

Kinder, he thought. *I must try to be kinder.*

"It's all right, dear," he said. "Private joke. For noncoms and privates only."

"What's that supposed to mean?"

"Do your duty, dear. Do your duty. That's all we did when we came through here from Lacata, from Sicily."

"But you were an officer ... a major."

"Yes, dear."

"Oh, the war!" She dismissed it, all squeezed up in three words like an accordion.

The shopkeeper concealed his embarrassment (*or amusement?*) in a dry-lidding of his weapon eyes, half turning away. One purple-veined hand stroked the dark blue velvet of a chair back.

White spots accented Katherine's cheeks. "Well?" she said.

"Well what?"

"What am I supposed to do?"

He shrugged. *It's the indifferences that drive her mad. Never give her a clue what to expect.*

"I've made my point then?" she asked.

"Let's say you've established a beachhead." And he could all but hear the stick mixed words of her mind: *"Still in the war. Won't he ever leave his toy guns?" That's what you're thinking. Ah, my dear, I know you too well. I know you so much better than I knew Dora. God! I must try to be kinder!*

Nectarine in her voice: "Darling, you know that I ..."

"Oh, for Christsakes!" His breakfast eggs began to taste sour in the back of his throat. *Why does merely the sound of her voice make me flare?*

She was not deceived. Victory was in sight but not won. Not yet. Readily watchful dove. "This is special, darling. This is the place where Lorna got ..."

The darting of his mouth lines told her her mistake.

"So that's it! This wasn't a simple little foreign expedition this morning. Just to browse! This is something you and Lorna cooked up!"

"Perhaps we'd better come back after lunch," she said. "Let's go to that place the man from Pasadena recommended. We could have lobsters, a salad, perhaps some melon."

This is what happened Friday in the dress shop, he thought. *She pressed me too hard. She always presses too hard. Except in bed. Too softly hard. Catch her using a bed for a trampoline!*

"Are those your final terms?" he asked. *Why can't I keep the coldness out of my voice?*

"I'm only thinking of you," she said. Her hungry gaze went to the shopkeeper's hand on the blue velvet chair.

"Huh!" His mouth tucked in with little tic-seals.

"Such a beautiful chair," she murmured. "That one. It'd look so nice with our other pieces." A sigh, lifting, collapsing.

I must force my careful attention upon being kinder.

"One piece," he said. "You can get one piece. No more."

Again she was not deceived. The victory was gratuitous, and not, therefore, a victory. "Now you're being your old, sweet self," she said. And again she watched him, speculating.

"My pleasure," he said.

She turned toward the shopkeeper, encountered bright eyes, benign mocking.

A deep breath against the armored foundation garment. She resumed a semblance of her poise. "I am interested in early Florentine also. Our upstairs sitting room must have ... something."

"I congratulate you, madam." The hopping accent. (*Selling a sofa to Caesar's wife. Dead Caesar's wife.*) "The Florentine is our best. We have recently acquired some particularly fine pieces."

One old Roman hand lifted in invitation to precede him.

She'll pay ten prices for something made last month in an antique-faking factory for tourists!

"Oh, that's pretty!"

She's found something else already! I thought he was going to hook her with that blue velvet monstrosity. This is probably more expensive. No dickering now, dear! Pay the first price! Christ! I cannot listen! He tried blanking his mind to their murmurous voices, but still the words poured through to feed his rage. He turned. "I'll call a cab."

"I'll have my boy call your cab, sir," said the shopkeeper. He excused himself from Katherine, moved away: grey-green color wash fading through vellum scratching curtains.

Katherine looked at her husband. Behind the dove mask, the *undove* moved impatiently.

He nodded a prepared nod, smiled. He knew she would recognize the smile. It said: *"I forgive you for all your mistakes, my dear. Even when you're impossible, I forgive."* A stubborn smile, and he knew that its image was burned upon her memory out of a thousand such incidents. *Dora never saw my forgiving smile,* he thought. *I wasn't kind to Dora.*

"We can go to the Forum right after lunch," said Katherine.

"Since when have you wanted to go to the Forum?" he asked.

She took the words without rising to them as she always had. Suddenly, emotion was running white hot in the air between them. Her eyes caught his attention, compelled him. In the gloom, Charles abruptly saw two faces: two frozen shades, four polar eyes: the image of Dora overprinted on the reality of Katherine— the shock of bitter wax flowing out of sweet honey. A twin reality with new meanings.

I paid Dora with coffee, chocolate, and cigarettes. Katherine takes it out in ... what? Antiques? There's no real difference between them. The world's full of Dora Pucettis. It's full of Katherines. It's full of ...

"This is what I'm getting," said Katherine. "Do you like it?"

She put a gloved hand on a pedestal-footed octagonal table upthrusting in the careful clutter. A figure dimly golden painted on it. *Wings?* He stepped closer. Horrible saccharine pseudo-Romance: a Roman eagle snared in laurel intertwined by a misty ring of doves.

"Isn't it lovely?" she asked.

The shopkeeper swished back through the curtains. "Your taxi comes, sir." He saw the intense downpouring attention. A shutter-blink velvet smile jumped across the old face. "You like it, sir? The design is by Giordano. Very old. It is symbolic of Caesar's standard." Dry chuckle rendering sere lips. "The Roman peace."

Caesar's standard come to this! The last of all the Romans! Hysteria climbed his mind. Katherine's hand fluttered against his arm. The deadly, subtle shirring of feathers. And he heard her voice as from a great distance: "You're very sweet, Charles. So kind to buy me this. Charles? Charles! Why are you laughing, Charles?"

Eagle doves, doves eagle, eagle doves doves eagle eagle doves ... All the eyes staring at him. Slowly, the drunken, reeling overflow of images receded. He quieted, looked up at Katherine, encountered sudden mockery in her gaze. She smiled for the first time this day, and her voice dropped all of its pressing sympathy; it came to him with the soft pounding of a muffled drum.

"This piece makes me very happy, Charles. You see, I wanted something that would remind *me* of Rome ... too."

WILFRED

If you'd ever heard Louis Donet sing, you never would've tied him up with Wilfred Long. But that's where you'd have been wrong. They *were* the same person—in the flesh, that is. Where his character was concerned, though, he was like a chameleon—as if changing his part to fit different backgrounds.

I first met the man when he still was Wilfred Long. He was fresh from the Continent and the Academie des Arts Princips. There was a thin coat of Parisian mannerisms over his British veneer, and beneath it all was the hard shell of ego sealed from the world. He wore that Continental air of a man who has just heard a long, dull story.

The Brunswick Recording Company brought Wilfred to New York in the middle twenties because of a reference from Sir Hugh Blakely-Smythe of the Philharmonic Society to Hal Radcliffe, our managing director.

In the course of time, I received the usual list of "facts" with which to prepare the public for our new find. I leafed through the list and realized I'd need an artificial glow to be able to give even a faint glimmer to Wilfred.

I picked up the phone and called Hal. "Look," I said, "this Wilfred Long, the name, it's …"

"I know," he said, "but it has to stand. Do what you can."

I heard the receiver click, cradled my own, and slammed out of the office. Right then I needed something that could be had only at Vincentes, the best speak in town. "A chicken ranch," I told myself. "I work in a chicken ranch where all the roosters cackle and want to take credit for the eggs."

George Bates was sitting in my favorite booth, and I slid in opposite him. George directed the recording orchestra that played for most of our contract vocalists. He was a native of Cincinnati, a little guy—I'd say about five feet six and kind of stout. A piano player by profession, he had the shortest fingers of any pianist I'd ever seen. He was always getting mad at me, the way I'd ask him to play something like Chopin's *Raindrop Nocturne* where his fingers would get a workout. George had the coldest temper of any man I've ever known. His controlled ferocity could make you shiver even if you weren't the object.

He looked up at me as I sat down. "Hullo, Felix," he said. "I gave 'em a breather. We're makin' *My Old Kentucky Home* with Jules Preston, an' they just tossed out the sixth one."

"What's the matter?" I asked.

"The usual stuff," he grunted. "We get wax in the cutting channel, distortions, squeaks, noises, everything. Why don't they invent something so we don't have to go to all this trouble?"

He frowned and gulped his drink. The waiter came up with my regular double scotch.

"Finish that," George said, "an' come up an' give us some luck."

I downed the drink, and when the shivers had stopped, nodded. "Okay, George. But you better cross your fingers for me, too. I gotta make a singer by the name of Wilfred look like copy. I won't be able to show my face in a newsroom for a year."

"Wilfred," he repeated unbelievingly. "Let's have another."

We got back to the studio about a half hour later, and I took a seat high up in the back while George collected the orchestra. They'd just repainted the studio, and the smell of turpentine mixed with the odor of the floor compound the sweepers used was doing things to my stomach. I wished I was anything right then but a publicity agent for a platter palace. I looked around me. What a racket!

Preston, the vocalist, was slouched in one of the front seats with his hat over his eyes. George went over and poked him in the ribs. "Okay, Press. Let's try it again."

The singer tipped back his hat, stood up, and walked over to the big square horn that led into the cutting room. We didn't have any of these fancy electrical pickups in those days. The vocalist had to stand in front of the horn with the orchestra members crowded as close as they could get behind him. They always had to shout at the damn horn and then hope like hell they were on the wax. It was a common thing to make the same disc over six or seven times before it got the okay. On an average of once a week, some yokel would come bouncing in right in the middle of the one cutting that everyone knew was going to be perfect. The door couldn't be locked because of some damn fire rule, so they'd set up a red light and a sign.

That's how we met Wilfred. He barged in just as they were finishing the seventh try on Foster's classic. A trolley was passing by on the avenue, and its clanging seemed to fill the room.

George hushed the orchestra with a resigned air and slowly turned on the intruder. We all waited expectantly for the slightly unkempt stranger to wilt under George's famed vitriolic tongue. Wilfred was taller than George by a good three inches, and he had bushy hair, which made him seem even taller; there was a supercilious set to his red features. Continental look, I believe you'd call it. We'd seen bigger ones routed by our bantam champ, though, and didn't doubt the outcome of this one.

"You saw the red light and thought you'd come to the right place, eh, junior?" George asked in a deceptively soft tone. He strode up to Wilfred, pointing his baton as if he wanted to skewer the man. "Well!" he shouted. "This is a recording studio, and we don't like bastards like you wandering in here and flirting with our girls! Get the hell out!" He gestured with his baton. "And next time, don't believe everything the taxi driver tells you!"

We guffawed until the room seemed to expand. George was in rare form.

Wilfred cleared his throat, looked George up and down with an infuriatingly aloof glance, and stepped past him. The baton was knocked aside. "Droll fellow," he said, "but that sort of humor always fails to amuse me."

He walked over to the horn, a big affair about eight feet across. "So this is a recording studio," he murmured. Swiveling, he fixed Preston with his eyes. Even from the back of the room, I could see the almost hypnotic gleam.

Preston stopped laughing and stood there with a silly grin on his face.

"You're the vocalist," Wilfred said in an accusing tone. Before Preston could recover, Wilfred continued, "Well, I'm Wilfred Long. You're to show me how this thing is done so I can make a few records tomorrow."

"So that's Wilfred," I said to myself. "Oh, brother. Oh, Brother!" I groped into my pocket and brought out my flask.

By this time George had regained his voice. "Oh," he said apologetically. "You're the new singer."

We shifted our eyes to George with an amazement that lasted only until we saw the glint in his eyes.

"Well," he shouted boisterously, "I guess I jumped too soon. Come on over and sit down while we run through this thing again. You can ask all the questions you want. Just sit quietly until I give you the sign." He grabbed Wilfred's arm. "Say your name's Wilfred?" he asked and turned toward the orchestra. "Boys, this is *Wil*-fred."

The accent on the first syllable seemed to go unnoticed as George ushered the singer to a seat in the background.

While the boys went back to Kentucky, I examined our new addition. So help me, he looked like a Wilfred. He didn't look like a Will or a Fred; he just looked like a character who had been created for the whole name. There are some men who can carry the name well, but when it's attached to someone like this it's like kicking a man when he's down. Wilfred's eyes held a round, owlish expression which was made almost ludicrous by over-hanging eyebrows slanted steeply toward the nose. The eyebrows appeared to be leering while the eyes gave a gentle, wise admonishment. Under his clothes Wilfred looked flabby, and his neck was short, with a roll of fat just above the collar. He didn't look paunchy; he merely gave the picture of a man who has been fat and reduced only in odd spots.

The eighth cutting received a grudging approval from Sayles in the work room; George gave the orchestra the "ta-dumpha" wave with his baton, and they began picking up the pieces and filing out in whispering, rustling, and clattering groups.

A little smile hovered around George's lips as he stepped up to Wilfred. "Any questions?" he asked.

"Not at all," Wilfred said. "Really quite simple, isn't it?"

"Quite simple," George agreed.

I had about five of my friends down from the front office the next day to watch the fun, and we just managed to squeeze into an empty space along the back wall. There was a schoolroom, giggly undertone in the room. Wilfred strode in at about one minute before rehearsal deadline and took his place before the horn. He stood there, glancing through some sheet music and seemingly unaware that the room was packed. George appeared just as the second hand whirled straight up and, knowing how unpunctual he usually was, we took this as an omen.

Wilfred and George bent their heads over the music for a minute, then George straightened. "Mr. Wilfred Long will sing 'Duna,'" he said.

A deprecating smirk flitted over one side of Wilfred's face. We all clapped, and he bowed slightly.

They rehearsed the song three times—a remarkably small number—and each time, George's grin became broader. Wilfred's voice was … well, I guess *common* is the word that best describes it. I turned to Callahan of Booking, who was standing beside me. He shrugged his shoulders.

After the third rehearsal, George nodded to Wilfred and shouted into the horn, "Cut this one!"

He returned to his stand, motioned the orchestra in, and raised his baton, lifting slightly on his toes. He appeared more like someone about to lead a series of yells than an orchestra. The buzzer sounded, and they went at it.

The music was wonderful—most especially the violins. It's the string section that really can sabotage a singer. The brass, woodwinds, and tympany can destroy a musical effect as quickly, but a voice usually can hold its own against them through contrasting tonal values. Let the violins run wild, though, and the singer might as well be shouting down a rain barrel.

When they finished, we waited for the cut-down to the center of the platter and started clapping. George put one arm around

Wilfred's shoulder and motioned toward us. Wilfred acknowledged our ovation distantly. He was beginning to see the light.

It was about an hour and a half wait for the casting and playback, so we adjourned to our own business. The playback would be an anticlimax anyway, we thought; we'd seen the show. I was anxious to hear it, though, if only to watch Wilfred while it was being run. At about twenty minutes after the hour, I wandered back to the studio. There was a crowd of people at the door, all listening to Wilfred tell what he had said to the Duke of Montmarte. His sang-froid seemed to have returned.

"So I told the duke the fox couldn't have gone that direction," he was saying.

I turned around and went back down the hall out of earshot. I suddenly felt sorry for the poor dope. Didn't he know the silly picture he made? Could anyone really be that dumb? I turned the corner and bumped into a little blonde tester from the factory named Lisa Engman. She had a package in her hands.

"Whooof!" she said. "Felix, you scared the daylights out of me." Her voice was about three tones above a falsetto. "What's in this?" she asked, holding up the package. "They told me to treat it like fragile china."

I glanced at the tag. "Darling," I said, putting my arm around her and taking the package, "you are looking at the rise and fall of a guy by the name of Wilfred Long. Let's take it into the cutting room, and I'll buy you a drink after we've had our fun."

Sayles was standing by the cutting room door as we passed. I winked and handed him the package, then went up the hall to spread the word. Lisa and I squeezed ourselves into the studio and found a couple of empties along the far wall. We started to sit down but were interrupted by a commotion at the entrance. Radcliffe was coming in with Callahan. Room was made for them near the door. I looked around for George and found him down front with several of the orchestra members. Wilfred was the last to enter. His composure seemed to have deserted him. He stood by the exit as if ready to bolt or do a death scene.

A hush came over the room as the music started, but as it progressed, we leaned forward like a nest full of baby robins grabbing at a worm. The voice coming out of the horn was good—maybe better than good—and the orchestra was properly in the background. I looked at George. He had scrunched down in his seat, and a nerve at his temple was jerking. His complexion had taken on a boiled-cherry hue, dark and violent against his white collar

The recording wasn't easy to explain—in fact, the only explanation was that it had happened before. If there was one thing you could say about the recording business in those days, it was that the platters were unpredictable. Through some acoustical quirk, Wilfred and the loud orchestra had hit the right combination. They didn't seem to go together any more than Gilbert and Sullivan, but they made beautiful music.

When it was over, Wilfred turned to George with a positively glowing expression. He looked as though someone had just run a heater over his face. "You know," he said, "when we were making that record I thought you were a little loud, but I guess you know more about this business than I do."

"Yeah," George said. "I guess we do."

He brushed past Wilfred and went out the door. I had one devil of a time following him. There was a crowd milling around Radcliffe and Wilfred. Radcliffe had the broad smile of a man whose hundred-to-one shot has just romped home. He was shaking Wilfred's hand as though it was a pump handle.

I found George at Vincentes, and we drowned our woes.

"That damn pipsqueak and his lousy voice!" George kept repeating. "That damn pipsqueak ..."

That was the beginning of a really wonderful hate.

Wilfred's contract read for five masters, and when he'd completed those, the company signed him for ten more. He'd cut three of the new batch when he got an offer from a Broadway company to do the lead in *Star Night*, a musical being produced by Royce and Bodington. This sort of thing always was good publicity for the platters, so the company gave Wilfred a leave of absence, stipulating in the contract with his producers that all the throwaways and posters mention Brunswick—the usual procedure.

Royce and Bodington had heard all of Wilfred's recordings and assumed his voice was of the same quality. They had no reason to assume otherwise and didn't even bother to hear him before completing the contract.

I wasn't at the first rehearsal—or any of them, for that matter—but I understand it was something new on Broadway. It was all over town in a couple of days. They started Wilfred on one of the more difficult scores, a duet with the feminine lead, Eugenia Moran. Royce and Bodington heard about twelve bars of it and motioned for the conductor to stop. The orchestra trailed into silence and Royce, a big, blustery fellow, stood up in his seat.

"This is no time to make jokes," he shouted. "Sing with your right voice, the one we hear on the records!"

Wilfred ignored him and ordered the maestro to continue. Somehow they struggled through the rehearsal, and toward the end, Wilfred's voice seemed to become a little better—or maybe they merely became more accustomed to it.

"A liddle tightness in de t'roat, mebbe?" Bodington inquired when it was all over.

Wilfred brushed right by him and followed Eugenia Moran down to the dressing rooms. They let him go. There were a lot of bucks tied up in Wilfred's contract, which maybe accounted for part of their reluctance to antagonize him. Besides, artists were supposed to act that way.

The only person who failed to notice anything wrong with Wilfred's voice was Miss Moran. Of course, she could have been too busy listening to herself.

Then, too, a baritone so close to her probably was a novelty. Tenors usually took the romantic leads.

Two days before the show opened, I received two tickets through the office mail. I buzzed George, and he said he had a couple too.

"The whole damn orchestra and Radcliffe got Oaklies," he said. "Wilfred wants to show off. You got 'em because you're publicity."

"You going?" I asked.

When George quieted down, I said, "Maybe it'll be a flop."

There was such a long silence that I thought George had hung up. "You still there?" I asked.

"Yeah," he said. "Maybe it'll be a flop."

Opening night, I took my tickets and Lisa Engman, the blonde from cutting, and went to hear Wilfred. They were playing at the old President Theater, and the place was aglitter with lights, jewels, white faces and shirt fronts and bright talk. The usher led us down front, and I had to admit Wilfred had given us good seats. They were about a third of the way back from the orchestra, right in what is called the acoustical focus. We stepped past some expensive knees and sat down. A few minutes later, George and Gladys, his wife, came in. They had the seats beside ours. George shifted around so that he was sitting next to me.

"'Lo," he said.

I nodded and leaned over him to speak to his wife. "Gladys, this is Lisa Engman."

They made a few polite remarks, which I don't remember. George pushed me back—rather rudely, I thought. He was in a pretty rough mood.

"You still think it'll be a flop?" he asked.

"What do you think?" I countered.

"Could be," he said, and turned to glance back over his shoulder. "That bastard sure must have sent out a lot of Oaklies."

George's voice was none too quiet, and a woman behind us must have heard him. She sniffed so loud she could be heard for six rows. Gladys leaned over and shushed George. The introduction started on time or it could've been a family row.

By the middle of the second scene, we knew it wasn't going to be a flop. They had done things with props and lights, and the music was good … catchy. It would have taken a worse voice than Wilfred's to knock the box office from under that show.

George made only one other comment during the evening. He leaned over and whispered in my ear, "That bastard is still getting the breaks."

I looked at Moran, whom our Wilfred was fondling with more than the required intimacy during their love scenes. "Yeah," I agreed.

This Moran was what could be called a dish. She looked as though she'd just come from a conference with a snake and an apple. Wilfred appeared interested enough to take a bite himself.

George gave me the slip when the curtain came down, so I said, "To hell with it!" and went out and had myself a time with Lisa. It was about two AM when I got back to my hotel, and there was a call at the desk for me. I took it, went over, and crawled into a booth. It was George's wife.

"I'm sorry I bothered you," she said. "I was worried about George. He brought me straight home and then went out, but he just came in."

I heard a hoarse voice in the background say, "Who'n 'ell you talkin' to now?"

"Okay, Gladys," I said. "Put him to bed with an ice pack. He's had a large disappointment."

It didn't come as a surprise to any of us when Wilfred and Eugenia Moran began seeing a great deal of each other. What with those torrid love scenes, one thing and another, I guess they convinced themselves they really were in love. It has happened before and most likely will happen again—many times. Both of them were married, but that rule isn't supposed to apply to artists.

I'd met Wilfred's wife once—in Mendel's. I'd gone in to buy a new tie, and there was Wilfred and a mousy-looking woman. The term had been coined for her. Mousy she was and dressed in gray. A rather big nose jutted out above a wide, thin-lipped mouth, and her forehead was tall and smooth.

Wilfred was trying on a new suit, a tweed thing. I believe he fancied himself a type—the English gentleman, y'know. All he needed was a monocle.

I walked over to him. "Quite a piece of burlap you have there, Wilfred," I said.

He didn't stop admiring himself in the full-length mirror, but he glanced at me in the reflection. "Maude," he said, "this is Felix Jacobsen. He works at Brunswick. Say hello."

The little gray woman stepped away from Wilfred and gave me her hand. "I'm delighted," she said, and she made me believe it. I took back all the things I'd been thinking. Her smile was beautiful—full of warmth, affection, and … oh, a grand love of life.

"Mrs. Long, where has Wilfred been hiding you?" I asked.

She looked back at her husband, and a haunting, poignant expression flitted across her features and was gone. "Oh, I've been busy opening a new house out at Great Neck," she said. "A home is such a bother. Really, all I need is a stable."

Again she favored me with that smile. "Why don't you come out and ride with me some morning? Wilfred never has time."

Hearing his name, Wilfred looked away from the tailor with whom he was speaking. "What'd you say?" he asked.

"I only said that you never seem to have time to ride with me anymore."

Wilfred turned away, muttering. "Silly beasts," was all I caught, but his wife's face looked as if he'd slapped her. The expression vanished so quickly that it was almost as if I'd imagined it.

"Do come out," she said. "I'd enjoy becoming acquainted with one of Wilfred's friends. I know so few people over here."

I murmured a banal, "One of these days," and took my leave. Wilfred hardly noticed my going.

I heard later that Maude came from a wealthy British family. Wilfred was a crown citizen, of course—South African—but not many people knew it until he was picked up at Nuremburg and the trial was splashed all over the papers. He always was pretty much a mystery man, and he really didn't look the type.

Well, along in the fall of that year, *Star Night* closed shop in New York and went on the road, the understudies taking over. Eugenia Moran went to Reno "for her health," the tabloids quipped, and Wilfred disappeared. I don't mean he vanished in the usual front-page sense with police hunting him; he just didn't show up at any of his regular places, and gradually the talk died. He was resurrected for a short while when news of Eugenia Moran's divorce broke, but it didn't last. We simply forgot about him.

I first learned that Wilfred was back in town from a friend of mine—Lee Adams, a reporter on the *Sun*. It was about eleven months later. Lee said he'd seen Wilfred in the customs line getting off the *Muritania*.

"You sure it was him?" I asked.

"Yeah, it's him. Got a face full of whiskers, though—regular Evans Hughes badger. But you can't miss 'im; it's the same Wilfred. He was standing in the *D* line."

We both laughed.

It wasn't until a week later that I ran into Wilfred for myself. I was leaving Vincentes just as he was entering. He was with Eugenia Moran.

I grabbed his arm. "Wilfred, old boy," I said. "When'd you get back? And what's with the bush?"

He regarded me with a cold stare. "Wilfred?" he inquired, freeing his arm. "Are you acquainted with someone by that name who resembles me? My name is Louis Donet."

I turned to Eugenia.

"Excuse me," she said, looking up at Wilfred. "Allow me to introduce Mr. Felix Jacobsen. He's director of publicity at the Brunswick Recording Company, darling." She turned to me. "This is Mssr. Louis Donet of the Paris Opera."

"Louis Donet!" I protested. "Why, this ..."

But Wilfred already had my hand. "Delighted," he said. "It's such a pleasure to meet Uzheenyaa's friends. We must see more of each other." He looked down at Eugenia. "I understand the Brunswick company is seeking a new baritone."

"We simply must be going," Eugenia interrupted. "We'll see you some other time, Felix." She turned back to Wilfred.

It *was* Wilfred. I knew it!

"We have a big night ahead of us, haven't we, darling?"

"Uh, oui, cheri," he murmured, looking into her eyes and then returning his gaze to me. "It has been delightful meeting you, Mr. Jacobsen." He gave me a courtly little Continental bow and turned away.

I stood there watching them as they disappeared into the club. "What the hell's the pitch?" I asked myself.

As it turned out, I was the first of the old crowd to meet the new Wilfred, but we all received the same greeting. He brushed everyone off cold—all his old acquaintances at Brunswick, the show, everyone. I understand Radcliffe almost had apoplexy. There was one possible exception, of course, and that was Eugenia. But I'm not sure to this day about her.

In a week's time, Wilfred was the favorite topic of conversation in all the dives across town. "Have you seen Wilfred Long—I mean, Louis Donet?" the conversation would begin.

There'd be a long round of laughter and a few more rounds of drinks.

You have to say this for him, though: he carried it off. I don't think it was demonstrated any more fully than at the trial when his ex-wife (there was some kind of a European divorce) sued him for her commission on his income. It developed that she had picked Wilfred out of a South African church choir, taken him to London, and financed his voice training. She had a contract, too, for ten percent of his income. When, as Louis Donet, he refused to pay, she hired two high-powered lawyers (Cole and Hamilton) and went after him in the courts.

The courtroom was as jammed for the trial as the little studio had been the day George Bates had taken his flop. Wilfred was up against a different situation here. Mrs. Long took the stand. Her hair was turning gray, and a slim shaft of light from one of the tall windows along the left wall caught her head in a yellow-and-silver halo. She was every bit the English lady sitting there and telling her story in a calm, dispassionate voice.

"He was a nothing—a nobody," she said. "I took him and made him into something of which he could be proud and of which I could be proud." Using the same calm tones, she leveled a finger at Wilfred and said, "No one could take pride in this ... this ..."

She was too much of a lady to use the correct term, but her story became all the more convincing because of her restraint. There was a stirring through the court, and the judge rapped for order. Wilfred, sitting at the trial table, hadn't moved or changed his bored expression.

"Continue, Madam," the judge said.

"There is no doubt that this man is Wilfred Long," she said. "I was married to him for five years. He hasn't a mannerism with which I am not familiar."

The judge leaned down from his bench. "It is quite possible, madam," he said, "that you could solve this case in a simple manner. Did Mr. Long have any peculiar markings on his body which would not be known generally?"

Without a blush, she looked directly at the judge and said, "He has a cherry birthmark on his right thigh."

This time the judge had to rap his gavel repeatedly before the noise subsided. "One more such outburst and I shall clear this court," he said. He turned to Mrs. Long. "You may step down, madam."

In the silence that followed, we could hear someone coughing in the rear of the courtroom. The judge leaned over and addressed himself to Wilfred's attorney. "Is there any objection to your client stepping into my chambers for a personal examination?"

With a tired, disinterested wave of his hand, Wilfred arose with his attorney. He raised his eyes to the judge in a condescending manner. "I've never seen this woman before in my life," he said. "She must be mad. However, if it will satisfy those present, I will submit myself to this distasteful ordeal."

The judge rapped his gavel once and stood up, the spectators arising with him. "There will be a ten-minute recess," he said. "Will counsel for the plaintiff accompany us, please?"

Mrs. Long's two lawyers arose and, with Wilfred and his attorney in the lead, made their way around the clerk's desk and into the judge's private chambers. They were gone the full ten minutes. A hush fell over the courtroom when the door reopened and they filed out. The sessions clerk arose and rapped his gavel, calling the court to order. Everyone stood until the judge had taken his seat, and then we sat down again. The lawyers and Wilfred made their way to the trial table, all seeming to wear the same inscrutable expression. It was maddening. I searched their faces for a clue to what had happened but could see nothing. The judge cleared his throat.

"I have before me," he said, "documented evidence that supports the claim of Mr. Louis Donet that he is the said Louis Donet." (He was referring to a French passport and birth certificate, both of which, it turned out, were forged by a Russian émigré in Paris.)

"On the other hand," the judge continued, "I have the claim of Mrs. Maude Chester Long that Louis Donet is one Wilfred Long, an alleged defaulter on a commissions contract. Viewing all the evidence, I am forced to the conclusion that Mrs. Long is laboring under the delusions brought about by a remarkable resemblance between Mr. Donet and her ex-husband. Mr. Donet has no such birthmark as she describes."

There was pandemonium. The judge pounded his gavel steadily, then gave it up and took a drink of water. He leaned forward, and only those of us in the front rows heard him say to Mrs. Long: "If at a later date, madam, you are able to bring before me sufficient evidence to substantiate your claim, I will reopen this case. Meanwhile, it is dismissed for lack of evidence."

Wilfred had done it again.

(Years later, when it was too late, we learned that the birthmark had been tattooed into oblivion by another Paris artisan. Wilfred had been thorough.)

I bumped into George as I was leaving the court and had to shepherd him through twenty bars on the way home. We both were in pretty rough condition when we got to his place. Gladys, ever understanding, opened the door. She saw how it was right away.

"George, George, where have you been?" she demanded.

"I been out fin'in' out how to get ahead in the worl'," he told her and collapsed face forward onto the carpet.

I leaned against the doorjamb. "It takesh genyush to be a first-clash heel," I said. The opposite doorjamb suddenly did the funniest thing. It split into four doorjambs with a Gladys standing beside each one. Each Gladys had a kind of accusing and hurt look, and each one said, "It isn't right to hate someone like that. It just isn't right." Somebody pulled a curtain over the scene.

I awoke the next morning inside a giant object that throbbed in a million places. Reaching upward with one hand, I felt the object; it was my head. There was a sudden crashing noise by my ear. I forced open one eye and saw Gladys clinking a creamer against a coffee cup. She was in a dressing gown and had a paper under her left arm. I saw a picture and the familiar face of Wilfred and grabbed the paper. The story was all over page one. Mrs. Long was returning to England, it said. I threw the paper into a corner, got up, and took my head down to the studio—stopping off at a bar on the way.

It was four days before George came back to work. The first trumpet had taken over for him, and they'd gotten along as best they could. George had a lot of fast talking to do up front, and they put him on probation. He came into the studio in time for the two o'clock session—it was a Tuesday, I remember. I was downstairs in the cutting room, trying to get up a game for that night. George stood in the doorway for I don't know how long before we noticed him. He was well oiled. There were a few "Hi ya, George!" calls from the gang, but he didn't seem to hear them.

"Wilfred is going to sing for us," he said.

"You mean Louis Donet?" I asked.

Everybody laughed ... everybody, that is, except George. He fixed me with a baleful glare, and the laughter died in self-conscious splutters. After that, we always referred to Louis Donet as Wilfred whenever George was around.

Donet was signed by Brunswick to do five platters starting the first of the following month—November, it was. Nothing was said about Wilfred Long's unexpired contract. I don't believe he fooled anyone in the front office; it was more likely that they'd been reading the papers.

While we were waiting for him to put in his appearance at the studio, the news was released that he'd been engaged to do a concert at Carilon Hall, a place referred to in the trade as "... where the dowagers dangle." We all figured he was cashing in on his trial publicity but had to admit it was good box office. The hall was sold out two weeks in advance.

I collared George the day before the concert and showed him a copy of the program and two tickets I'd managed to wangle from Bennie, the scalper.

"Sorry, Felix," he said. "I've had enough. You can't touch him."

This was very quiet for George, so I played my trump and opened the program. "Look," I said, "he's going to sing 'Sylvia' and here, 'Ah, Sweet Mystery of Life' and ..."

George grabbed the program.

"With that voice it'll be murder," I goaded him. "We've been waiting too long to miss the payoff."

"Do you think we could get the concession selling the rotten tomatoes?" George asked, returning the program.

"I'll meet you at Vincentes at seven tomorrow night," I said.

He nodded and went off down the hall.

It started to rain about five o' clock the next afternoon, and both of us were soaked by the time we got to the hall. It had been George's bright idea to walk. The rain didn't seem to have cut the crowd any, though. Carilon Hall was filled with all that tinsely chitter-chitter-chitter that usually accompanies a gathering of the intelligentsia. We barely got into our balcony seats before the house lights dimmed, turning off the small talk. The curtains parted, showing a big Steinway, and a pianist by the name of Torrell came on stage and took his seat. There was a slight wait, and then Wilfred appeared from the wings. A scattered wisp of applause echoed through the house, and he bowed. The pianist struck the opening chords of "Sylvia," and Wilfred began to sing—I mean, Louis Donet began to sing. This voice and this stage personality didn't belong to Wilfred Long, not the Wilfred Long I'd known. We could see the dowagers in their plush boxes below us lift their lorgnettes and lean forward as he delivered those low, vibrant, passionate notes. You could almost count the delicious shivers running up and down their fat spines.

Well, we had to admit it: he was good. No … he was better than good. He was tremendous. He had stage presence, and that voice … ah, that voice. Where in hell had he found those pagan pipes?

During the intermission, we stayed in our seats. George was leaning back with his eyes closed. "You know," he said, "when I close my eyes and try to forget it's that bastard singing, I almost enjoy myself." He opened his eyes and looked at me without lifting his head. I had to turn away. Unrequited hate is as terrible to witness as unrequited love.

Overnight, Louis Donet was in. Brunswick put him on a long-term contract after reading the morning paper reviews; he was booked solid for two years in advance. Then he married Eugenia Moran, and they left on a combined tour and honeymoon in Europe. They were gone five months. During that time, we slid back into our accustomed rut at the studio. You know how it is with a regular job—one month looks just like any other.

Wilfred returned to us on a Monday. I came into the office about eleven o'clock that morning and passed Radcliffe's door; it was open just a crack. Inside, I could hear Radcliffe arguing with a vaguely familiar voice. "I will have it or else," the vaguely familiar voice said, and Wilfred burst out of the office, slamming the door behind him.

I went into my cubicle and called Radcliffe. "Well?" I said.

"So you've been peeking in keyholes again," he growled.

"We have a Monday morning special on murders," I told him. "Two for the price of one. What is it our prima donna will have or else?"

"He will have a special orchestra for his recordings!" Radcliffe shouted, and slammed the receiver down.

I looked at the phone and thought of what this would do to George. An open slap in the face—it would break him.

It did.

When George came back from his three-week bender, he didn't have a job. I offered to help him, but he turned me down with the same damn quotation from Shakespeare and just disappeared. There wasn't even a farewell party. Just blooey! A little man by the name of Feldman was imported from Chicago to take over. Damn good musician and a nice guy, too, but he just didn't seem to fill George's shoes.

I heard from some of the crowd that George had gone back to Cincinnati and returned to his old job of piano accompanist for a local symphonic group. They said he was doing a little teaching on the side. After a while, we put him in the back of our minds.

Things were pretty rocky for me at about that time. Sales had hit a terrible skid, and I was receiving my share of the blame as it filtered down from the top. Our full sales chart looked like a profile of the Matterhorn, and it seemed I was the only one who'd admit what was wrong. I believe this was because I was the only one around the office who hadn't made a foolish prediction about this new "fad," radio. Odds had been given quite freely that radio wouldn't last more than six months—then a year—then two years. "Who wants to sit at home and listen to music?" they said. Now the betting was on how long *we* could stay in business.

I gave the company another year to last at the outside and decided to quit the ship. This decision was abetted by an offer from Rheinhardt & Sellars, the San Francisco advertising firm, and a different kind of an offer that I had made to Lisa Engman the night before. The answer to both offers was "Yes."

Radcliffe came into my office that morning wearing a face like ten years of ulcers. "Jacobsen," he said. (He usually called me Felix.) "Jacobsen, you've got to do something about this publicity. It's this lousy publicity that's killing our sales." (Evidently he'd just come down from the directors' meeting.)

I stood up, picked the wire basket full of flimsies from the previous day's copy off the desk, and placed it on his head—hat fashion. It slid down over one eye, and he stood there in a shower of onionskin paper, mouth hanging open, while I put on my hat and walked out the door. I'll wager that was the most silent resignation they'd ever had—nothing but the slither of paper.

Lisa and I were married and in San Francisco in two weeks. It was the wisest move I ever made. A man doesn't really appreciate life until he's married and has a family. (Two boys and a girl.)

Three years kind of whizzed by, and one Friday I had to go to Portland to install a new branch manager there. In Portland, I crossed paths with Wilfred again. The first thing I saw as I drove uptown from the depot was a scare-face poster announcing Louis Donet, world-famed baritone, at the Civic Auditorium. "Saturday and Sunday," it said. This was Sunday.

I had a damnable time getting a ticket, but finally I remembered Susy Paulus, drama editor on *The Journal.* I'd fixed her up with some tickets once in New York. She had just one.

It was a half hour to curtain time when I got to the auditorium. I felt slightly foolish among all those strangers—digging up old memories. Opening the program, I glanced down it, really not seeing anything until a name leaped out and almost smashed me senseless. "George Bates, accompanist." I couldn't believe it. Things still were hazy when the program started. To this day I can't remember the music. The whole thing was a jumble of lights and faces.

Wilfred looked the same, but I was shocked at the change in George. He was thin, very thin, and his eyes held a haunted, almost feverish look. His playing hadn't suffered—he had the same nimble, talented fingers—but that face.

After the show, I went backstage. I saw George standing in the hallway, smoking a cigarette, and was a little at a loss on how to greet him. Finally, I walked up and stuck out my hand.

"George, you old son-of-a-gun," I said. "Long time no see."

He dropped his cigarette, and the look on his face was almost pitiful. The old memories must have flooded back all in one big wave.

"Felix," he muttered as if he couldn't believe it. "Felix, boy, where've you been all these years?" He put his hand on my shoulder. His eyes were bright.

"Oh, around," I said, and gestured with my hand. "Donet in there?" I nodded toward the door.

"If you mean that bastard Wilfred Long," he said, "yes, he's in there." George took my arm. "Come on. Let's go get us a drink and pick up the loose ends."

Before we could start, the dressing room door opened, and Wilfred stood there in a mandarin dressing gown. He started to speak to George in his same old condescending manner.

"George, how many times must I tell you that the audience pays to hear me sing, not to listen to your piano playing? You deliberately tried to drown me out in the third stanza of my first number tonight. I won't ..."

He saw me for the first time. "Hello, Felix," he said (just like that) and turned back to George. "Don't forget it next time." He closed the door.

George and I went out and found an all-night speak on Third Avenue. We crawled into a little booth with a curtain across the front. As we sat down, I noticed that George's face was as gray as the bar mop that had been left on the table. I ordered two double scotches out of habit, and when the waiter brought them, sat there toying with my glass. George still hadn't spoken since we'd left the auditorium. Abruptly, he looked up at me and grinned. It was the old George, that grin. I breathed a sigh of relief. I hadn't realized how tense I'd been.

"You're wondering why I'm working for that SOB and why I take that stuff," he said. He moved his glass in a little circle in its sloppings and looked down at it. "Well, it's this way: I'm waiting for him to make a slip and go back to Wilfred Long for just one second. He knows it, too. He can't go on forever. I'll be there when it happens to hang it on him for his first wife, for myself, and for all the others—there've been plenty." He laughed bitterly, picked up his drink, and gulped it.

His laugh frightened me—the suppressed venom in it and that quavering overtone which is next to madness. I searched for something to change the subject. "How's Gladys?" I asked.

The glass dropped out of his hand and clattered onto the table. He ignored it and looked past me.

"Dead," he whispered.

"Oh."

I didn't know what else to say, and there was a long silence.

"She had a cancer," he added. "That was almost two years ago. I couldn't afford good doctors."

I had to take George home to his hotel room that night, and it was almost like old times. Only there was no Gladys waiting for us at the door. It filled me with deadening nostalgia. When I'd tucked him in, I went out and got myself plastered good.

The next day I had a lot of business to do explaining things to our new manager, and I didn't get a chance to see George or Wilfred before they left for Seattle.

It was a month later and I was back home when I learned that George had died in Chicago. I was reading a copy of *Variety* on my way to the office and almost skipped over the item. His name wasn't even in the headline. The only reason there was a story was because he'd been Donet's accompanist. The obit said he'd had a heart attack.

I was in pretty rotten shape for work that day. George had been ... well, I'd thought a lot of him. I found out the funeral was to be in his hometown and wired a Cincinnati florist. One of the saddest damn feelings I ever had, sending those flowers.

It's funny how you pick up the loose ends on a story such as this one. Reading about George's death caused me unhappiness— oh, it had been deep enough—but when you're alive, you soon forget about the dead. They come back to you only when they're prompted by some little thing with which you've associated the one who's gone. George had faded out of my mind, and I hadn't thought about him for six months when one day down at the office ...

It was one of those bright San Francisco days, and I felt less like working than ... well, than almost anything. But I had the Farber Fisheries copy to get out, and it had to be done. My secretary interrupted the second skull session over the layouts.

"There's a man here to see you about a fine arts campaign," she said.

I looked at the card she handed me. "Reuben M. Feldman." The name didn't mean anything at first, and then it clicked. Feldman, the fellow who'd taken over when George got the sack. I dismissed the gang and told her to send Feldman in.

It was the same fellow, all right. And the funny part of it was, he didn't recognize me. I was merely another advertising executive and had been patted into the conventional shape—a little thicker here and grayer there.

Feldman came bouncing across the room on the balls of his feet. "How do you do?" he said.

"Hello, Reub," I greeted him, rising from my chair.

He stopped in midstride and took a closer look. I could see he recognized me but couldn't remember my name.

"Felix Jacobsen," I said.

"Felix Jacobsen," he repeated. "Brunswick, wasn't it?"

"Sure," I said, motioning toward a chair. "Business can wait. Sit down and give me the news from the big burg."

He sat down in the leather chair across the desk from me. "Well, I don't know where to start. How long's it been?"

"I'd hate to say," I said, and we both grinned.

"You hear about George Bates?" he asked.

"Yeah."

"And you remember Louis Donet, of course."

Did I remember Louis Donet?

"He and the Moran just got divorced," Feldman said.

"No! When'd that happen?"

"Shortly after Bates died. She went to Reno."

"Where's Donet now?"

"Down in Florida someplace. He's singing tenor in a road show. Another dame ... and you know the romantic parts those tenors get."

"He can't sing tenor," I said.

"You're right," Feldman agreed. "I've heard him, and you're right. Such music shouldn't be, but he does it. He sings *Pagliacci*. You wouldn't believe it. A second Caruso he thinks he is yet. The new blonde thinks tenors are wonderful, though."

"He change his name?" I asked.

"No, but you should see him. He's shaved off his beard. Remember the beard? And what with no hair on top, he's a sight to scare little kiddies. He's got some more weight, too. Looks like Humpty Dumpty. The people are laughing themselves sick." Feldman threw up his hands and laughed.

I had a great reunion with Feldman. We hadn't known each other too well, but we'd known all the same people. It was like meeting each one of them again. I took him home to dinner, and the kids loved him. He knew some stories about a little pig who wanted to grow up and scrub the pigpen bright and shiny; the pig became toothbrush bristles. It shocked Lisa, but the kids loved it. I was really sorry to see him go.

Well, the years went by as they do. There were … let me see, about seven, I'd guess. I remember this day very well, though. It was a Friday, and I'd been up the whole damn night with Hank— he's the youngest. I was reading the paper on the way to work, or at least I was pretending to read it. One of the pictures on an inside page caught my eye. There was a face in it that looked familiar in spite of the German uniform. "Reich Musik Führer Wilfred Long at the opening of the Berlin opera season," the caption said.

"Well, I'll be damned," I thought. "So he's changed his name back to the original." The fact that he was tied up with the national socialists and that new chancellor, Hitler, didn't seem strange at all. I guess I'd gotten to the stage where nothing Wilfred did could surprise me. My education had started abruptly the day he'd burst into the studio and bowled George over. Good old George.

I put the whole thing out of my mind, and there followed some years when the past just became more remote. I didn't think about Wilfred again until the spring of 1942. We were invited to a cocktail party that evening. Lisa and I hadn't been out of the house since before the war, so we hired a YWCA girl to sit with the kids and decided to make a night of it. The party was at Lawrence Coulard's. He's an executive with a pineapple import company we handle.

It was a bracing spring night with just a little breeze coming in from the bay and maybe a touch of fog in the air. We put the car top down and enjoyed the breeze. The Coulards live out toward Bolinas—quite a drive, but it didn't seem as though it was any time at all before we were there. At that, we were late. Lights and noise were bubbling out of the house. We parked the car at the end of a long line, got out, and walked up the stone steps and through the open doors. The butler took our wraps and announced us to a room that seemed to pay no attention. I noticed Lawrence coming toward us down a hall. He grinned and waved his hand.

Suddenly I was startled by a voice calling my name. "Felix! Felix, dear boy!"

I turned around, and there was Eugenia Moran plowing her way across the room with a drink in one bejeweled hand. She looked a good deal older and somewhat more painted than I remembered, but there was no mistaking that long, lovely face.

"Felix, it's been so long," she said as she came up. "But perhaps I shouldn't mention that. Hello, Lisa."

Eugenia grabbed my arm and began dragging me toward the punch bowl. I made futile signs to Lisa, but she waved and wandered away with Coulard. She knew all about Eugenia Moran. I finally wound up in an alcove corner with the ex–Mrs. Donet. She still had her grip on my arm.

"Felix, where have you been keeping yourself?" she demanded. "I was back in New York last month and saw all sorts of our old friends. They all asked about you, but of course I couldn't tell them a thing."

Like hell, I thought.

"My, you still look so handsome," she rattled on. "Time hasn't changed you a bit. Still the same old dashing Felix."

She broke off her monologue, put a hand to her hair, and looked at me in what she must have imagined was an arch manner. It was my cue, I suppose, to say she hadn't changed a bit either. I decided to break it up by being politely rude.

"Say, whatever happened between you and Wilfred Long or Louis Donet or whatever you want to call him?" I asked.

Eugenia pouted. "You're a rude boy," she said. "But I adore you anyway." She reached out and patted my cheek with that cold, diamond-studded hand. "So I'll tell you."

Looking out the window beside us, she paused for a long minute. When she began to speak, it was as though another person had control of her body; her voice and manner both changed.

"We were in Chicago, you know," she said. "Louis had just finished his engagement there. It was a dreary night—rainy and cold." She shivered. "Louis went up to the room, and I stayed in the bar to have a nightcap with George. Poor boy, he grieved so over his wife's death. Drank constantly. He got quite drunk that night and kept referring to Louis as Wilfred. He swore a great deal—really dreadful words. I didn't know what to do. Finally, I left him and went upstairs."

She pursed her lips before continuing.

"Louis was lying on the bed with all his clothes on. He looked … well, he wasn't a handsome man, you know. He'd opened his belt and thrown back his coat. I sat down at the dressing table to take off my dress. But it was rather difficult—buttoned in the back. It was too late to call a maid, so I asked Louis if he would unbutton me."

Eugenia paused again, and when she continued, her voice was lower. "Only I said, 'Wilfred, will you come unbutton me, please?'"

She was silent for so long a time that I thought she wasn't going to continue.

"Yes," I prompted.

"That's all," she said. "I heard the bed spring croak and waited. After a few minutes, I noticed that there was no sound in the room. I turned around, and Louis was gone. I never saw him again. I didn't learn until the next morning that George had died in the bar. His heart, you know. I waited several weeks and went to Reno. Louis and I hadn't been getting on so well."

She lifted her hands and stared at her fingers. "I often wonder what would have happened if I hadn't called him Wilfred. I feel quite guilty sometimes. Perhaps he wouldn't have gone to Germany and become a filthy Nazi."

"Perhaps," I agreed. "But who can say?"

Well, that's about all there is to Wilfred's story—all but the concluding item, which had to wait until the war was over to bring all those things back to me. It was a story in yesterday's paper that told how Wilfred Long, awaiting trial for treason, hanged himself in his cell with a strip torn from his blanket. Perhaps there's a moral in this somewhere, but I really didn't intend that there should be. I just keep going over this thought that ran through my head when I read that story. I thought, *Well, Louis Donet is dead.*

THE IRON MAIDEN

T o Pete Waller, coming across the park toward it at 1:28 on a Saturday morning, the Belroc Arms looked sinister—which he knew meant left-handed, and he felt all left-handed at the moment, on a fool's errand.

The building towered as a black outline punctured by three golden squares—windows of an apartment on the corner. Not Hal Kerrigan's apartment, which was toward the center. All the windows were dark there. This fact almost stopped Pete, but he remembered the vow of friendship: "Anytime, pal … anytime."

Pete took a deep breath, swallowed. Haloed streetlights fringed the park, and there was a wet smell of dead leaves around him. From up the street on his left came the brush-whirr-rasp of a mechanical sweeper growing louder, muffled motor whispers echoing against the stone buildings. Pete darted across the street, used the key Kerrigan had given him, took the elevator to the top, and let himself into the apartment.

The door made a thump-click as it closed behind him. The room was sonorous with sleep-breathing, and he tried to determine if it was one person breathing or two. One, he thought. He started across the familiar room, collided at shin level with a harsh edge that made a crash of sound. He barked, "Sonofabitch!" and rubbed his shin.

The sleep-breathing stopped. Kerrigan's voice came out of the dark: "Whassat?"

"I bumped my shin," Pete said. "Who moved the damn table? Uh … you awake, Hal?"

"Who's 'ere?"

"It's me, Pete."

"Pete?"

"Yeah, Pete. Is there … I mean, are you alone?"

"Chrissakes, Pete. You're about as subtle as a tank. What if I had a … guest?"

"That's what I'm trying to find out."

"I oughta take away your damn key."

There came a scratching, fluttering sound, rattling of a lamp chain, a click. Warm yellow light flooded the room, striking golden glints on a red wall. The light revealed an oblong living room jammed with a clutter of both living room and bedroom furniture. Clothing on hangers had been thrown over most surfaces. A rolled rug lay bent across the back of a basket chair.

In the center, crowded on all sides by the furniture, stood an oversized square bed with golden covers over black silk sheets. Sitting upright in the bed, his hairy chest bare, was the object of Pete's visit, a darkly tanned black Irishman with blue eyes and hunting hawk features—Hal Kerrigan.

Pete stared around at the mess—walls, color scheme. It was all different from his last visit less than a week ago. Two of the walls were now red, two black, the ceiling golden. Everything had been grey and cream before. Chinese brocade draperies of black with red-and-gold dragons covered the windows at the end of the room. The dragons undulated to a breeze pouring in from an open window. Through the clutter of furniture, Pete could see little wedges and trapezoids of a grey-and-gold rug.

Kerrigan reached for a folding alarm clock tucked onto an end table beside his bed with a full pipe rack, a bronze tobacco humidor, and a pair of brown slippers. He peered at the clock, owl-eyed, and muttered, "One thirty-four! For Chrissakes, Pete!"

Pete hobbled farther into the room, still rubbing his shin, then stopped, confronted by a tall mirror leaning against a chair. The mirror was pitiless, revealing a tired, hatless man with dun brown hair, brown eyes, a rather round face with a small nose and skin that looked decidedly pink. It always looked pink—baby skin. He tore himself away from the mirror, flopped down on a corner of the bed.

"What's all the mess?" he asked.

"I met a dame—interior decorator. What you doing bumbling in here at this ungodly hour?"

Pete looked up at the black marble fireplace behind the bed, noting something that hadn't been changed by Hal's interior decorator—a pair of holstered .45 automatics with Marine Corps insignia, each with a name burnt into the leather: Pete and Hal. They always struck him as out of place in this room.

"Hal, I got a problem," Pete said.

Kerrigan fumbled an open pack of cigarettes from the floor beside the bed, lit one, and tossed the pack across the golden blanket toward Pete, who ignored it.

"What's her name?" Kerrigan asked.

Abruptly, Pete got up, threaded his way across to the automatics above the fireplace, returned to the bed with the one bearing his name, and began field stripping it. His fingers worked with a casual, deceptive rapidity: snick, click, swish, click, swish, click, snick.

Kerrigan smoked silently, knowing there was no hurrying Pete in this mood.

Presently, the gun lay disassembled, spread out on the blanket. Pete began reassembling it, spoke without looking up. "You're in bed kinda early tonight."

"We were at a house party until 4:00 AM yesterday, and decided to play some tennis. Afterward we went sailing, and I just didn't get to bed until 9:00 PM."

"Whatta life you lead!"

"What's the problem, Pete? Tell your old Uncle Hal. You didn't come all the way up here at this hour to show me how fast you can strip that .45."

"I don't know how to say it," Pete said.

"You got some babe in trouble?"

"Nothing like that."

"Is it your job? I could have my old man transfer you anywhere in the company you—"

"No! I'm happy in the shipping department. If I learn enough, maybe I can be boss there someday, but ..."

"You wanta be promoted tomorrow?"

"Hal, you embarrass me. Sometimes I'm ..." Pete broke off, shrugged.

"You sorry you saved my skin there in that rice paddy?"

"Don't say that! I'd have ..."

"You'd've done it for anybody, I know. But you did it for me. What you want, Pete?" He waved an arm. "Take it."

"All I need's some advice ... from your experience. I just ... don't know. Maybe I better skip it." He started to get up.

Kerrigan snaked out an arm, dragged him back. "Oh, no you don't! You don't wander in here in the middle of the damn night and then leave without saying why."

Pete shook his head. "This is ... well ... I dunno."

"Look! Petey boy, it's Hal. What's mine is yours. Anytime. Advice? That I provide at no extra cost. So give."

"Hal, I dunno what to do about her."

"Which her?"

"Virgie."

"Virgie?"

Pete took out his wallet, extracted a photograph. He gazed at it a moment. It showed a blonde young woman in a bikini, proportions about 40-28-36. He sighed. She didn't make him feel sinister at all—just left-handed.

Kerrigan pulled the photograph from Pete's hand, whistled softly. "Mmmmmmmmmmm," he said, then peered more closely at the photo. "Oh, no! Not *that* Virgie!"

"I thought you'd recognize her," Pete said. "She's in shipping, too, as you know, and ..."

"Ahh, Pete." Kerrigan threw the photograph face up on the golden blanket.

Pete stared at him. "You ... uh ... *know* her?"

"Before I went out and got myself that nice green uniform. I dated her once, just once. I know others who've tried. Give it up, Pete. That's the original iron maiden."

"Hal, I just gotta ..."

"You in love or some crazy thing?"

"Maybe. I guess so. I dunno."

"That figures. With Virginia, you never know anything."

"Hal, don't say that. You don't know what happened."

"The hell I don't! You went out on a date with her and afterwards a little parking somewhere and ..."

"What's unusual about that?"

"Wait a minute, son," Kerrigan said. "You parked. One thing led to the next thing, and pretty soon you're getting eager."

Pete ran a finger under his collar.

"The dress came off," Kerrigan said. "And the slip. They were easy. And then you ran into it."

Pete stared at him, pale faced. "I didn't know girls wore those things anymore," he said. He didn't ask himself how Hal knew about it.

"It's the modern chastity belt, son," Kerrigan said. "It's called a foundation garment. You should come up into the store sometime and look around."

Pete tried to swallow with a dry throat. He felt like a fool.

"It slowed everything down to a fumbling walk," Kerrigan said. "She had time to think, and she changed her mind. *That* is what happened."

"I dunno what to do about her," Pete said.

"Drop her," Kerrigan said. "That's my free advice for tonight. Find yourself another doll."

"I don't know any other girls."

"Pete, the world's full of ..." Kerrigan stopped, stared at Pete. "Hey, fella, what about all those stories you fed us in the bull sessions? The babe in Passaio, the little wench in Amegate?"

"Hal, you know I was the youngest guy in the outfit. I lied about my age to get in. You know that."

"A terrifying thought occurs to me," Kerrigan said. "Answer me, friend: are you a virgin?"

Pete blushed.

Kerrigan slapped his forehead with his palm. "Holy Colonel Magee!"

"Okay, laugh!"

"Pete, I'm not laughing, believe me. I'm sad."

"What am I gonna do?"

Kerrigan sighed. "In a thing like this, one cannot hold one's friend by the hand through the entire operation. You know that. However ..." He shook his head. "Does it have to be Virgie?"

"Yes!" Pete looked away. He knew he had spoken too loudly, betrayed himself, but he wasn't quite sure what he had betrayed.

Kerrigan stubbed out his cigarette, said: "Better ..." He paused. "... let us say more *experienced* men than you have tried and failed."

"I still ..."

"Okay, okay." Kerrigan held up a hand, bent his head. "Say no more. A friend comes for advice; I give advice." He shook another cigarette from the package, lit it, stared through the smoke. "Have you tried night swimming?"

"Hell, *I* thought of that. She's afraid of what might be in the water, she says."

"In the water?"

"Frogs and stuff. You know."

"Well, have you tried just right out asking her—yes or no?"

"Aw, come off it, Hal!"

"Yeah." Kerrigan stared at his cigarette. "There's gotta be some way to get her out of that armor." Presently, he asked: "Did I ever tell you the camera ploy?"

"Camera ploy?"

"Somewhere in all this stuff's a 35-millimeter camera. You take that camera ... lots of dolls are exhibitionists, see. Tell 'er you're the arty type and you ..."

"Nude pictures? For Chrissakes, Hal! I couldn't."

"Did you come here for my advice?"

"Well ... yes."

"Okay. Here's what you do. You take her to dinner—some quiet place with atmosphere, candles, wine, that sort of thing. Take your time over ..."

"Hal, I couldn't ask her to ..."

"Just listen, son. You introduce her to the idea very slowly. It's almost as though it's her idea. Tell her how much you admire her beauty. Everything inspirational."

Pete nodded. There was something hypnotic about the flow of Kerrigan's words.

"Tell her her hair is like brilliant sunshine," Kerrigan said.

"Yeahhhh … brilliant sunshine."

"Photogenic, you understand? Say there's something French about her. Aiyah! The French have a way with them, understand?"

"Her grandfather's French Canadian. She told me."

"All the better. Now, for dinner, I know just the place—that Gypsy Cellar over on 64th. Violins, the works. Arrangements, lad, arrangements—it's all in your arrangements. Tell her you admire the gypsy in her."

"Yeahhh."

"You're at dinner, soft music, soft cushions—tell her she's a lovely, natural thing. Natural, got that?"

"Yeah, natural."

"Explain that only the natural things of the world are worth having."

"When do I spring the camera?"

"Easy, lad. You have to go slow, but slow on these things."

"Okay, but …"

"After dinner, you adjourn to one of those jazz joints across town, Ferreti's or Johnson's Tub or one of those pizza cellars out by the university. There's one called the Sweet Spot has a good combo. Nothing like hot jazz to get a woman in the mood."

"Jazz, okay. Then what?"

"You bring her back here."

"Here? You mean here in your …"

"You've got your key. I'll be gone next weekend. The place'll be all straightened up by then."

"I spring the camera then, huh?"

"Didn't I tell you slow? You gotta be cautious as a cat, son. I'll have the cleaning woman lay a fire in the fireplace. Good music— you know how to work the stereo over there. You get the fire going and stand her over by the fireplace while you …"

"Stand?"

"I said stand. Don't interrupt. Then you sit down on the floor and admire her. You just admire. From a distance."

"How far?"

"Far enough that you don't look too eager. While you're admiring, you use your hands like a frame—make a little square with 'em and stare at her through it. All the time you're telling her how much you'd like a picture to treasure."

"I got a picture; the one she gave me."

"But not a *natural* picture, something to express the *real* Virgie, got that?"

"I think so."

"She's standing here against the fireplace, and you tell her the setting fits her perfectly except for one thing."

"What thing?"

"The clothes, lad. And if she gets out of that armor, you're on your own."

Pete shook his head. "Hal, I dunno. You really think this'll work?"

"It never fails."

"But what if she ..."

"Don't knock it until you've tried it." He glanced at his bedside clock. "I don't know about you, but I need shut-eye. Let's sleep on it. You can sack out here with me."

Pete heaved a deep sigh. "Okay. I guess you oughta know about these things."

Presently, darkness again enfolded Hal Kerrigan's apartment. The Chinese brocade draperies rustled faintly to the breeze.

Pete cleared his throat. "Hal?"

"Mmmmph."

"Hal?"

"Yeah?"

"When you're with a girl ... I mean, what's it *really* like?"

"Oh, for ... go to sleep, son. Trust your Uncle Hal and go to sleep."

O O O

The sun came up. The sun went down. Up, down—seven times, and once again it was Sunday with sunshine touching the grey-and-gold rug at 8:18 AM.

The telephone rang. Pete answered it. He felt dopey with lack of sleep ... and angry. "Hullo? Oh, hullo, Hal. No, I'm alone. Okay, see you in a few minutes."

Pete dressed and flopped down on the grey semicircle of the davenport in front of the black marble fireplace. He stared moodily at the dead ashes in the fireplace, shifted his attention to two empty wine glasses on an oval coffee table at his left. A sneer curled his lips.

The outer door opened. Hal breezed in, throwing his hat across the room. "Hiya, Petey boy! Whatta weekend! How'd you make out?"

Silence.

Kerrigan threw his coat over a chair, sat down across the davenport's curve from Pete. "You all worn out, friend?"

"Sure."

"Wanta tell your old Uncle Hal?"

"No."

"Gentlemen don't tell; that's the boy."

"Hah!"

"Whatta you mean, hah?"

"Just hah!"

"Didn't you follow the program?"

"Program!"

"You know, dinner at …"

"Dinner at her place with her family: brussel sprouts, tuna and noodles."

"Oh?"

"Great dinner. They wanted to know how well I knew you, the boss's son and everything. And Virgie told them about the rice paddy thing. How'd she find out about that?"

Kerrigan shrugged. "My old man, probably. The whole store knows it. Don't think anything about that. He likes you."

"She even knew about the .45s over your mantle, said a girlfriend told her." He glared at Kerrigan. "Is that right?"

Kerrigan raised his right hand. "So help me. It must've been the jewelry buyer, Miss Franchot."

"Yeah, okay. So I told them it wasn't really sentimental, only a sort of joke. And I told them how much dough you won betting on me."

"Stripping the .45, you mean. Sure. Remember the time we took the five hundred iron men from Sergeant Keeler? Man! The look on his face!"

"Yeah, I told them."

"Keeler had a good boy going up against you, too—old Krouty. But man, you took him by eight seconds." Kerrigan took a deep breath. "So it was a great dinner with her folks. Well …"

"Just great. Family staring at me all through dinner. How much do I make a year? What with the boss's son being my best friend, my prospects must look pretty good, huh? Taxes are getting worse, though, aren't they?" Pete leaned forward. "Hal, did you know that a set of good living room furniture costs upwards of six hundred dollars?"

"It was pretty bad, eh?"

"It was awful."

"Did you go out afterward?"

"To the Sweet Spot, sure."

Hal grinned. "They're great, aren't they? Man! That sax sound. They're laced with it—a real coal-colored noon beat."

A touch of animation replaced the stony glare on Pete's face. "They're pretty good. I'll give you that."

"She liked it, huh?"

"She liked it."

"So you stayed awhile and then came up here."

Silence.

"You did come back here?"

"Sure, we came up here—the fire, the stereo, the hands, the whole bit."

"So?"

"She told me I shouldn't get dirty ideas from you." He glared at Kerrigan. "How'd she know about that?"

Kerrigan gulped. "Pete, I swear to you, I never …"

The glare continued.

"I swear," Kerrigan said. "So help me, you saved my life. I wouldn't lie to you about this. I never."

"Then you must have some dame who's doing a lot of talking."

"That's always possible."

Pete sank back, stared at the black fireplace. He hated his own feelings of inadequacy, his suspicions, this apartment, Hal, life, the store—everything except Virgie.

"Now that you've given up on Virgie," Kerrigan said, "maybe I could fix you up with a cute little ..."

"Who said I've given up?"

"Well, you just as much as implied ..."

"I didn't imply anything. She was absolutely right about you. I shouldn't have tried that camera trick. It's cheap."

"That's one of its big advantages." Kerrigan shrugged. "But you did strike out!"

"And how I struck out!"

"But you didn't give up?"

"Sic semper et cetera," Pete said. "I'll tell you—the lights in here were still down pretty low, the stereo was going, and I was sitting here feeling like a fool. So she came over and put her arms around me and said it was all right, she understood—men have these animal urges and everything."

"Animal urges. That's very good."

"It was kind of sooty in here, those dark walls. I kissed her. Her lips were moist and ..." He broke off, stared moodily at the fireplace.

"Well?"

"A funny thing: she shaped her mouth up funny, almost like a poodle and she made this little noise."

"Noise? What noise?"

"It sounded like *nusssss* or 'nice.' So I kissed her again."

"Yeahhhhh."

"Pretty soon she's saying, 'Please, Please, Please.'"

"Yeahhhhh."

Pete cleared his throat.

"So?" Kerrigan demanded.

"Oh, nothing."

"Whatta you mean nothing?"

"Nothing."

"Let me guess," Kerrigan said. "Off came the dress and the slip and you ran into that armor again."

Pete swallowed.

"Right?" Kerrigan asked.

Pete nodded disconsolately. "She's saying, 'Wait. No. Lemme think.' And I'm trying to get that thing unfastened and it's like it was put together with steel girders. I was all thumbs. I kept thinking if it was a .45 I could strip it, but this was too much."

"What'd you say?" Kerrigan asked.

"Huh?"

"Just then, what'd you say?"

"What'd I say what?"

"About stripping a .45."

"It was just a crazy thought. I was half nuts."

"No, wait. You had an inspiration."

"I did?"

Kerrigan leaped to his feet, grabbed one of the .45s from its holster over the mantle. He whirled, faced Pete. "You know what you're gonna do?"

"At gun point?" Pete asked. "Are you crazy?"

"No, not this," Kerrigan said. He put the gun back in its holster, returned his attention to Pete. "You're gonna get one of these foundation garments. You're gonna strap it onto a couple of pillows. And you, pal, *you* are going to practice field stripping that armor until you can get it off those pillows in nothing flat!"

O O O

Pete stared at the contraption on the floor of Kerrigan's apartment. The thing was pink in a shade that clashed with the grey and gold of the rug beneath it. Pillows protruded from each end. Two straps stretched over a pillow at the top. Garter snaps dangled limply from the bottom. A zipper reached up the right side with hooks over it. Part of a similar hook-and-eye arrangement lay unfastened on the left with a flap turned back. This revealed a second layer underneath, which suggested with its crossing bands of elastic an illustrated anatomical section of muscle tissue.

The whole thing possessed an obscene hint of fibrous flesh, Pete decided. It looked dead in a horrible, decapitated way.

Kerrigan stood over it in a maroon robe, a martini in his left hand. He sipped the martini, reached out a foot, and rolled the contraption over. This revealed tight lacings all the way up the back. "Almost takes the heart out of a man," he said. "You sure this is the same kind?"

Pete nodded.

He stood at the corner of the davenport, cracking his knuckles, knowing this betrayed his nervousness but unable to stop.

Kerrigan glanced at the moving hands, frowned. "What's eating you? This is just something to disassemble. Think of the .45 and how you beat Krouty. Practice, that's all. Speed."

"That lady on the phone when we ordered it," Pete said.

"She bother you?"

"I didn't like the way she laughed. All those questions about size and color and price range and ..."

"Why didn't you just make up a size?"

"All I knew was to describe it," Pete said. He blushed and hated himself for it.

"Take it easy, pal," Kerrigan said. "We'll just start in easy. Just get down there beside it and ..."

"Maybe I should come back tonight and practice. I really shouldn't take the day off this time of ..."

"I *ordered* you to take the day off," Kerrigan said. He downed the martini, put the glass aside. "You're helping me on a very challenging problem." He squatted beside the pillow-stuffed garment. "Come down here now, and let's analyze this thing." He touched one of the shoulder straps. "Y'know, these'd probably just pop right out if you yanked them. Give 'er a try."

Pete dropped to his knees beside Kerrigan, said: "I don't want to ... well, tear it."

"Yes, you do. You're the rampaging male. She'll love it."

"You sure?"

"Sure I'm sure. Go ahead and try it."

Pete put out his right hand, withdrew it.

"Close your eyes and imagine it's Virgie inside it," Kerrigan said. "Go ahead."

Pete wet his lips with his tongue, caught the strap in a desperate grip while Kerrigan held the pillow. Pete wrenched the strap. There came a small tearing sound, and it pulled out of its binding seam.

"Strong hands, that's what it takes," Kerrigan said. "Now, how about those snaps?"

Pete felt the challenge of the problem grip him. He took a deep breath, bent forward more intently. "Maybe if I roll them between my fingers they might just pop open." He demonstrated. "Hey! It works!"

Kerrigan got to his feet, said: "What the mind of man can do, the mind of man can undo. Fasten that thing back together best you can while I get my watch. We'll run a few time trials." Presently, he returned carrying a stop watch, said: "I borrowed this from the store. We may as well do this scientifically. Don't try for speed the first time. Just get the feel of the thing."

Pete nodded, began popping snaps, working zippers. He crouched back on his heels when it was done. "How long?"

"A minute and fifty-four seconds. Let's put 'er back together and try again."

"I don't like you calling it *her*," Pete said.

"What else would you call such a thing?" Kerrigan asked. "Here, I'll help you reassemble ... *it*."

"Okay!"

He went at it again ... and again ... and again. Kerrigan called time after the twenty-fifth run with the time down to thirty-seven seconds. "That's enough for today," he said. "Take my car and go for a drive or something. Think about it. I'll see you tomorrow night after work."

"Thirty-seven seconds," Pete said. "That's not bad."

"Not bad, not good. It's just a beginning. See you tomorrow."

"It looks kind of ... used," Pete said.

"It'll look worse before we're through," Kerrigan said.

By Thursday, with the time down to nine seconds, the *contraption* did indeed look worse, Pete decided. It looked wilted, and frayed cloth showed around the snaps. Both shoulder straps had been torn loose. Only one garter strap remained.

"What time is it?" Pete asked.

"Nine thirty-five. You getting tired?"

"Yeah."

"Take a break. How you feeling generally?"

"My hands are tired." Pete stood up, stretched. "I feel like I've unfastened that thing ten thousand times."

"Almost five hundred," Kerrigan said. "Think you can cut your time any more?"

"Gosh, Hal, I don't see how. There're just so many connections. I have to get each one."

"You got this date with Virgie tomorrow night?"

"We're going dancing at the lake."

"You feel ready?"

"As ready as I'll ever be."

"Tell you what—knock off. Rest your hands. I think any more training's just a waste of time. You can overtrain on a thing like this, you know."

"I guess so."

"You're not scared, are you?"

Pete swallowed. "Maybe a little."

"Don't be, pal. You've got it made. Blitz! She won't know what hit her."

"I don't like that kind of talk," Pete said. He cleared his throat with a cough. "Hal, I been thinking. Maybe I shouldn't do this."

"*What?*"

"Well, it's not really fair ... kind of."

"Fair! Is it fair what she's been doing? Leading you right up to that armor and cutting you off?"

"Maybe it's not her fault exactly."

"Not her fault, he says. You think she *really* wants to stop?"

"Wellll ... I dunno, maybe not."

"You know damn well she doesn't want you to stop."

"I guess you're right."

"It's your duty, Pete." Kerrigan lowered his voice. "You're really saving her from her inhibitions."

"I guess you could look at it that way."

"Think of how she's teased you," Kerrigan said.

"You really think she's been teasing me?"

"I *know* she has."

"Yeah! You could call it that."

"It's nothing else. Now you get in there and fight." Kerrigan glanced around the apartment. "You want to use my place?"

"If it's okay with you."

"Be my guest. *Be* my guest."

O O O

It was Saturday high noon in the apartment, and Pete reclined on the davenport in Kerrigan's maroon robe. He dangled a torn length of pink strap in his left hand, studied it with a pursed-lip frown of concentration.

A hesitant knock sounded at the hall door.

Pete ignored it.

The knock was repeated.

Pete raised his head. "Yeah?"

"It's me, Hal." The voice sounded muffled, conspiratorial.

Pete stuffed the strap into a pocket of the robe. "Come on in."

Kerrigan let himself in the front door, crossed to the davenport, and draped his coat over it. He leaned on the coat, looked down at Pete.

"Hi, Hal," Pete said.

Kerrigan glanced around the apartment. It looked neat—everything in its place, nothing disarranged. He returned his attention to Pete, noted a smudge of lipstick across Pete's neck.

"You're looking pretty good," Kerrigan said.

"Hal, we're getting married," Pete said.

Kerrigan's lips moved without a sound, then: "You're getting *married?*"

"Yeah." Pete frowned up at him. "You sound like you don't think it's a good idea."

"Oh, it's a great idea. Great, great."

"We think so."

"What'ya been doing here all this time if you were just going to get married?" Kerrigan demanded.

"Are you sure you're happy about this?" Pete asked. "You sound kind of funny."

"I'm delighted! I'm overjoyed."

"I was gonna ask you to be my best man."

Kerrigan passed a hand across his eyes. "Sure, Pete. Sure."

"I owe it all to you," Pete said. "She was too inhibited to get married. I proposed every night last week, but she kept putting me off."

Kerrigan pointed to the place on the rug where Pete had practiced disassembling the *contraption.* "You mean … while we were working with that … every *night?*"

"On the phone after we got through. I was hoping I wouldn't have to go through with it." Pete blushed.

"But you went through with it?"

Pete dropped his feet to the floor, sat up. A look of animation came over his face. "Hal, I watched the luminous second hand on your mantle clock. Hal, seven seconds! Think of it: seven seconds!"

"Yeah," Kerrigan said. "I'm thinking."

THRILLER

AND

ADVENTURE

The Wrong Cat

It was early dawn when the headless dog was thrown over the fence into the wisteria beside the cottage patio.

A fat golden cat skittered sideways to circle the dead dog and get to the cottage door. It mewed twice.

Mary Cloister heard the familiar call, but first she put the coffee pot full of water on the range, adjusted the flame. The glass coffee pot magnified the blue light of the gas flame. She paused to admire the color, wondered if she could capture that combination of blue light and sparkling water on canvas.

Again the cat mewed—this time angrily.

"I'm coming, Puss, I'm coming," Mary called. She belted her short red corduroy robe tighter around her slim waist and opened the door. Puss rushed in, brushing her legs with dew-damp fur.

Mary stepped out onto the patio, took a deep breath of the morning breeze off the sea. Her favorite view spot was near the wisteria and the fence. She crossed the patio in anticipation of the sight of the blue seawater and white fishing boats below.

Before she could begin absorbing the peace of the view, she saw the monstrosity that had been a dog—brown-and-white fur streaked in gore and an unthinkable horror where the head had been.

"Oh, my God!" she closed her eyes, put her hands to her face, turned, and ran into the cottage, slamming the door. "Oh, God!"

She sank onto one of the two ladder-back chairs by the maple table, closed her eyes. "Who could be so cruel?"

Puss brushed against her legs, purring. When she didn't reach to pet him, he butted her ankle with his head. "Meow!" he demanded.

She pushed his head away with the side of her foot, leaned on the table.

Now she could be sure the pattern that had begun yesterday was deliberately malicious.

The dead rat in the mailbox could have been trapped there. The knocking on the roof last night could have been squirrels. The sounds at her door—well, the wind blew strongly off the bay.

She stroked her cat's head, murmured, "That poor dog."

Across the kitchen, her Tyrolean clock began to chime the hour—7:00 AM. She stared at the clock. Jim had given it to her, and for the first time in many weeks, she began to cry.

Immediately after Jim's death, she had cried often. She and Jim had been married only two years before the accident. A drunken driver on the wrong side of the freeway, and that had emptied the happiness out of her life.

Mary had tried to return to her painting career. But the city seemed involved in a conspiracy against art. Then Jim's law partner, Ron Devin, had found the cottage looking down on Santa Maria Bay. He'd insisted she bring her paints and brushes for the summer.

"You need a long rest away from … memories," he had said.

In the way women know such things, Mary knew Ron loved her. But also in the way of such things, neither had ever mentioned it—or even looked as if it were true.

The cat leaped into her lap. "It's too soon to think about someone else. It's been barely a year," she said aloud, but the picture of Ron's slim face and sun-streaked blond hair came into her mind. She glanced toward the window.

The wisteria that framed the view forced her mind back to the horror in the garden. She shivered.

Until yesterday, the cottage had been good for her. And now—just when the sun-warmed peace of Santa Maria Bay had begun to ease the pain in her chest—this had to happen.

From the stove came a bubbling hiss. The coffee was boiling over. She jumped up, and the cat sprang to the floor with an indignant shake.

"Sorry, Puss," she muttered as she turned off the gas. She stared at the mess of coffee grounds and water spreading slowly across the white enamel stove top.

Maybe somebody's trying to scare me away, she thought. *But who? And why?*

She crossed to the refrigerator, took out a red-and-white can of cat food.

With a knife from the drain board, she levered a thick slab of the food into Puss's bowl. The operation took her near the window over the sink, and she knew if she looked out that window she could see the dead dog.

She carefully turned away without looking.

Who would want to scare me away—and why?

The only person she had met here was George Brett, owner of the general store and bait shop. *Oh—and that poor brother of his, Willy.*

She considered Willy. *Could it be that poor half-wit? But what would be the point?*

She sighed. The first thing to face was burying the dead animal in the yard. Until that was out of sight, there could be no peace for her.

Puss finished eating, mewed at the door.

She let him out, returned to the window over the sink, steeled herself to glance toward the wisteria.

The body was gone!

It couldn't be gone! She was sure the dead dog could be seen from this window, but there wasn't a sign of it.

With quickening alarm, she crossed to the door, stepped onto the patio. The sun was hot on her head as she moved toward the wisteria.

There was a crushed spot in the foliage, nothing else.

In sudden panic, she whirled back into the cottage, slammed the door. A missing dog was more terrible than the carcass in the wisteria.

This is foolish! She told herself. *Country-style juvenile delinquents are having a game with me. Or—or some animal has dragged it away.*

Mary nodded to herself. The dead dog had become a symbol. She felt if she let this incident completely shatter her peace she might never find her way back.

As a beginning therapy, she stepped once more into the sunshine, forced her reluctant steps toward the wisteria.

It took a few minutes to regain calmness. She made herself gaze out at her favorite view of the bay.

This midmorning light flattened the water far below, and only one boat was in sight, a ketch with red sails hanging limply. Not a breeze stirred. Her artist's eye measured the light, and she wondered what she could do with that matte look to the water.

The only sign of life between her and the bay was the bait shop store far below. It gave her some comfort to think of George Brett, the owner, puttering around there.

The thought came to her as she stood there that peace and loneliness were only a fraction apart. When she had arrived at the cottage, she had rejoiced in the absence of neighbors; now she longed for the security of nearby humans.

A quick movement to her left caught her eye, and she whirled just in time to see a disturbance in the hedge beyond the wisteria.

Panic choked her. She swallowed. Somebody was hiding there. "Who—who's there?" she managed.

"Just Willy," said a gruff voice. The hedge parted. A stocky man pushed through, stepped onto the patio. "Just Willy," he repeated.

She caught her breath. Willy. Brett had explained him in a hoarse whisper: "My brother. Willy ain't quite right. But he's harmless."

"What are you doing?" she asked. And she asked herself, *Was the dog Willy's doing?*

Willy giggled, looked down at the ground. "I just came to bury the poor little dog," he said.

She stared at him. "*You* buried the dog?"

"Yes'm." He frowned, worry wrinkling his face. "Didn't you want the poor little dog buried?"

Mary managed to swallow. She spoke carefully, as one would speak to a child. "What do you know about the dog? Did you put it in my garden?"

Willy shook his head slowly. It was a heavy, bearlike movement. He looked at her out of tiny, intensely blue eyes. "No.

I come by and seen the poor little dog. Didn't you want him buried?"

Mary felt sure he was telling the truth. Willy was too uncomplicated for much falsehood. "Do you know who—who killed the dog?" she asked.

Unexpectedly, Willy raised one big arm, clamped down on his own wrist with the other hand. It was a powerful gesture, full of implied violence. "If I did, I'd sure *get* him," he muttered.

She took a step backwards. Just how harmless was Willy?

He dropped his hands. "I wouldn't hurt the little dog," he said. "I loved him."

"Was—was it your dog, Willy?"

"No. But I knew him."

The way he said that: "I knew him." A normal man might mention a human friend in just the same tone. "Why were you walking by my back fence?" Mary asked.

"I come by here every morning," said Willy.

Mary found the thought unsettling. "You do? Why?"

"I come by to say good morning to your pretty cat."

We're all alone here, she thought. *What could I do if this poor half-wit became violent?*

"I'm glad you like my cat," she managed. Then: "Why were you hiding in the hedge?"

"Wasn't hiding," he said.

Without warning, tears filled Willy's eyes. One ran down his cheek, and he wiped at it with the back of his hand. "I was looking for the poor little dog's head," he said.

For a moment, Mary couldn't speak. She was aware of pity for Willy, but no words came.

Willy swallowed, said, "Head should be buried with the body."

He turned and ambled off around the house, saying, "Got to get back to the store."

Mary sank onto the stone bench near the house, took three deep breaths. Willy had told the truth. She felt a deep certainty of this. So he probably wasn't the one trying to frighten her. If that was the real meaning of these … incidents. If someone was trying to frighten her away, who could it be? And why? She gazed at the bay. Was she in someone's way?

Something brushed her leg, and she gasped. Then she heard deep purring and put her hand on a cat's reassuring fur.

"Poor Puss," she said. "Your mistress is falling apart."

The cat moved from under the bench, leaped lightly into her lap.

It wasn't Puss!

She pushed it away sharply, stared at it.

This was a black tom with a white bib and wide whiskers—and fatter and bigger than her golden Puss.

At her abrupt motion, the strange cat flattened itself to a cautious crouch, then streaked for the wisteria.

Mary stared after it. *I'm really falling apart*, she thought, *when a cat frightens me.*

But where was Puss? He wouldn't let a strange cat get this near his territory.

"Puss," she called. She stood up and crossed to the cottage door. "Puss. Puss!"

No sign of her cat. She stepped inside, moved into the tiny living room. "Puss?"

Mary felt her fingernails cutting into her palms as she glanced around the bedroom. No cat. She tried not to think of the headless dog.

A tentative mew at the door made her sigh with relief. She returned to the front door, swung it open.

The black-and-white tom stalked in, mewing sharply as it marched past her, its tail held high. The message was unmistakable: "Why were you so long opening the door?"

Mary stared at him.

Without looking left or right, he crossed to a maple rocker, leaped onto the red cushion, turned once, and went to sleep.

A chill moved down Mary's back. There was no sunlight on the chair, but within a half hour or so, the only sunlight in the room would be right on that cushion.

Puss had learned the same thing and often spent his mornings there.

How did this strange cat know? And where was Puss? A cat in a strange room will always look it over before settling down—but not this silly black-and-white creature.

For a moment, Mary considered throwing the strange cat out. But the feeling of company he gave her was too valuable.

"When Puss comes home, you'll get chased out fast enough," she muttered.

She kept reminding herself of this to keep from worrying about her cat, but by midafternoon, Puss still hadn't returned.

The black-and-white tom slept on in the patch of sun until the light moved across the room. Then he jumped onto the window seat and waited for the afternoon sun to find him there.

At first Mary pretended to be amused by his confidence—but her mood soon gave way to apprehension.

Whenever Puss slept in the sun, Mary would stroke him lightly as she passed by and he would answer with a rumbling purr.

She tried it with the black tom, and his angry yowl made her recoil in astonishment. This was a "do not disturb" cat.

Several times she approached the phone to call Ron Devin in the city—but each time she drew back. It was as if that unspoken attraction for her dead husband's partner stopped her each time.

Even thinking about going out into that cottage yard took an effort of will, but as the afternoon drew on, she realized she would have to go outside and then into the cellar for firewood. By 6:30 she knew she could put it off no longer. She couldn't wait for darkness. She steeled herself, told herself the fear was silly, but as she emerged from the house with her flashlight for the cellar, she felt hate around her. There was no doubt in her mind that someone was trying to scare her away.

She lifted the shake doors of the cellar, breathed through her mouth to avoid the sour mustiness of the dirt-floored cellar as she descended. One stab of the flashlight's beam toward the fireplace wood pile, and before she could help it, she screamed.

Lying neatly on top of the wood was the dead dog's missing head.

The flashlight began to slip from her fingers. She used both hands to steady it for a moment. With an effort of sheer will, she snatched a quick armload of wood from the edge of the pile, then raced for sun and sanity.

She pushed through the door into the kitchen, locked the door behind her, and dumped her wood into the woodbox.

Panic gave way to anger. She pounded one fist into the palm of the other. "Enough is enough," she said.

She strode into the living room, determined to throw out the strange cat, no matter how much it yowled.

But the black cat was gone, and her own golden Puss slept serenely in the patch of sunlight.

"Sure looks pretty in the sun," said a voice by the door.

She screamed and whirled. "Willy! What are you doing here?"

Willy grinned, stepped farther into the room. "Brought back your pretty cat."

She swallowed. "Thank you, Willy."

He took a step closer. "Had to put my cat outside," he said. "Your cat got pretty mad when he saw Blackie."

"Is the black cat yours?" she asked.

Willy nodded proudly, his tiny blue eyes sparkling. "Yes. Do you like my pretty kitty?"

Mary managed a nod. "He made himself at home."

Willy grinned. "He used to live here. He belonged to the nice lady who died."

Who died? Mary wondered. *Nobody told me.* She swallowed in a dry throat. "Did you know the lady who died?"

Willy shuffled into the patch of sunlight that spread gold across Puss's fur. He stroked the cat, and it responded with a deep purr. "Sure is a nice cat," he said. "I took him to see my house."

Mary tried frantically to think of a way to make Willy leave without antagonizing him. "Did—did your cat go home?" she asked, thinking she might suggest his black cat was hungry and he should attend to it.

Willy shook his head. "No. He likes it better here. I have to keep him closed in my cabin." His jaw went slack. "Poor lady. She was sure nice to that cat." He jerked his head toward Mary. "She liked her cat just like you do."

Mary nodded, took a careful step toward the kitchen door and the phone.

"She got all choked," said Willy.

Mary's eyebrows rose. "The cat?"

"Naw. The lady. Her eyes sort of bugged out, and she was real dead, so—"

Mary took two more steps toward the kitchen. Willy was not only half-witted, he sounded psychotic. In a wildly irrelevant way, she recalled reading that simpletons seldom went crazy. Not enough mechanisms to go wrong.

A sudden idea came into her mind. "Willy, would you do me a favor?"

"I'd like that," Willy said. "I did lots of nice things for the lady who got choked."

"Yes," Mary said. *What in God's name was he talking about?* "I found the head to the dog, Willy."

He seemed interested. "Where is the poor little dog's head?"

Mary almost said, "Where you put it," but she restrained the thought. "Down in the cellar," she said. "You have to go outside to go down there."

Willy grinned in delight, shambled toward the door. "I'll get it and put it with the rest of the poor little dog," he said.

Mary took a deep breath of relief as Willy shuffled out the door. She hurried to close it when it opened again and Willy leaned in at her.

"Lady," he said gently.

She paused in the center of the room. "Yes?"

Willy smiled, and his little blue eyes almost closed. "If you get choked, I'll take care of that pretty gold cat of yours, too."

Mary forced the corners of her mouth in a caricature of a smile. "Thank you," she managed.

The door closed, and she heard Willy's progress around the house. Three steps took her to the door. She slammed and locked it. She hurried through the house to the back door, checked its double locks.

Through the thin flooring beneath her feet, she could hear Willy in the cellar. She forced the picture out of her mind of the halfwit removing the gory head from the woodpile.

But his voice came through the floor to underline the unseen movement. "Poor little doggie. Poor, poor little doggie. Willy's going to put you back together. Poor little doggie."

Still crooning, Willy crossed the cellar, mounted the stairs to the patio behind the kitchen.

Mary returned to the living room and sank into the maple rocker.

On the window seat, Puss opened one eye, mewed lightly.

Mary set the rocker into gentle motion, tried to organize her thoughts. When Willy spoke of "the woman who had been choked," she had not believed him, but now doubts hit her.

Perhaps Willy had made it all up.

But the cat had acted so much at home.

Skepticism reasserted itself. *What I need is sane and logical conversation,* she thought, realizing as she did that it was the first time since coming to the cottage that she had thought seriously of returning to the city.

She pulled herself from the armchair, went through to the wall phone in the kitchen.

With one hand on the receiver, she paused, wondering if she was using these incidents as an excuse to call Ron. She shrugged. *What if I am?* she thought. *I was never meant to be a hermit.*

The lawyer's voice came on the phone at the second ring, and she felt suddenly shy.

"Mary!" he said. "How are you? Is Santa Maria taking the— are you feeling better?"

She pushed the receiver hard against her left ear. "It's—it's beautiful here, Ron. I wish you could see it."

His voice sounded light and happy. In her imagination, she could see his big desk with its afternoon clutter of papers. "I wish I could, too. Maybe ..." His voice trailed off, then became stronger. "Why don't I drive up one of these days?"

"Why not tomorrow?" she asked. The receiver felt damp in her hand.

He laughed. "It's Saturday. Why not?"

Mary took a deep breath. "Well—well, fine, then." She wanted to tell him how frightened she was; she didn't know how to begin.

"Mary." His voice changed, deepened. "Is something wrong?"

She closed her eyes, forced her voice to sound easy. "No. No. Not really. It's just that something rather awful happened this morning, and I haven't quite gotten over it.

"What happened?"

"Some kids threw a dead dog onto my patio," she said. "I found it when I came out this morning." She took a deep breath.

There was a moment of silence on the phone, filled only by a faint line hum. Then he said, "Couldn't the dog have been ill—or perhaps poisoned? And just happened to die where you found him?"

Her hand was perspiring so freely it slipped a bit on the receiver. She gave up her pretense of calm. "Ron! The dog had no head! Somebody had cut off its head!"

"Good God!" He hesitated. "That has a nasty sound to it." Again silence, then: "Have you called the police?"

"No—I—what could I actually tell them?"

His voice hardened. "Look, I'll be up tomorrow. In the meantime, promise you'll stay inside and keep the doors locked. This doesn't sound like kids. It sounds like a nut."

She promised, although the doors had been locked ever since she'd gotten rid of Willy. Still, the first thing she did after hanging up was recheck the doors—and the windows.

As Mary went into the living room, Puss woke up, stretched in the sunshine, and curled up the other direction.

Mary glanced at the clock. Almost 8:00. Night came late in the summer. She wished for a moment she had insisted Ron come right up, but that would have sounded hysterical. She wondered if she should have told him what Willy had said about the woman who had been choked—but was glad she hadn't. The ravings of that poor simpleton would have convinced Ron she was a nervous wreck.

The phone rang, and fear clutched at her chest. She forced herself to cross the living room and kitchen slowly, answering it on the third ring. "Hello?"

"Mrs. Cloister?"

Mary smiled her relief. It was the warm voice of Brett at the store. She could picture him, with his shock of brown hair standing almost on end—the gentle expression of his eyes—the work-calloused hands. "Hello, Mr. Brett," she said, more enthusiastically than she had intended.

"Say, I'm sorry to bother you, but I got to worrying about Willy. Has he been up there pestering you, Mrs. Cloister?"

Mary frowned at the phone. "Why do you ask?"

Brett chuckled, and again his voice warmed her. She pictured him in her mind—thinking suddenly how strange was the similarity between Brett and his brother, yet the bright blue eyes so alarming in Willy were friendly when lit by Brett's intelligence. And the stocky build, so simian in the brother, looked strong and protective in Brett.

"Well," said Brett, "Willy was late this morning, and he said he'd been up at your place. I got to thinking, and I was afraid he'd been pestering you. He acts sort of queer sometimes—but he don't mean no harm."

Mary took a firmer grip on the phone. This was her chance to clear up the biggest question in her mind. "Mr. Brett, who used to live in this cottage?"

"Last party was a fishing fellow from the city. Before that, a young couple lived there all one summer. Why?"

Something felt wrong in the answer. Mary shook her head, glanced around the kitchen. "Who—who fixed this place up?"

"Must have been the young couple," Brett said. "The wife was an artist with some magazine. She had pretty fancy ideas."

Mary's eye swept the provincial wallpaper, the ruffled priscillas, the almost overdone cuteness. "Oh? Maybe I know her," she said. "Which magazine?"

Brett named one of the most sophisticated fashion publications in the country. Mary gasped in disbelief. No artist who worked for that magazine could have overdecorated this kitchen. "Are you sure?"

He cleared his throat. "Yes, Mrs. Cloister. She was always talking about it. Seemed pretty proud of her job."

Mary readjusted her grip on the phone, thinking of the woman Willy had said was choked. "Are you sure someone else— some other woman didn't live here just recently? Maybe an older woman—?"

Brett's voice became less friendly. "What do you mean?"

"Oh—just something Willy said."

The warmth returned to Brett's voice as he chuckled. "Pay no mind to Willy, Mrs. Cloister. He just ain't right." He cleared his throat. "You want I should bring you up some groceries?"

She thought, *I'll need to fix lunch for Ron tomorrow, but I'd better think through a list first*. She said: "No, thank you. I'll need some steaks and things in the morning, though—I may walk down."

"Glad to bring them up," he said.

"No, thank you," Mary said. "I'm not sure of everything I need yet."

"Give me a call when you need me," he said. "I'll come myself instead of sending Willy."

"Thank you," she said. She considered telling him about the dog but hesitated to add to his worries about his brother. "You're very kind."

"That's what neighbors are for," he said. "It's hard on a woman all alone. A body gets to thinking too much." He paused, then added, "If you ever feel jumpy or anything, you just call me."

"I will," she said. "Thank you, Mr. Brett."

After she had hung up, she felt jumpier than ever. Perhaps she should have had him bring up some groceries and check the place.

Soon it would be dark. With a shudder, she remembered the sounds that had disturbed her the previous night.

After a late supper that was more a snack than a meal, Mary again went around the cottage, checking the door locks.

The cottage was so far from its neighbors that it had no window shades—just red checked curtains that barely pulled across the night-darkened panes.

She started her fire, sat down before it with Puss in her lap—tried to read. Soon she realized she was just turning pages. Her awareness remained focused on the poorly covered windows.

Was someone out there? And if so—why?

She scratched Puss under the chin, glad of his company. "Well, Puss, I'm scared." She tried to smile. "If that's the idea of all this—it's succeeding."

The door shook suddenly, and her eyes widened in fear. She stroked the cat as if Puss had been frightened too. Her stomach felt like one big knot.

"Just the wind," she said.

Again she tried to read—and again failed. She snapped the book shut in anger at her own nervousness.

At the slap of the book's closing, Puss leaped to the floor, mewed at the door.

What if someone forces his way in as I let Puss out? Mary wondered. She stood up, made herself walk to the door, held it open while Puss marched out.

It was pitch black outside. The wind from the bay blew harsh and cold. She closed the door quickly.

That's one cat that stays out tonight, she told herself. *I'm not opening that door again for anything.*

She consoled herself with the thought that Puss often stayed out all night—it wouldn't hurt him.

The only thing to do was to go to bed, she decided. She refused to check the locks again, turned off the lights. With the lights out, each window didn't seem to be watching her.

After she got into bed, Mary found herself wishing she had told Ron to drive up this evening. He might have taken her back to the city and the safety of her apartment.

This is nonsense! She told herself. Muscle by muscle, she forced each part of her body to relax—starting with her toes. She stretched, willed a drowsy mood to fill her mind.

Without warning, the bed shook as something heavy hit it. Mary gasped, jerked erect in bed. "What—?"

A deep purring came out of the dark.

"Oh, Puss! You scared me." She sank back onto her pillow, felt the bed quiver as the cat sought a comfortable spot near her feet.

Mary's eyes began to close; the drowsiness returned—and then she remembered: Puss had been locked outside!

She eased to a sitting position, reached out in the darkness, brushed against soft fur.

The cat snarled angrily, and she drew back with a gasp.

It was Willy's black-and-white tom, the cat that had belonged to the woman who "was choked."

Mary stared into the blackness, hardly breathing in her effort to hear any strange sound. A pulse drummed in her neck.

Was the front door opened? How could this cat have entered?

The sensible part of her mind told her to get up, check the door, and see if it had blown open.

Slowly, she swung her legs from under the covers, felt the braided rug under her bare feet.

Again the strange cat snarled, disturbed by her movement.

Her hand moved to the light over her bed, pulled back.

The only sound had been from the cat. If there was another— her mind hunted the word—another *intruder*, it would be better not to advertise that she was awake.

She felt a terrible exposure moving through darkness— wearing only a flannel nightgown. It was as if she walked toward danger instead of running from it.

A tiny orange light, flickering from an almost burned-out log in the fireplace, greeted her as she entered the living room.

Mary took a deep breath, crossed to the hearth, picked up a piece of firewood. With the makeshift weapon in her hand, she felt somewhat safer.

She could see the front door by the firelight. Tightly closed.

How had that black tom entered? Not down the chimney— the fire. Mary frowned. Could a window be open from the top? The wind—she'd have felt a cold draft.

She moved toward the lamp, reassuring herself with the round splintering feeling of the firewood in her hand. The lamp chain felt cold. She pulled it—*click!*—and sighed with relief as yellow light drove back the darkness.

A rattling and rolling sounded from the roof. She looked up, stifling a half scream.

"What was that?" she asked, forcing her voice into the silence.

It came again—a rumbling crash—followed by repeated knockings and rolling.

She'd tried to blame the squirrels the night before, but tonight it was much louder.

The thought of giant squirrels dropping oversized walnuts onto the roof brought a hysterical giggle into her throat.

Again the noise rattled and tumbled down the roof.

It could only be one thing. Someone must be throwing rocks onto the roof—a cruel joke.

Mary crossed to the front door, the firewood clenched in her hand. She held her face close to the tiny window in the door, flashed on the porch light, peered out.

Something moved out there. For just a moment, she saw a man, a shadow against shadows. Then he was gone, swallowed by night beyond the wisteria.

The half-second glimpse was enough. Willy!

Mary tried the doorknob, making sure it was locked.

With a swirl of her gown, she raced for the kitchen, double-checked the lock and bolt on the back door.

She turned on the light over the stove, crossed to the table, and sank into a chair. Willy! What could she do against that poor, confused mind?

She put the firewood on the table, stood up, and crossed to the telephone. The kitchen linoleum was cold against her feet. Her first thought was to call Ron, but he was three hours away in the city. Perhaps Brett? She nodded. He would know how to handle Willy.

She found the number, lifted the phone off the hook, put it to her ear.

Silence.

Not even a line hum.

The kitchen felt so cold, the night so dark and windy. She clicked the phone hook, knowing before she did it that it was useless. Someone had cut the wires.

For some terrible reason, Willy wanted her to be alone and frightened.

She swallowed hard—once, twice. *At least he can't get in.*

Then she remembered the black–and–white tomcat. How had it entered?

Her glance strayed toward the kitchen window. The curtains barely stretched across the dark glass, with gaps at each side where anyone could look in.

She debated between the concealment of darkness and the reassurance of light. Darkness offered some security. She moved to the switch, plunged the kitchen into darkness, and hurried to the front room.

Again she glanced at the poorly covered windows, reached for the lamp, then gasped as it went out before her fingers touched the chain.

The main switch! It was just inside the cellar door. No way to get to it without leaving the safety of the cottage.

Again the hysterical laughter grew in her throat. *Safety of the cottage!*

As her eyes adjusted to the darkness, she became aware again of the glow from the dying fire. For a moment a flame flickered brightly, then settled to a dull ember.

Mary stood barefoot in the center of the braided rug, head turned to catch any sound. Despite her flannel gown, she shivered, tensing every muscle against the chill and the fear.

She could almost touch the silence and the dark.

Three heavy blows struck the door. Mary felt each in her chest as if she had been hit.

Oh, God! There he is! She stared toward the dark-hidden door. The heavy knocks came again—then a voice.

"Hello, Mrs. Cloister! Are you home?"

With a gasp of relief, Mary recognized Brett's voice. But what was the grocer doing outside her door at midnight?

She crept to the door, peered through the little window. Automatically she flicked the switch for the porch light before remembering she had no electric power.

"Yes?" she called. "What is it?"

"It's me," said the friendly voice. "Mr. Brett from the store. Are you all right?"

"My lights and phone are out," Mary shouted through the door. "Can you call someone for me?" Dimly, she could make out the white shadow of his face—so like Willy—yet so importantly different, with the light of intelligence in his eyes.

"Can I come in?" he asked. "Maybe I can fix them up for you."

She answered with a question: "What are you doing here?"

"Saw Willy coming this way. Thought I better check. You all right? Better let me come in and look around."

Her hand moved toward the doorknob. She jerked it back. "I'm not dressed."

"Better let me in," Brett persisted. "I could check around for you."

She didn't like his insistence. "No—no, thank you. If you'd just phone someone for me, that would be enough."

He rattled the knob, and she jumped away from the door.

"Open the door," he said. "You shouldn't be all alone and scared."

"I'm all right," she called.

Again the knob rattled. "Open up!" he demanded.

She gasped. "Please. Please go away."

Then, incredibly, she heard the sound of a key being fitted into the lock.

She moved as quickly as she could in the darkness, felt her way into the bedroom, and eased the door closed.

The black–and-white cat mewed angrily as her foot hit against the bed.

"Hush!" she said sharply, straining for any sound from the living room. Yes. There it was. The slight creak of footsteps, then a crash as Brett ran into the rocking chair.

He cursed angrily, gave the chair an audible push.

Mary shuddered, furious with herself for not running for the kitchen with its back door.

She felt her way around the bed, shaking the black-and-white cat. He protested loudly.

Oh, damn that cat! She thought. The least disturbance sets him off.

A dim light showed under the bedroom door. *He must be using a flashlight now,* she thought.

She groped with trembling hands for her robe, slipped into it. She could hear him fumbling at the knob of the bedroom door.

He swung it open.

The flashlight beam blinded her; she blinked away from it.

Her voice sounded steadier than she expected. "What are you doing in my house?"

"I'm awful sorry to scare you, Mrs. Cloister," Brett said in a soft voice. "But you shouldn't be here all alone. That Willy can be dangerous."

"You told me your brother was harmless," she said, her mind racing. *Keep him talking,* she told herself.

Brett chuckled softly. "Willy takes spells," he said.

She could just see the outlines of his face behind the light. "Why do you have a key to my house?" she demanded.

"Lady who was here gave it to me," he said.

Fear rose in her throat like gall as she remembered Willy's tale of the lady that was choked. "You said a man lived here."

Brett shifted the light to his left hand, took a step into the bedroom. "Did I? Well, maybe before him, she was."

Mary forced her voice steady. *Don't let him stop talking.* "It was you who left the dog on the patio, wasn't it? Why did you do it?"

Brett cleared his throat. "It was sort of a little lesson. Wanted to show you bad things can happen when a woman's all alone."

Suddenly he turned his head toward the darkness of the living room. She heard the sound that had distracted him: footsteps. Hope grew in her mind like a light.

"Who's there?" he asked, his voice shrill.

"Just Willy," said a deep voice from the darkness.

The hope died. She wanted to cry. Now there were two of them. How could she get around Brett *and* past his half-witted brother?

"You get out of here, Willy," Brett said. "Go home."

"I just want my cat," Willy said. Then, as if suddenly noticing, he added, "Why's it dark?"

Brett seized on this excuse. "Willy," he said in a gentler voice. "You take this here flashlight and you go down cellar and turn on the lights. There's a switchbox down there."

"Willy, wait!" Mary cried. Anything was better than being left alone with Brett. "Wait, Willy! You have to help me."

"Where's my cat?" Willy persisted.

"Willy!" she said. "You have to help me. Your brother's the one who killed that pretty little dog."

"Where's my cat?" Willy demanded.

"Damn it!" Brett snapped. "How do you expect to find your cat in the dark, you dummy?"

Willy moved close to his brother, another dark shape behind the flashlight. "Give me the light," Willy said. He took it and moved away toward the door.

Brett followed swiftly, a gross shadow. The front door slammed, and she heard the lock snick closed.

In the deeper darkness after the light, Mary plunged toward the bedroom door.

But Brett was quicker. She rushed into him in the doorway, felt her arms seized in a strong grip.

He pulled her against him, released her left arm to embrace her. "There, there," he said. "Don't be scared. I'm right here."

His face came closer. She smelled whiskey and tobacco. She tried to twist away, felt the wet touch of his lips against her cheek.

What can I do? She asked herself as she tried to push away and found herself ineffective against his rough strength. Her knees felt like rubber.

Do I dare hurt him? She wondered. *If I kick or scratch, could I hide in the dark house? Or would it be better to play up to him—wait for my moment of escape? Or would that just make him angry and murderous?*

She felt his hand move on her back up to her head, force her face toward his.

The living room lamp sprang on behind him, silhouetting them in the square of light from the doorway.

She could see his face, heavy lips wet with passion, the little blue eyes glittering. He blinked in the light and said, "Damn!" His grip relaxed.

In a burst of revulsion, she forced herself free, stumbled backward till the bed hit the back of her legs. "Get out of here!" She almost screamed the words. The black-and-white cat on the bed meowed in protest.

Brett arranged his face in what he must have thought a pleasant expression. "Now, what's wrong with me?" he asked. "A widow needs a man now and then."

"Get out!" She looked around for a weapon, regretted she had left the piece of firewood in the kitchen.

The black-and-white cat snarled angrily as she pressed backward around the bed. Her foot kicked a shoe. She wondered if she could distract Brett long enough to get her hands on the shoe—use its spike heel for a bludgeon.

He took a step toward her, and she spoke quickly. "What happened to the woman who lived here before I did?"

Brett shook his heavy head. "What's wrong with me?" he asked. "Am I so ugly?"

With one toe, she moved the shoe from under the bed, kept her gaze on his little blue eyes. "No," she lied, trying to smile. "I wouldn't call you ugly."

"She did," he said, and moved closer. "A woman shouldn't live alone. I told her that. But she called me ugly."

He's mad! Mary thought. *God help me!* She forced her voice steady. "So you had to get rid of her, didn't you?" The shoe was by her right foot now. In a second she would dip down and grab for it.

"She called me ugly," he said again. His voice carried honest bewilderment. "I told her to be quiet. I didn't mean her to die. I just wanted her to be quiet—and not say things like that." Incongruously, he chuckled. "She's real quiet now."

Mary was afraid she would faint. "What do you mean?"

"She's sleeping like a top," Brett said. "Right down in your cellar." His tone went solemn. "It's what she would have wanted. She loved this cottage."

From the other room came an angry rattle of the outside door. "I want my cat!" Willy shouted.

Brett's glance flickered over his shoulder; he began to turn slowly toward the disturbance.

Mary snatched for the shoe.

But her shoulder hit the bed. The cat protested with a furious yowl.

Brett whirled back to her as she raised the shoe to strike.

He caught her wrist, shook her arm till the shoe fell to the floor.

Now Willy was pounding on the living room window. "You give me my cat!" he demanded.

"Damn dummy!" Brett muttered. "Now he's looking in the window. A man and woman like to be alone—without some damn dummy peeking in at them."

Mary wanted to sob but didn't dare give way. She forced a grotesque smile. "Why don't you make him go away?" *That stupid cat,* she thought.

"I'll just close the bedroom door," Brett said, releasing her arm and turning back to the door.

Mary focused on the cat, desperation forcing her mind to work at a furious pace.

Brett had reached the doorway.

Mary scooped up the surprised cat, hurled it at the man's back.

The cat screamed in fury and fright, dug angry claws into Brett's shoulders.

With a startled curse, Brett whirled a grotesque dancing circle in the doorway. He clutched for the hissing, panicky cat. Its claws tore at his shoulders. A stumbling step carried them into the living room. Brett still grappled for a hold on the black-and-white fury.

A groan of pain escaped him as he ripped the animal from his shoulders. He flung it to the floor, kicked at it as it streaked under the couch.

Mary rushed past Brett, fumbled at the front door, tore it open, shrank back as Willy confronted her.

Willy filled the doorway, the hatchet from the cellar in his hand.

Brett grabbed her, whirled her toward him, his face contorted with pain and anger. "You damn bitch!" he snarled. "You dirty little—"

His hands were at her throat.

She kicked and fought, but his grip tightened. She could sense pain and approaching unconsciousness, but abruptly she was free. The hands released her throat. Brett jerked away.

Willy! The half-wit held his brother—his strong hands restraining the other's strength as easily as Brett had managed Mary.

Gasping for air, Mary stumbled out the front door, fled through the garden into the road.

Headlights from a car climbing the hill blinded her. She waved her arms in a frantic signal. "Help!" she screamed. "Please help me!" *Oh, God!* She prayed. *Please be a friend.*

The car skidded to a stop on the gravel, bounced with the sudden braking. The driver jumped out.

"Mary!"

It was Ron's voice. *How could it be Ron?* She wondered dazedly.

"For God's sake, what happened?" he demanded.

"Ron! Oh, Ron!" She threw herself at him. "Oh, thank God!"

He held her close. "Take it easy. I'm right here."

"Are you real?" she asked. "Where'd you come from?"

"I didn't like the sound of that headless dog," he said. "I decided I'd better come up tonight instead of tomorrow."

She began to sob. "We have to get out of here. He's—he's out of his mind."

"Who?" Ron held her close.

"Mr. Brett."

A voice spoke out of the darkness beyond the headlights, "He hurt a little dog." Willy stepped into the light, carrying the black-and-white cat cradled in his left arm. There was blood on his hands.

Mary closed her eyes, pressed closer to Ron. She remembered the hatchet.

"Who are you?" Ron demanded.

"Just Willy," the man said, stroking the black-and-white cat. He grinned. "My brother was mean to a poor little dog. I fixed him the same way he fixed the dog."

Mary moaned in horror. She would have fallen if Ron hadn't held her.

Willy shuffled out of the light, walked away down the road. "He hurt my cat, too," he announced to the night.

THE YELLOW COAT

[This story recently appeared in Fiction River: Pulse Pounders, WMG Publishing, 2015.]

There was a separate type of fear in each of the three men running up the open hillside in the late summer evening. They paused for a moment beside a row of rotten poles that marked an old fence line, and the way each man rested exposed his fear.

The man in the yellow coat stopped a little ahead of the others and turned, watching his companions more than he did the back trail. He was out of place here—a city man with narrow shoulders padded out by the coat and with the thin face of a drugstore diet. Even his yellow coat from a walk-up store was out of place, a bit of cheap color amidst the rich gold of the dry grass.

And this city man's fear was of his two companions and the hills around him, which had no street signs. He was Skeeter Ricco, and his type seldom live beyond the age of thirty.

Indian Karl Daggert sat on a fallen log facing the valley, where darkness already was gathering up the shadows of the day into one mass of blackness. Anyone watching him would have said he was completely relaxed, but there was an almost imperceptible twitch to a muscle on his high, tanned cheekbone. His nightshade eyes did not waver from the way they had come.

Karl Daggert feared those who followed, for this fleeing on foot was not part of his plan.

Little Rollo Eckstrom, fat and dumpy with heavy jowls, sat in the tall grass a little lower on the hillside. The look of fear upon his face was a natural part of him. Many had seen it there. It was the mark of cowardice, which is stamped on the child and never leaves the man.

And Rollo's fear was centered on Indian, Karl. He had seen that twitching cheek muscle before. Karl was going to kill a man. Rollo feared that it would not be Skeeter Ricco of the yellow coat. It had always been the odd man before, but this time ...

Ricco tensed. "Hear that?"

They listened. From far down in the valley, across the dimming silver of the river where they had abandoned the car, the sound of baying dogs floated up to them.

"They got dogs after us, Karl."

"Yeah, Skeeter, I hear it." Karl rose to his feet, unfolding in angular sections. "Bloodhounds." He looked down at Rollo. "Come along, Rollo boy. Follow papa."

He turned and picked up a bulging leather satchel that had rested beside Ricco. "Lead off, Skeeter. I'll carry the bag a ways."

The man in the yellow coat turned and led the way up the hill. After a few steps, he began to speak. "I s'pose you guys are blamin' me for not pickin' a car that'd ride those ruts."

Karl spat in the grass.

Behind him, Rollo remained silent, his body cold with fear— of the law that followed and the killer ahead.

Ricco continued, "Well, I ain't never been in this country before. You oughta blame Rollo. He was born here. He shoulda warned me."

Karl shifted the satchel to his left hand without changing stride. "Shut up," he said. Then, half turning his head added, "What's on the other side of the ridge, Rollo?"

The little man swallowed the dryness in his throat. "Hedgehog Creek. Say, Karl! There's a limestone cliff on the other side and some caves. Maybe we could ..."

"Creek!" The tall one stopped just below the ridgetop and turned. The others stopped with him. "Use your head, fat boy. If that creek's big enough, those dogs don't mean a thing to us." He listened a moment to the sound of the baying, seemingly louder now. "Come on! Let's get to that water!"

They hurried over the crest.

Once below the ridgetop, shadows enveloped them. Fallen logs and thickets of salal and salmonberry became a dark mass through which they threaded their way. Halfway down the hill, they hit a trail slanting to the right. Through the open trees above them, a dusky half-light showed the pathway leading down into deeper darkness.

Rollo, in fear of Karl slowing his steps, was twenty feet behind the others when he reached the trail. He was just in time to see Karl whip a thin blade from his waistband, dart forward, and plunge it into the swaying yellow coat. Ricco pitched forward onto his face, quivered slightly, and was still.

An almost audible sigh of relief escaped Rollo's lips. He waddled up, his hand on the .38 in his pocket.

Karl faced him, standing over the fallen man, the knife in his hand strangely devoid of any blood.

"He got us into this," Karl was saying. "Now he can get us out. The dogs'll wait here and hold up the men while we get away. Come along."

Rollo waited, his fingers still damply clutching the gun.

"What you want?" Karl's eyes were on the hand in Rollo's pocket.

Rollo swallowed, dredged up a thin flag of courage that was held aloft by greed—a need to get something out of the ordeal they had already survived. But might not survive unless Rollo could maneuver through these dangerous waters. He moved his hand in the pocket, made sure the .38 was prominent.

"I want part of the money. Just my share," he said, as if he needed to explain it.

Karl scowled. "And who decides your share?" As if the fat boy deserved half of what remained.

Rollo looked at the satchel, could not know how much they had actually stuffed in there during the frantic minutes of the robbery. "A thousand," he said. A nice round number.

Anger flashed across Karl's face, but the baying hounds made him change his mind. With a look of disgust, he opened the leather satchel. "A thousand?" He began hefting out stacks of bills, ten banded bundles like valuable decks of cards. "There, a thousand."

Clearly not half of what the satchel contained, but that was the number Rollo had demanded. Karl snapped the satchel shut.

Rollo picked up the bills and held the jumble in his hands. Since they had to run, this was going to be a problem. "How am I supposed to carry this?"

"That's not my problem," Karl said, then glanced at the body of Skeeter Ricco in his bright but now bloodstained coat. "Use the yellow coat. Skeeter doesn't need it anymore."

Rollo felt sick. He held the bills in his hands, stared at the body, and Karl trudged off as the barking dogs came closer. Rollo didn't want to leave the money behind. Finally, after too long a hesitation, he set the bills on the moist forest floor, knelt, and tugged the coat from the dead man's limp torso, working the uncooperative arms out of the sleeves.

Karl was already hurrying down the path. Ricco tumbled the bills into the coat, then folded the waterproof fabric over them, folded again, and finally had a neat package that was possibly worth dying for. He grabbed it up and ran after his companion.

Karl was already almost to the creek, brooding. *The thousand doesn't matter,* he thought. *Let the little jerk have it. They'll find Ricco's body, and since he waited outside of town with the car, they've seen only two of us. Now they'll think there's only one left—a short, fat boy. At the creek I think we'll split. It'll be too bad if they find Rollo—too bad for Rollo.*

Behind, Rollo's fear had returned. *What will Karl do now? He doesn't need me.* But the little man's fear of those who followed was greater than his fear of Karl; so he stayed close, even knowing how murderous the man was.

Abruptly, Rollo heard Karl's feet clatter on a log plank bridge, and from his childhood he remembered this place.

"That's Watson's Hole crossing," he called, and hurried to catch up.

"Shut up and listen!" Karl whispered.

Above on the ridge, they heard the dogs, their barking now a frenzy of yapping and howling.

"They found 'im," Karl said. "That'll bring the men up on the run." Then, "Here's where we split up, Rollo boy. We're going to confuse 'em. You head upstream and I'll go down. When we're clear, we'll meet at the Lockton Hotel in Savannah. First one there registers under the name of Skeets. Got that?"

Fear had muted Rollo's tongue. "Go it alone?" He gulped.

Karl hurried on. "Don't take chances, but if you're caught, clam up. Now good luck."

Rollo heard a soft splash in the creek below the bridge. For a moment he waited, almost willing to brave Karl's wrath and follow. But he thought better of it. He had a thousand dollars, and Karl was short tempered. It didn't occur to him that he could have shot Karl in the back coming down the ridge and then taken all the money. One didn't think things like that about Karl Daggert.

He turned and lowered himself clumsily over the opposite side. The water was marrow chilling, creeping up his pants legs. His teeth began to chatter. Slipping and clutching at limbs, he made his way upstream.

Downstream, Karl waited until Rollo's progress could no longer be heard, then he began to follow, leaving subtle spoor along the banks—a hand print in the mud, a broken limb. He did this for perhaps a hundred yards, then turned and made his way back and under the bridge....

On the upstream side, Rollo hadn't gone more than a quarter of a mile before he stumbled into a deep hole hollowed out by a low waterfall. He almost lost the yellow coat with its wrapper of bills and, when he had rescued it dripping from the creek, he turned and faced the falls. It was so dark he couldn't see the water, but from the sound, he judged that it couldn't be dropping more than three feet.

Suddenly, an inspiration hit the little man. This was limestone country, and sometimes behind a waterfall was a hollowed-out place deep enough for a man to hide. There wasn't room to stand behind this fall, but if he sat in the water, there might be breathing space.

Above the noise of the water, Rollo heard the sudden confused yapping of the dogs at the bridge. It spurred him into action. He waded into the hole and ducked under the falling water. Clutching the waterlogged coat, he scrambled ahead and lifted his face from the stream. He emerged into damp air, abysmally dark. Falling water seemed to echo from the darkness ahead. A steady trickle ran down his neck and under his clothes.

Rollo sent an exploratory hand ahead and found no back wall. Feeling his way, he inched forward on his hands and knees. The cave floor went up slightly and then down. A shallow stream ran under him, its bed hard against his palms. Cautiously, he crawled farther and farther into the blackness. Maybe there'd be a dry spot ahead. And the farther he went into the hole, the safer he felt. There was a protective, secret air about the place that he seemed to remember from childhood caves.

Abruptly, he came to a turn, felt his way around it, and his exploring hand reached into nothingness beneath him. He could hear a stream gurgling over rocks ahead and below. The sound of the falls behind him was muted now. Slowly, in the cramped space, Rollo turned around and eased backwards down the wet incline.

Without warning, his feet slipped on the slimy rocks. He fell, clutching, sliding, and scrambling, down a slick wall, to be brought up with a splash standing at the bottom in about two inches of water. He held the yellow coat against his chest as though it offered protection. Around him, he could hear the deep rolling swish of much water passing over a smooth bed.

As his first fear receded, stories from his childhood came crowding back into Rollo's mind—about dogs that ran into dark holes and were never seen again, the legend of an underground river running through the limestone and boiling to the surface near Boomer Island on Bell Lake. That had to be the answer.

All of this came back to him in the blackness, and then his position underground enveloped him. Fear returned with a sickening ball in his stomach, tightening his chest.

What if he should become lost down here—as had the dogs?

With one hand, he reached up and tried to climb back the way he had come. The slimy limestone gave no footing. Turning to his left, he moved ahead cautiously. Maybe there was another way out. His feet encountered a ledge. He leaned over and felt it with his hand. It went up about two feet. He stepped out of the water, lifting his head slowly for fear of hitting the ceiling.

Hesitantly, Rollo felt his way forward and encountered a smooth, slippery wall. He turned and leaned against it. Trapped! He tried to fight down the panic, but it overwhelmed him, and he slid to the ledge.

For a long time he sat shivering, tears running down his cheeks.

Finally, he gained new strength and began a frantic mental groping. His mind came to focus on one item: cigarette lighter. He reached under his coat and felt in a vest pocket. The lighter was still there. He brought it out, flipped open the lid, and spun the wheel. A tiny light flickered upward. It threw dancing shadows on the green-and-black walls.

Looking up and to his left, Rollo could make out the small underground waterfall down which he had fallen. Above it, the ceiling was rainbowed with icicle-like stalactites. The falls cataracted over a sheer face for more than fifteen feet. He could never make it back.

To his right, the ledge on which he sat extended in an undulating stalagmited path along the river, disappearing in the darkness. The oily black waters ahead of him gave off a faint, rippled gleam of light.

Rollo stood up and, looking downstream, came to a decision. Karl was down there on the surface somewhere. Maybe there was another exit. He snapped off the light and replaced it in his vest pocket.

With one hand on the wall, the other clutching the yellow coat, he made his way down the ledge for as far as he had been able to see it. Stopping where he guessed that spot to be, he brought out the lighter and peered ahead.

In this manner he made his way down the underground river. Sometimes he was forced to wade, and once he had to cross the stream to a ledge on the opposite side. Fear gripped him all the way, lest he lose his footing and be swept away into the oily darkness. Whenever he flicked on the lighter, he searched the ceiling for an opening. Several times he paused to explore small streams coming down the walls, always to no avail.

The farther down the river he went, the greater his fear became. Fear made his steps cautious, and this was what saved him when he came to the end of the ledge.

It was just a small sound, much like the noise an oar makes when dipped into the water. Stopping, Rollo took out the lighter. Its flame, smaller now, showed him the end of the ledge and a deep boiling hole where his next step would have been. In fright, he stepped back. Ahead, he saw what was making the noise. The river made a sudden descent, waves washing against a black wall. Under the wall, the water disappeared.

Flicking off the lighter, Rollo sat down. So this was the end. He placed the yellow coat beside him. Thought of the coat made him realize it was very cold in the cavern. His teeth began to chatter.

Almost idly, Rollo wondered if he'd have enough courage to take the easy way out—suicide. He reached into his pocket and pulled out the automatic Karl had given him for this job. He pointed the gun across the cavern and pulled the trigger. There was a dull click. Working the action, he pulled the trigger again. It was the same. And again. And again until the gun was empty. The ammunition was wet. He threw the gun into the blackness and heard it splash.

He took out the lighter and pressed the wheel. The flame flickered up. By its light Rollo watched the long wavering line where the river rolled under the wall. In a short while the flame died down farther and farther, ending in a tiny smoldering spark on the wick. Rollo threw the lighter after the gun. It made a smaller splash.

The sound of the lighter hitting the water and the mental picture of the dull metal object being swept in a slanting course to the bottom of the river brought a new thought to Rollo's mind.

What if the river actually did come out in the lake? Then if a man went in here he could come out on the surface. It was a long chance, but there was nothing but death in the cavern—slow death at that. The other way would be faster and with the added spice of a chance—just a chance.

With that thought, Rollo stood up and began taking off his clothes. He folded them neatly and placed them one by one on the yellow coat with its bundles of money. Later, armed with a ladder and a flashlight, he could return for the money.

Lastly, he placed his shoes on the pile and stood up in his thin underwear. At this point he almost lost his nerve. Maybe there was another way. But he knew there wasn't.

In a momentary surge of courage, he felt with his toes for the rim of the ledge and fell rather than dove off. The icy current gripped him immediately and sucked him downward. He felt a slimy wall brush his right hand, and then he was up in blackness with his head out of water. He imagined the cavern's rough ceiling above him and gulped another lungful of air before the current sucked him under for a second time.

This time the waters took him downward—down, down, and down. He felt the pressure growing almost unbearable on his ears, and then it turned and swooped upward at an incredible speed. Once, his shoulder hit a wall, sending blinding pain through his body. Feebly, he tried to help. He moved his hands aimlessly upward. Breath! He had to have breath! Then he was on the surface, more dead than alive.

Listlessly, he paddled with his right hand while gasping for breaths that were half water. Somewhere in his mind, he realized that his left shoulder was broken. But it seemed to make no difference.

The magnitude of what he had done was enough to wipe out all the shame of all the cowardice of his past. Even if he were to die now. He felt exhilaration deep within him. He had done a brave thing—in desperation, yes, but on his own initiative.

With his good hand, he turned himself over and began to float. A current was taking him somewhere, and the waters had lost their first chill. He looked up and saw the moon low on the hills, highlighting a long line of thunderheads in silver.

Cloudbursters, they'd called that kind of thunderhead when he was a boy.

His bad shoulder grated on rocks, sending a flash of pain radiating through his body. Rollo realized that he had drifted onto a beach. Turning over to protect his shoulder, he found bottom with his knees and half scrambled, half climbed out. There was a darker mass of bushes ahead. The beach shone in the moonlight. He turned to the right and limped along the rocks.

It was hardly fifty feet from the spot where he emerged to the place where he caught the almost invisible gleam of firelight back in the trees.

O O O

Indian Karl Daggert had made short work of his trip to the lake. Holding to the deepest spots in the creek, he had scrambled downward, always careful not to touch anything that would hold scent.

At the lake he'd stripped off his clothes and tied them and the satchel with the remaining money into a neat bundle, using his belt as a rope. This bundle he'd rested on a log, which he'd pushed ahead of him across the lake to Boomer Island. It hadn't taken long to find that he was alone there. On a low spot in the center he'd built a small fire and dried his clothes.

For a while he'd watched the lightning in the hills, thinking of Rollo up there. Several times he'd smiled at the thought of how easy it had been.

Karl was squatting beside the fire, thinking of how good it would be to have some food, when Rollo stepped out of the bushes across from him. For a moment the tall man's mind refused to register on what his eyes saw. Rollo—it couldn't be!

Then the pudgy man was beside him, sobbing in relief and babbling something about a cavern and a river.

For a moment, blind, killing rage seethed in Karl's mind. *The fool! He became frightened! So he followed me!*

Then reason replaced the hate. *So he followed me. Well, there's nothing for it now but to think of some way to use him.*

Aloud, he said, "Sit down by the fire." For the first time, he noticed Rollo's shoulder. "What's wrong with your shoulder?"

"Broken," Rollo said.

There was momentary surprise in Karl's mind at the lack of servility in the fat man's voice, but he passed over it. "Sit down. There's nothing we can do for it now."

Obediently, Rollo sat. The fire was warm on his face, but the chill air was cutting against his wet back. He thought of asking Karl for a coat but stifled the words. Somehow, the old begging and whining didn't seem right now.

The sky began to grow light around them. Rollo could make out the shapes of trees beyond the firelight. A bird called in a thicket at the opposite end of the island. It was answered from somewhere behind him. He heard something wrong with the bird calls, but his weary mind refused to register what exactly was different.

In spite of the pain in his shoulder, in spite of the cold, Rollo leaned back, found soft moss beneath him, and went to sleep.

From the other side of the fire, Karl watched his companion. His mind picked up first one idea and then another, only to reject all. *The little fool! Everything was perfect!*

So intent was he on his thoughts that he failed to hear the soft rustle of bushes behind him until a voice barked, "Reach!"

Involuntarily, he started to raise his hands, then caught himself and dived across the fire toward the bushes. From his left, a rifle spoke once, dropping him into the flame.

Tall men stepped out of the trees and pulled Karl's body from the fire, smothering the flames.

Rollo was leaning up on his good arm, trying to shake the sleep from his eyes, unable to understand what was happening. One of the tall men was standing over him, a rifle pointing at his chest.

"Okay, bud," the man said. "How do you figure in this?"

Rollo looked across the fire at Karl's body—Karl, dead?—and instinctively he knew the form this story should have—just as he'd always known how his stories should go.

"He held me hostage as a guide," he said.

"Yeah?" The man's gun was unwavering. "Who're you that you know so much about this country?"

"My name's Rollo Eckstrom. Why, man, I was born not more than two miles from here. This fellow and another guy got acquainted with me in a Louisville bar. They asked all kinds of questions about where I was from and was there many banks around. Said they was investment counsels or something like that. We went outside to go to another place and got in their car. First thing I know, the other guy has a gun on me—and here I am."

Rollo paused for breath. The gun hadn't moved.

"They fought over the money last night," he went on. "This one killed the other. He was going to kill me, too. He broke my shoulder so I couldn't swim and took my clothes. My name's Rollo Eckstrom, man! I'm no bank robber."

The gun was pointing away now. "Where'd they leave you when they robbed the bank?"

"They left me tied in a car just outside of town. My name's …"

"Yeah, you're Rollo Eckstrom all right. I'm Pete Jenkins— Sheriff Pete Jenkins. We went to school together, Rollo. Remember?"

Rollo looked into the other's face. Through the adult flesh, he recognized the youthful features of a childhood friend, one of the few people he'd ever known who hadn't called him "Rollo" in a patronizing way. "Pete Jenkins," he said.

"Yeah." The other's voice was kindly now. He stooped and put an arm under Rollo. "Come along. We'll get you to a hospital."

On the island's far shore, four rowboats were drawn up. Three of the deputies dumped Karl's body into one of the boats. Rollo and the sheriff got into the stern seat of another.

In the early morning light, the voice of one of the deputies drifted across the mists rising from the lake surface. "Water's high."

Another voice answered. "Cloudburst at Haven Springs early this morning. Nobody killed, but it washed out half a dozen houses."

The full boats shoved off, grating against the gravel beach. A deputy took up the oars in Rollo's boat and headed it toward the dark line of trees on the opposite shore. The oars made misty circles in the black waters, and the rowing sound reminded Rollo of the cavern and the river disappearing beneath the ledge. Under the overcoat that had been thrown over his shoulders, Rollo shivered.

"He didn't fool me a minute," Sheriff Jenkins was saying. "He went upstream a ways, leaving marks, then doubled back. That was it, wasn't it?"

Rollo nodded his head dumbly. *Yes, that would have been Karl's way.*

"We didn't see the fire on the island, but we drove around the lake, and one of my men smelled wood smoke. After that it was easy. We just …"

The sheriff broke off. "Hey! What's that over there?" He pointed to an object floating in the lake to one side of their path and almost obscured by the mists.

The deputy at the oars changed his course, and the man in the bow picked it up. It was the yellow coat, arms still tied, but the ends open and its contents gone.

Dimly, Rollo imagined the swollen river picking his clothes off the ledge, the yellow coat with them, and swirling them up the same channel he had taken.

The deputy turned and threw the coat on the floor slats at the sheriff's feet.

"Just an old coat," the sheriff said. He picked up the limp cloth and dropped it over the side.

Rollo turned and watched the yellow splotch on the water for a moment, a kind of dull despondency settling over him.

Then he turned toward the sheriff and in a low voice began telling the whole story, the true story: his four years with Karl, the other jobs, then this bank robbery, the car getting stuck, the flight into the woods and the journey through the cavern, his dive into the underground river and passage to the lake surface.

Sheriff Jenkins heard him through in silence. The deputy facing them at the oars—his face seemed familiar somehow—smiled once or twice.

When Rollo finished, the sheriff began to chuckle, then to laugh coarsely. "Ho, ho, ho, ho! Rollo, you slaughter me! Same old Rollo, all right. You, a bank robber! Ha, ha, ha, ha, ha! Rollo, you haven't changed a bit!"

For the rest of the journey, Sheriff Jenkins chuckled intermittently.

When they reached shore, they told the story to the rest of the deputies. They looked at him often and laughed. Rollo ignored them, keeping his eyes downcast, his mind on the yellow coat waterlogged in the lake.

THE HEAT'S ON

Arson squad Lieutenant Barnie Ellis strode across the fire-blackened hotel room in five angry steps, leaned out the window. He took a deep gulp of the early morning air.

It should have smelled sweet at 4:00 AM. It didn't. When dirt burns, its stink is pervasive and unmistakable.

Four stories down, on the sidewalk, he saw Fire Captain Coddington talking to a slender man in a dark suit. "Captain!" Ellis bellowed.

The fat fire captain tipped his head back, shaded his eyes with one pudgy hand. "Yeah?"

"Where in the blithering hell is McCoy?" Ellis shouted. He put his arm on the charred windowsill, drew it back again.

"Up there," called Coddington in a high, wheezy voice. "Or he damn well should be."

Ellis spread his big hands in an empty gesture, shook his head. "Come on up!" he bawled, and pulled his head back into the room.

He strode across the blackened shell, stepped into the hall. "McCoy!" he yelled. "McCoy!" Where had that eager beaver got to?

Ellis had been jerked out of sleep by the telephone at 3:30 AM—McCoy with a "suspected arson." That made three times in six months McCoy had suspected arson.

Ellis had dragged himself out of bed, hustled down here, and now—no McCoy.

He looked up and down the dingy hotel hall. Again, he yelled, "McCoy!"

Ellis thought he understood McCoy. The young man wanted to get on the arson squad; it was the reason McCoy had become a fireman in the first place. Ellis sighed. McCoy would find out fast it wasn't all beer and Skittles.

Especially with eager beavers getting a man out of bed at 3:30 in the morning. Jesus!

Quick footsteps sounded on the stairway. Ellis turned toward the sound. About time. He waited for McCoy to emerge on the stairway.

Instead, a brown felt hat came into view, and then a familiar, lean face—Curt Onstott from the DA's office.

Ellis met him at the top of the stairs. "Curt!" He knew the tall, thin lawyer well, had worked with him on several cases. "I didn't know the DA's office was in on this one."

Onstott wrinkled his nose. "What's that stench?"

Ellis swung back toward the fire scene. "A man died in the fire," he said shortly. "Where's Captain Coddington?"

Onstott jerked a thumb toward the stairs. "Coming," he said. "About two flights behind." The slender district attorney paused in the doorway, glanced around the blackened hole that had been a cheap hotel room. "Well, Barnie," he asked, "was it set?"

"How the hell can I tell this quick? What's your office doing on this?"

Onstott was a tall man, but he still had to look up to talk to the bulky Ellis. "We've lost two witnesses in fires this past month—witnesses on the same case."

Ellis froze in midstep. "What case?"

"That damn Tonelli thing—numbers and bookmaking. The man who died here this morning—Yorty—was a key witness."

Ellis moved farther into the fire room. Half of one wall—where the bed had stood—showed the charred, alligator-hide markings of intense heat. Deep charring reached toward the window. Below the sill lay the soggy, begrimed remnants of lace curtains. He flashed a quick look at the lean DA's man. "If Yorty was so important, why wasn't he guarded?"

Onstott had the sort of thin, mobile face that shows its feelings fast. Right now he looked disgusted. "Hell, if we put a guard on every witness, there'd be no one left to mind the store."

Ellis gave the soggy curtains a kick, glanced out the window. Where the hell was McCoy? Below him in the street, he could see one fire engine—a pumper—pulled diagonally into the curb. Near it, two firemen poured streams of water from a hose onto a soggy mattress. The mattress had stopped steaming.

Ellis turned back to Onstott. "We'll give the place a real going-over for you, Curt. But I can't promise we'll find anything. It looks pretty cut and dried."

"No arson?"

Ellis grimaced. "I told you it was too early—"

Coddington came wheezing through the doorway of the fire room, paused to catch his breath. "Four flights!" the fat fire captain gasped. "Did I hear you say arson?"

"No sign of a setup," Ellis said shortly. "Where the hell is McCoy?"

Coddington held up a pudgy hand, took a series of fast, deep breaths. "Wait till I can breathe." He took several more breaths, then gasped a little as he spoke. "I ran into two of his team on the way up. They said McCoy pulled them off the overhauling and dashed off to the phone. That was the last they saw of him."

Ellis stared. "You mean he just took off? That doesn't sound like eager beaver McCoy."

Coddington spread his hands wide. "That's all I know." He frowned thoughtfully. "Wait a minute. His wife's pregnant—due any minute now. Maybe he got a rush call and took off."

Ellis looked doubtful. "Maybe."

"Who's this McCoy?" Onstott asked.

"You met him in my office once," Ellis said. "Skinny, blond kid."

Captain Coddington wheezed a short laugh. "Just a young fireman who sees a pyro behind every smoke." He turned to Ellis. "What set him off this time?"

"Something about a mark on the floor," Ellis said slowly. He looked at the assistant district attorney. "What was that about *two* witnesses dying in fires, Curt?"

Onstott pulled a cigarette package from his pocket, hesitated, then shoved it out of sight again. "We lost the other witness in that Swinburne Hotel fire last month."

Ellis nodded sharply. He had been sure that's what Onstott would say. The Swinburne fire was the last time McCoy had suspected arson. Something about a ring mark on the floor, the same thing McCoy had said about this one.

Coddington crossed the room to the window, looked down on the activity below, and sighed. "Happens all the time," he said. "Guy gets drunk, lights a cigarette, and passes out. The real miracle is when the whole building doesn't burn out."

Ellis took a careful look at the floor, pointed suddenly to a brown ring on the ash-stained yellow linoleum near Onstott. "What's that?"

Onstott moved away from the ring, looked down. "What's what?"

"That mark on the floor by your feet." Ellis moved over for a closer look, took a metal tape measure from his coat pocket. Coddington moved in closer.

"What about it?" Onstott asked.

Ellis knelt for a closer look, ran his thick forefinger across the mark. Hardly an indentation. Still, there'd been a mark just like it on the floor of the death room at the Swinburne. He measured the diameter. "Fourteen and a quarter inches."

Coddington bent closer. "Could have been there for months," he said. "Doesn't have to mean anything."

Ellis straightened, slipped the tape into his pocket. "I'd sure as hell like to talk to McCoy," he said. "I wonder if he saw anything else."

Onstott drew his black eyebrows into a worried V. "If you find anything, be sure to keep us posted. I don't know who the hell we're going to get to testify against Tonelli now."

"Witnesses smoke in bed too," wheezed Coddington. He moved impatiently toward the door. "Let's get the hell out of here and get some air."

Ellis glanced again at the ring on the floor, then met the worried look on the face of the assistant district attorney. "I've got my men on the way over," he said. "If there's anything to find, they'll find it."

Onstott stepped around the ring, walked over to the blackened doorway. "Arson isn't usually a syndicate crime," he said. "Bullets are more in their line."

"They can buy talent," Ellis said.

With a grimace, Onstott moved toward the stairs. Coddington had already started down. Onstott paused. "I'm going to grab some breakfast before I report. Can you get away?"

Ellis nodded. "Maybe by the time I get back, McCoy will have shown up."

But McCoy wasn't there when he got back. A call to the firehouse told Ellis that McCoy was off shift. Four calls to McCoy's house went unanswered.

By lunchtime, Ellis was bone tired. He'd worked late the night before. Today was Saturday—his day off—when he'd promised to take Jane and the kids on a picnic. He felt he should at least go by his home, try to make peace with Jane.

But first—what about McCoy? What else could the young fireman have seen? It would only take a minute to stop by McCoy's house on his way home. If Mrs. McCoy had gone to the hospital to have her baby, the neighbors would know it.

Nobody answered the front-door chime at McCoy's tract house. Ellis pushed the bell, waited. Rang again. He turned to go back down the stairs, paused.

What was that sound in the house? It sounded like running water.

Ellis froze, listening, turned, and punched the door chime again. The sound inside stopped.

Ellis was sure there was someone inside. He didn't like getting the runaround from the young fireman—especially when this was the guy who'd dragged him out of bed in the middle of the night.

Even the street was quiet now. Two boys sat on a curb in the afternoon sunshine, talking in low voices. A dog wandered silently across the lawns.

Ellis muttered his favorite short oath, went down the two steps, and followed the cement sidewalk to the back of the house.

Here, the steps were steeper, led directly to a tiny open porch and kitchen door. In two big steps he was at the back door, looking through the window into the kitchen.

Inside, he could see the back of Mrs. McCoy—a mop in one hand and bucket in the other, peering around the doorway toward the front of the house. *Must think she's hiding from a bill collector,* thought Ellis with a grin. He pounded on the door.

She almost dropped the bucket at the sound behind her. From the back, she had looked like a schoolgirl, her brown coil of hair caught in a blue ribbon—but from the front, her smock barely covered her advanced pregnancy.

She spotted Ellis through the window, put down bucket and mop, and walked across the wet floor, heedless of the marks her moccasins made. She opened the door a crack, then wider. "Lieutenant Ellis," she breathed. "What are you doing at the back door?"

Ellis smiled. "I rang the bell. I guess you didn't hear me."

"Come in," she said in a tiny voice. Her eyes were wide.

Frightened? wondered Ellis. He glanced past her. "Shall I step on your clean floor?"

She looked down. "Oh. No, better come around to the front."

But Ellis had seen something that interested him—a ring on the fresh-mopped floor. He pointed. "What made that mark, Mrs. McCoy?"

She turned, startled. "What mark? That ring?"

"Yes. What made it?"

She managed a tiny smile. "The bottom of the mop bucket. The water was too hot, and it made a mark in the wax. It'll fade. Why do you ask?"

"Just wondered." Ellis pulled his gaze from the ring. Smaller, but the same sort of mark. He met Mrs. McCoy's puzzled look. "Is your husband here?"

She looked over her shoulder quickly, then back. "No, Chris isn't here."

Ellis knew she was lying. "I think he is," he said flatly.

She bit her lip, looked up at Ellis. "You're right," she said. Her voice was barely audible. "Lieutenant, can I talk to you?"

He nodded.

She came out on the tiny porch with him, pulled the door almost shut behind her. "Lieutenant, I'm worried sick. Chris has been hurt, and he won't let me call a doctor."

Ellis felt his hands close into fists. "Hurt how?"

"I don't know. Maybe in the fire he was on last night. But he was—was being sick in the bathroom most of the morning. When I asked him about it, he said he had the flu."

"Maybe he has," Ellis said.

She shook her head so violently that the brown coil of hair flipped from one side to the other. "No. There's a big bruise on his stomach. I saw it." She looked down. "And he won't let me answer the phone—" She blushed. "Or the door."

Ellis stared over her head, thinking. So someone had gotten to McCoy and he had chickened out. "Where is your husband now?"

"In the bathroom, I think."

"Can he hear us?"

She shook her head again. "No. Not from here."

Ellis nodded. "Okay. I'll go around to the front again and ring the bell. This time let me in. You can always say I saw you through the front window and you had to open the door."

She nodded, threw him a grateful look.

At the front door, she opened it wide, beckoned him in. "Lieutenant Ellis," she said in a high clear voice. "What a surprise! I'll tell Chris you're here. Sit down." She waved toward a lumpy armchair, then left Ellis alone.

Ellis lowered his big frame into the chair, hoping she wouldn't overdo the surprised bit. In another room, he could hear a murmur of voices, and then McCoy appeared in the doorway.

"Hello, Lieutenant," McCoy said. His smile was tight. What Ellis thought of as McCoy's puppy friendliness was entirely missing. "Would you—would you like a beer?"

Ellis could sense McCoy hoping he'd say "no" and leave. He obliged. "No, thanks. I just stopped by on my way to make out my report. I wanted to get a few points cleared up."

McCoy perched tentatively on the arm of the couch as Ellis studied him carefully. If he hadn't been watching, he would have missed the twitch of pain that crossed the blond fireman's face.

McCoy forced a smile. "I'm sorry about that goof, Lieutenant, getting you out of bed and all. I don't think I can help you very much. I ... well, your squad must have the whole picture by now."

Ellis took a deep breath. McCoy was scared. He could almost smell it. "What made you think of arson in the first place?" he asked carefully.

McCoy looked over Ellis' head. "The—the speed of the fire, I think. But then I found that can of lighter fluid. I guess your sergeant told you about it. It probably spilled and spread the fire."

Ellis wrinkled his forehead, looked down at the rug. "You mentioned a ring—a mark on the floor—like the one in the Swinburne Hotel fire. What about it?"

"It was just a funny coincidence, I guess," McCoy said.

Ellis narrowed his eyes. They'd sure put the wind up with McCoy, he thought. The kid was as white as a ghost. "You don't look well," Ellis said.

"Flu," said McCoy. "Hit me suddenly. That's—that's why I didn't wait for you this morning."

Ellis decided abruptly not to challenge McCoy right now. Hell, he thought, there's even an outside chance he's telling the truth—but I doubt it. Ellis wanted more facts, and this scared boy wasn't going to give them to him. Mentally, Ellis crossed off any chance of seeing Jane that afternoon. He wanted to get back to that hotel.

"Well ..." McCoy said awkwardly.

Ellis pulled himself to his feet. "Anything else you'd like to say?"

McCoy stood up, followed Ellis to the door. "No. That's about it." His voice sounded easier now that Ellis was obviously leaving. "Are you sure you won't have that can of beer?"

Ellis was tempted to say "yes" just to watch the effect. But he wanted to get out almost as much as his host seemed to want him to leave. Scared witless, he thought. Good thing to find out early about a man.

It left a bad taste in Ellis's mouth. He pulled the car away from the curb with an angry jerk of the wheel. The one virtue a good fireman needed was courage. He would have said McCoy was a natural. And here he was—someone pushed, and he went into a yellow funk. They'd have to find out who was pushing, of course.

Ellis pulled the mic from under the dash, called his squad, and arranged for a tail on McCoy.

He headed toward the hotel where the morning's fire had been. One thing was clear in Ellis's mind—this had to be arson. No evidence at all. But too damn much smoke.

In the afternoon light, the Sander's Hotel looked more uninviting than it had that morning. Ellis saw no official cars; the street was back to normal. The signs of fire had been cleared away, except for a few burned chunks of mattress kicked into the gutter.

Ellis parked several car lengths away. A man named Yorty had died this morning on a mattress. This afternoon, the mattress was just a few charred chunks of cotton in the street. Ellis felt there was a moral here, but he couldn't frame it in words.

He slammed the car door, started away, then turned back to check the lock. This was a ratty neighborhood; no sense leaving anything for quick fingers.

Ellis stared at the car door a moment, thinking—then came to a quick decision. He unlocked the door, reached into the glove compartment, and took out the .38 police special he kept there. With a careful look to be sure he wasn't watched, he dropped the gun into his coat pocket.

He picked up the mic again—let headquarters know where he was going. No sense in foolish chances; the game was getting rough.

The smell was gone from the air, but the musty aftermath of the fire greeted him the moment he pushed open the glass door and stepped into the green-painted lobby.

On one side, a small man sat reading the pink sports section of the newspaper. Ellis recognized yesterday's baseball results in a headline.

The small man lowered the paper to gaze at Ellis, shifted his position slightly, and again raised the paper against the world.

Ellis stepped up to the worn desk, spoke to a tired-looking elderly man who smoked a stub of a cigar. "You the manager?"

"Yeah." The man's eyes were bloodshot, the eyelids drooped. "You a cop?"

They can always sense the uniform, even when you're not wearing it, Ellis thought. He shook his head. "Fire department."

"Fire's out," said the man.

Ellis fingered his wallet from his inside coat pocket, flipped it open to show his credentials. "I'm Barnhard Ellis, Arson Squad," he said. "What's your name?"

"Dittman," said the man. "Al Dittman."

No questions, nothing volunteered, Ellis thought. He pushed his wallet back into the pocket, feeling a bit awkward under the tired stare of the old man. "I have a few questions," Ellis said, "about your cleaning routine."

The old man slid off his stool, raised himself slowly to full height.

Ellis stared. The man stood even taller than his own six feet, two inches, but was so thin he waved like a blade of dry grass. "Cleaning!" exclaimed the man in his first sign of life. He put the cigar carefully on a blackened ashtray. "We run a good hotel. Got a certificate from the city. We can't help it if some bum smokes in bed. What's cleaning got to do with it?"

Ellis shifted his weight. "I'm not here to put in a complaint, Dittman." His eyes moved to the staircase and a small pile of trash near the foot of it. "Though maybe I should."

A guffaw sounded behind Ellis, and he whirled in surprise toward the small man trying to hide laughter behind his pink newspaper. "He's got you there, Al," laughed the man. "He's got you there. Living here is like living in the city dump."

"Shut up!" said Dittman, and the laugh ended as sharply as a clicked-off radio. Dittman turned back to Ellis. "What about our cleaning?"

Ellis kept his gaze on the tall, thin man—wishing he would return to the stool. Ellis wasn't used to looking up when he talked. "I'd like to see your ..." He hesitated, reluctant to say "mop bucket." "I'd like to see your cleaning equipment."

Dittman sank back onto his stool, picked up the cigar. "There ain't none," he said.

"What's that supposed to mean?" Ellis asked.

"We use a service."

"What kind of service?"

Dittman sighed. "I can't see what this—"

Ellis cut him off. "It isn't up to you to see. What kind of service?"

"One of those outfits you pay to come in at night and clean up. They bid for the job."

Bid, Ellis thought. *There* was a gratuitous offering. As though that relieved this creep from responsibility. "And what's the name of this efficient service?" Ellis asked, glancing again toward the rubbish near the steps.

The man behind the paper chortled briefly, broke off.

Dittman turned, still on the stool, to bend close to a card tacked on a wall near the mail boxes. "Cellini and O'Grady," he read aloud. "They're lousy."

Ellis pulled out a notebook, jotted down the name. "Phone number?"

Dittman read it off, then asked, "Anything else?"

"Yes. Who reported the fire?"

"Mulligan in 437," said Dittman.

"Can I talk to him?" Ellis asked.

"Can I stop you?"

Ellis bit at his lip to hide his irritation. "I mean, is he in his room now?"

The thin hotel manager shrugged. "Search me. Climb up and see."

Ellis nodded sharply, turned to the stairs, and reluctantly began the four-flight climb. *Christ, what a dump,* he thought. *And what a way to live.*

On the fourth floor, Ellis stopped to catch his breath. He thought about the people who lived in this class of hotel— derelicts, men living on alcohol and dead hopes—and older people with pensions that wouldn't stretch for a better address.

How did they manage these stairs? A less athletic group than the tenants of one of these old hotels would be hard to imagine.

Still breathing deeply, Ellis looked down the poorly lit fourth floor hall. Directly ahead of him was the room where the witness had died.

The musty hall angled to the right, revealing several doors in need of paint. The burned room was 425. He went down the hall the few doors to 437, raised his big fist, and rapped on the door.

Quick motion stirred in the room, then stumbling footsteps. The door opened quickly, and a pudgy man gazed blearily at him, supporting his wavering weight on the doorknob. "Whadja want?" the man managed.

Ellis caught the sweet-sour smell of wine on the man's breath, moved back a pace. "Mulligan?" he asked.

"Who wants to know?"

"Ellis, fire department. You the one turned in the alarm last night?"

Mulligan blinked at him, clung to the door. His once-white shirt was open at the throat, revealing a thick bush of red hair. "'Zat a crime?"

Ellis took a deep breath and, step by step, led Mulligan through a description of coming home. "I was dead sober," Mulligan complained, "at 2:30 in the morning." He had smelled smoke and phoned from the pay phone in the hall.

Mulligan indicated the phone by a wide wave of his arm.

"Did you see anyone?" Ellis asked.

"Jussa cleaning lady," Mulligan said.

Ellis sucked in a quick breath of air. "Here? On this floor? What was she doing?"

Mulligan raised a hairy-backed hand to support himself against one side of the doorjamb, leaned toward Ellis in an exhalation of sour breath. "What was she supposed to be doing, y' dumb fireman? She was mopping the floor."

Ellis glanced at the threadbare rug of the hall. "Mopping the carpet?"

"Christ, no!" Mulligan said. "I saw her on the stairs. She was carrying her mop and pail down to the lobby." He leered at Ellis. "You got a thing for cleaning ladies, Mac?"

Ellis ignored the man, reassembled his thoughts. He wanted to see the inside of Mulligan's room, find out the normal layout of one of these rooms. And it was high time he called the department. He decided to try for both. "Can I use your phone?" he asked.

Mulligan grinned. "Only phone's that pay phone in the hall."

Ellis nodded. "Okay. Was anyone else around—besides the cleaning woman?"

"No," said Mulligan. "And goodnight." He closed the door firmly.

Ellis was caught by surprise, decided to make the best of it. He had got all he was going to get here. He fumbled in his pocket for a dime, went over to the pay phone.

By this time they should have the word on how Yorty had died. He decided to call Captain Coddington instead of the sergeant. It was Coddington's fire, and if there was anything funny about it, the captain would be the first to know. He'd also have the grapevine report, the *unofficial* view from the top.

But Coddington was out. "He just *happened* to go to the Meadows," explained the fireman on the board.

Despite his disappointment at finding the fat fire captain out, Ellis had to smile. The Meadows was the local racetrack, and everyone in the department knew the captain's passion for the ponies.

The joke was the way Coddington always acted as if his visits to the track were infrequent impulses.

Ellis fumbled for another dime, dialed the DA's office. This time he was lucky. Onstott was in and had the coroner's report in front of him.

The thin assistant DA sounded disgusted. "Yorty died in the fire, all right—loaded with carbon monoxide. So there goes our homicide right out the window."

Ellis leaned close to the phone so his voice wouldn't carry into the hall. "Any question on identification of the victim?"

"No, it was Yorty, all right. It was the smoke that got him. The body's blistered but in pretty good condition, all things considered."

Ellis put that picture firmly out of his mind. "I'm at the Sander's Hotel right now. Thought I'd have a look around."

Onstott cleared his throat, sounded a bit apologetic. "Look, Barnie, isn't this police business now? You haven't an arson case, and—"

Ellis interrupted. "I can't argue that, Curt. But this whole mess doesn't feel right. You know that. It's full of things that don't add up?"

"Such as?"

"Let me poke around a little, and maybe I can answer that. Will you be in your office all afternoon?"

Again, Onstott cleared his throat. "As far as I know now." He hesitated. "Look, take it easy. Those boys don't fool around."

"Okay," said Ellis. "I'll finish up here and then check in with you again."

Ellis hung up the phone, then turned to look slowly up and down the narrow hall, not sure where he wanted to begin.

For one thing, he knew he wanted a talk with the other denizens of this fourth floor—and then there was that cleaning service. He glanced at his watch—4:15. They might close at 5:00, if they were there on Saturday at all.

He couldn't get the idea out of his head that the ring on the floor could have been caused by a mop bucket. He grinned to himself. It was the first time he'd ever heard of using mop water to start a fire.

Behind one of the doors, a phone rang, and Ellis paused in surprise. In this hotel, a private phone was a sound of affluence.

All the doors Ellis could see had numbers except the one directly opposite the pay phone. He found himself staring at its paint-chipped surface.

Supply closet? Probably locked. He tried the knob. To his surprise, it turned. The door opened with a loud creak of hinges.

One look and he turned away. It had been a broom closet once; now it was a hiding place for garbage. And from the smell, an occasional comfort station.

He pushed the door shut—but then another odor made him pause. Stale smoke?

Again Ellis creaked the door open, then took out his penlight and flashed it around. The smoke smell was very faint. Perhaps trapped in here from the morning's fire?

His light picked up a mark on the floor. Ellis bent closer, saw a clearly marked yellowish-brown ring.

He took out his tape, knelt quickly, oblivious now to the stench of the place. He nodded to himself as he read the tape. Exactly fourteen and one-quarter inches.

Behind him, a door opened and closed. But when he stood up to look down the hall, he couldn't tell which door it had been.

Was Mulligan watching from 437?

Ellis closed the door quietly.

An ugly silence hung over the hall. Ellis glanced at the pay phone. Another call to Onstott was indicated—but he suddenly felt that phone was too public. Besides, he wanted out of here.

A tiny red light glowed over a door at the opposite end of the hall from the front stairs. Fire exit? Service stairs? He'd better have a look.

Ellis headed for the red light, wondered why Mulligan's cleaning woman hadn't gone down this way.

When he opened the door, he saw why. Christ! Did every corner of this hotel harbor a pile of rubbish? The residents must empty their wastebaskets down these stairs. He made a mental note to call the fire inspectors but knew it would have small effect. They were understaffed and under pressure. Not their fault that these dumps existed on political *geetus*.

Ellis picked his way down the filthy stairs, still puzzling about the cleaning woman. More and more, Ellis was convinced that no professional cleaners ever came near this joint. They probably had a contract with a "service" all right, but the whole setup smelled of a kickback.

And what in the hell was a woman with a mop doing walking down carpeted stairs at 2:30 in the morning?

Ellis was pleased, though, by the way two things dovetailed. When he had seen that ring on the floor of McCoy's kitchen, he had wondered if a cleaning bucket had left the mark in the fire room. Now, first crack out of the bat, his questions had turned up a scrubwoman.

Above him on the steep stairs, he heard a door open. He turned to see the blocky outline of a man against the dim lighting from a dirty skylight.

Ellis walked a bit faster. Just one more flight to the ground level. He could feel the desire for fresh air welling up in him.

"Wait a moment," called the man above him in a gruff voice. "Your name Ellis?"

Ellis stopped on the landing where the steps right-angled between the first and second floor, glanced up. "Yeah. What is it?"

"I got a message for you." The man broke into an awkward run down the steps. "From your office."

From the office? Ellis wondered. How the hell would the office reach me through this punk, whoever he was?

A sound below him, from down the stairs, caught Ellis's attention. He glanced left, saw another man—this one mounting the stairs. The second figure could have been a brother to the first—ring-scarred, the eyes with that stare of secret ferocities.

Ellis didn't like his position here on the stairs. Back stairs, he corrected himself. Who ever used the back stairs?

The man from above stopped one step up, almost level with him on the landing. Ugly-looking pug. Neck thicker than his head. Fighter's shoulders with that bunched-up shape to them. His body was thick all the way down; it made his head look even smaller and rounder than it was.

"What's this message?" Ellis asked. He retreated to make room for the man, but it also put his back into the corner.

"Yeah, message," the man said. He was obviously waiting for his companion coming up from below.

Through Ellis's mind flashed the arithmetic of street fighting. This first pug was about five-ten. *I've got the reach on him,* Ellis thought. But the man outweighed him by at least twenty pounds—and here was his companion now—almost a mate in weight and empty stare. The companion stopped one step down.

"This is the bird," the one from below said.

Ellis could feel the menace. No doubt of it now. He had almost decided to punch first and apologize later when he saw the gun in the hand of the one who had come up from below.

Ellis knew the gun in his own pocket might as well still be in the car for all the good it could do him now. Better not reach for it and telegraph that he was armed. Later on, he might get a chance to use the .38. He watched the gun in the pug's hand, weighing his chances.

The armed man saw the direction of Ellis's stare and said, "Yeah, friend, that's right."

The other one stretched his mouth in a shallow grin that kept his teeth covered and said, "Like I said, Ellis, I got a message for you."

Ellis suddenly remembered young McCoy. Without needing the complete details, Ellis knew McCoy had met this pair—or their twins. They had syndicate written all over them. Deadly punks. Ellis fought against a sick feeling in his stomach. He had been through the police academy, but that was years back ... and besides, the first thing they told you was, "Try reasoning first."

"I think I get the message," Ellis said. "But I don't think your boss would like it if you got the department mad at you."

"Department," the man chuckled. Again his mouth stretched into that tight grin, and then he laughed shortly. Ellis saw a brief exposure of yellowed stumps and understood the tight grin, the concealing mannerism.

"You sure as hell can't make me look like a fire accident," Ellis said.

The moment he had spoken, Ellis knew the words were a mistake. He pressed back into the corner, wishing for more room, as the men exchanged a knowing look.

"You ain't got the message yet," said the one from the top. "We want you should remember this message. When you wake up—if you wake up—you remember it good. There's a kind of a postscript, friend. You stay nosy, and your wife, your Jane, she's gonna get the same message. You remember that, huh? And if she don't understand the message, then we'll deliver it to your kids."

Ellis felt sick fear spread through his muscles. *So that's how they got to McCoy,* he thought.

The man from below lifted the gun.

Ellis faced it, saw too late that was what they wanted. He sensed the blur of motion from above, felt the blazing drum-crash of a blow on his head.

Blackjack, he thought. Then there was darkness and stairs and falling all mixed up with a sound of breaking and a pain in his leg—and in his side. He sensed distant blows, knew somehow he was at the foot of the rubbish-strewn stairs.

The emptiness enclosed him.

O O O

Someone was groaning. With a feeling of unfamiliar detachment, Ellis realized it was himself.

Somewhere in the darkness he felt a sharp prick in his arm. Something rustled around him. There was a smell of disinfectant—a glare of light.

Again, this stranger—this distant self—groaned, and the emptiness returned.

There was a whistling sound, unmusical and unpleasant. Ellis grew aware that it was his own breathing past some kind of obstruction. A tube of some kind. He could feel it against his cheek.

A gurney rattled through the emptiness. Ellis had heard the sound many times—you couldn't come through the department's ranks without growing overly familiar with hospitals—and death.

But I'm not dead, he thought. *By God, I'm not dead!*

Voices talked, but too far away to be understood.

From the bottom of a long, deep, dark hole, Ellis felt consciousness return. With it came the pain. He floated back to wakefulness, aware of a bone-deep ache in his right leg—and a sharp stab each time he breathed deeply.

Carefully, slowly, he opened his eyes to a white-and-chrome hospital room. Outlines were fuzzy, but they steadied rapidly. He heard his own voice ask, "What time is it?"

A cheerful female voice: "2:00 AM."

"What day?" he asked.

"Sunday," the cheerful voice told him.

Nine hours I've been out, he thought. *Unless I missed a whole week!* But he knew he hadn't. The pain was too new.

"How do we feel?" asked the cheerful female.

"We feel like hell," Ellis said. He moved his head gently; it felt all there. "When can I leave?"

"When your leg gets out of traction," said the bright voice. She came around the foot of the bed, all white and fresh and starched.

Pretty little thing, thought Ellis, *if you like them sterile.* "Who're you?"

"Miss Birch."

"Why is my leg in traction?" asked Ellis, focusing on the contraption of metal and wire hung over the foot of the bed.

"I believe it's broken," Miss Birch said.

"Don't you know?" Ellis tried to sit up, couldn't. He turned his head to take stock of the room. Dresser. Armchair. Straight chair. Two closed doors—closet and bath? Extension-type table by the bed.

He glanced at the table, was relieved to see a telephone. But who was it he should call? His mind still fuzzed—whether from the blow or from drugs he wasn't sure.

Jane! The name washed into his mind on a cold splash of awareness. Jane and the kids! That thug had threatened Jane and the kids. He reached for the phone, but it was just beyond his grasp.

"Give me the phone," he said brusquely.

Miss Birch smiled brightly. "But it is two o'clock in the morning. You make your calls tomorrow."

"Goddamit, give me that phone!"

The smile vanished. "Now, now. Don't you want to see your poor wife? She's been so worried."

"Jane! Where is she?"

"Right out in the hall. And a very jumpy young man is waiting to see you too. Says he's an assistant district attorney."

Onstott, Ellis thought. "Tell him to wait. Tell him I'm delirious or something—and send in my wife."

"Doctor Greenleaf will be here very soon," said Miss Birch. "Mrs. Ellis can only stay a few minutes."

Ellis set his jaw. "Then get her in here right away."

Miss Birch frowned, swished away, then returned in a moment, followed by Jane.

Ellis tried to sit up, cursed the contraption on his leg that kept him in one position. "Jane! Where are the kids?"

"Home, of course. It's two o'clock in the morning."

Ellis waited till the nurse left. Jane showed signs of hasty dressing—a sports coat over slacks—but she looked terrific to him. "Are the kids alone?"

"Yes. Why not? They're old enough to take care of themselves." She smiled. "The important thing right now is you. How do you feel?" She crossed the room to the armchair by the window, started to sit down.

"Jane!"

She paused, arrested by the alarm in his voice. "What is it?"

"Close the door."

She crossed quickly, shut it, came over to the bed. "What is it, Barnie?"

"Listen carefully," Ellis said. "I don't have time to go into detail." Briefly, he outlined as much as he felt she should know of what his attacker had said. He wanted to scare her; to be sure she'd act without delay. When he mentioned the children, he knew he had succeeded.

She straightened, took a quick step back. Her voice was steady, but he could see the fear in her eyes. "Barnie, what should we do?"

"Exactly what I say. Call your brother. Have him pick you up right away at the hospital. Go get the kids and get out to your mother's place in Fairfield as fast as you can. Don't tell anyone but your parents and brother what's happened." He squeezed her hand, looked up at her. "Two things to remember: move fast and be careful. And for God's sake, phone me when you're safely there."

"But—I hate to just leave you—"

"Jane, believe me, it'll be much worse if I have you and the kids to worry about too. Promise me you'll do as I say. I'll have police guards out there as soon as I can. Your mother's place is safer, more open—keep your brother with you. I'll call Bill Torrance at the sheriff's office in Fairfield. We were at school together. He'll know what to do."

Ellis puased. "Would you hand me my coat from that closet?"

"Of course. Why?" She opened the closet door, took out his suit coat, brought it to him. "It's heavy."

"I thought you might need some money," he said, taking the coat and removing his wallet from the inside pocket. He touched the outer pocket. Good, the .38 was still there.

"Is there a briefcase in the closet?" he asked, inventing the briefcase to take her attention away from him long enough for him to slip the gun from the pocket, put it beneath his pillow.

"I don't see one." She took the coat, hung it up, turned back. "Barnie—"

The door interrupted her.

An older man in a dark suit came in, followed by Nurse Birch.

"Well, well," said the man. "I see our patient feels well enough to have a charming guest. How do you do? I am Dr. Greenleaf."

"The charming guest is just leaving," Ellis said.

Jane hesitated, then said, "The children—"

"Of course," the doctor said. "Why don't you drop by this afternoon?"

Jane bent, kissed Ellis's cheek. "I'll call you," she said. She hurried out.

Ellis faced the doctor. "How long am I stuck here?"

"Several weeks, I'd say," said Dr. Greenleaf. "You do have a broken leg, you know."

"What's this pain in my side?" Ellis asked, then listened to a dissertation on broken and cracked ribs, thinking how well the pugs had done their job. Professionals. The anger mounted in him, and he suddenly remembered the one who had chuckled, the rasping voice, the way he said "Department." *Could they have a fix in the department?* Ellis asked himself. *Oh, Jesus!*

"Miss Birch will give you something for the pain," the doctor said. "Don't worry about a thing. We'll take the best care of you, won't we, Miss Birch?" He beamed at her.

"We certainly will, Doctor," she chirruped.

Dr. Greenleaf patted his stethoscope, nodded briskly, and turned to the door. "Tell that assistant district attorney he can only stay ten minutes." He marched out, closing the door firmly behind him.

Miss Birch stood at crisp attention till the doctor was gone, turned back to the bed. As she bent over him, the door opened suddenly and Onstott stepped in.

"I have to talk to this man, nurse," he said briskly. "Police business."

Miss Birch smoothed the bedspread, moved the water glass and its crooked straw within Ellis' reach. "Very well," she said, "But please limit your visit to ten minutes."

A white-toothed grin lit Onstott's face. "Okay, honey," he said. He held the door open while she swished out. He clicked the door shut. "Nice," he said.

"If you like them crisp," said Ellis. He nodded toward the straight chair. "Park it."

Onstott jerked the chair close to the bed, pulled a small notebook from his side pocket. "I've kept the dogs off you so far," he said. "But now we need a statement. Did you lose much?"

Ellis tipped his head quizzically. "Lose much what?"

"Money. Cash. Green stuff. You *were* mugged in that lousy hotel, weren't you?"

Ellis stared at him. "No. This was a message from the syndicate, Curt. A warning to stop poking my nose into your damn bookie case." Ellis thought of the gun under his head. The professional pair had missed that—too confident. *Let them try me now—in here,* he thought.

"Brief me," Onstott said, his voice suddenly cold.

Ellis sketched in the details of the fight on the stairs and described the matched pair of thugs.

"Would you know them again?" Onstott asked.

"You're damn right I would!" Ellis said.

At the mention of the threat to Jane and the kids, Onstott paused in his notetaking, started to break in.

"I got them out of town," Ellis said. "That part's covered." He explained about the friend in the sheriff's office in Fairfield.

"That's Schaffer County," Onstott said. "I'll get on the horn as soon as I leave here. Don't worry about her. I have friends there too."

"Okay, let's get to work," Ellis said.

Onstott nodded, glanced over his notes. "Who knew you were in the hotel?"

"The desk clerk and some little guy in the lobby. And I talked to a drunk named Mulligan—the one who reported the fire."

"He's the one who found you and called an ambulance," Onstott said.

Ellis chewed his lower lip. "That probably clears Mulligan."

"Maybe. Maybe not. You could read it either way."

Again, Onstott glanced over his notes. "You'd almost think two different people were thinking up things to do."

Ellis reached over the table, got a cigarette, and lit it. "I've had the same feeling. Somebody very clever thought up the homicide-by-arson scheme. Someone a lot dumber is sending hoods around with threatening messages."

"I've a hunch the smart one may have a message for the dumb one before long," Onstott said. "And some messages are more effective than others." He looked at the traction arrangement over the bed.

Ellis grimaced as he tried to move his leg and failed. Onstott didn't look too good to him either. There were fatigue lines on the lean face.

"Is your case against Tonelli dead?" Ellis asked.

"As dead as the witnesses," Onstott glanced at the door, lowered his voice. "I had a reason for coming here myself. You'd better know what's on the grapevine."

Ellis shifted a little in a vain attempt to find a comfortable position. He stubbed out his cigarette, watched Onstott. "Yes?"

Onstott slipped his notebook into his side pocket, kept his voice down. "The word is clear and simple: there's a fireman mixed up in this. Tonelli is supposed to have made some crack about it. According to our tipster, he said, 'Why buy a cop when you can have your own pet fireman?'"

Ellis felt suddenly cold. Again he remembered the pug, the way the man had said, "Department."

The door opened, and Miss Birch put her head in. "Time to leave, Mr. Onstott," she caroled.

He swiveled toward her. "Almost finished," he said. "Give us fifteen minutes—"

"Oh, I couldn't—" she began.

Onstott held up one forefinger, shook it in schoolteacherly fashion. "You know, I bet you could ..." He let the sentence trail off.

She laughed suddenly, withdrew her head from the door.

Ellis hardly noticed the exchange. He was thinking. An abrupt idea had struck him—McCoy! Maybe the bruise and the fright were a blind ...

Onstott narrowed his eyes, watching Ellis. "You have someone in mind?"

"Maybe yes, maybe no. But I do have an idea how those convenient fires were set." He held up his hand as Onstott started to speak. "Hold it. I've some more checking first. If it checks, I'll brief you."

Again Onstott glanced at the traction apparatus over the bed, stared pointedly at the tape showing at the neck of Ellis' hospital gown. "You're in a swell spot to be doing some checking."

Ellis frowned. "Okay, so I'm a turkey ready to be roasted," he said. "How many people know which room I'm in?"

"It's no secret," said Onstott, "But I've got a cop posted in the hall."

Ellis nodded. "Good enough."

"I'll have a little talk with him," Onstott said. There was a hint of anger in his eyes, but he looked thoughtful, too. "Be right back." He turned to go, almost ran into Captain Coddington in the doorway.

Coddington was in uniform, and walked as erect as his chubby shape would permit. He nodded to Onstott, came over to the bed. "Hello. Hello. How do you feel, Barnie?"

"I could use a day's rest, Captain," Ellis said. "Do you suppose I could have tomorrow off?" In his mind, Ellis rejected the idea of telling Coddington that the syndicate had bought themselves a fireman. No sense in having the captain stir things up, muddying the water.

Coddington laughed and wheezed as he sat down in the armchair by the window. "Hell, Barnie—you never lose the old sense of humor, do you?"

"Ha!" said Ellis grimly. "You hear me laughing?"

Coddington's face sobered. "They said you were mugged," Coddington said. "First time that's ever happened to one of my boys, and I want you to know that whoever did it is going to pay."

"Yeah," said Ellis. "But this was no mugging." He sketched in the encounter on the stairs.

Coddington frowned. "Son of a bitch," he said.

Ellis noted the jaw muscle working on the captain's face, the angry pallor.

"I lived through it, Captain," Ellis said. "I've been hurt worse than this. Not by intention, sure, but—"

"This is—police business!" Coddington blurted. "No place for a fireman around this kind of violence."

Onstott came back in the room, nodded to Coddington in the armchair. "Attended any good fires lately, Captain?"

Coddington emitted his wheezing laugh. "We're trying to put out the fires for your office," he said. "Look what you let happen to one of my best men." He waved a pudgy hand toward Ellis. "I hope you're going to take better care of him now."

"We are," said Onstott shortly.

Coddington clutched the arms of his chair, kneading them with his fingers. "Do you really think someone tried to kill you?" he asked Ellis.

"No," said Ellis. "They were trying not to. This one was to tell me to keep my nose out. The next time may not be as gentle."

"What do you mean, 'next time'?" Coddington demanded. "You aren't poking any more fingers in this pie. It's police business."

Ellis sank back into the pillow, stared up at the ceiling. "As a matter of fact, it's *my* business," he said. "They made it that when they sent those thugs after me." He raised his head, looked at Onstott. "Give me a little time, and I'll tell you exactly how your witnesses died."

"Tell me now," Onstott said.

"I said, give me time. I haven't got it quite clear, but it's coming."

"For Christ sakes—" Onstott began.

"Get off my back!" Ellis snapped. He felt queasy. The pain in his leg and chest took second place to a sick worry.

Onstott took a step toward the bed. "It's my business to ask questions," he said in an overcontrolled voice.

Coddington interrupted. "Time enough for questions when Barnie feels stronger." He turned to Ellis. "Right now, the important thing is to get you back on your feet."

"Okay, okay," said Onstott. "But tomorrow, we talk." He glanced at his watch. "I mean, later today."

Ellis nodded. "Fair enough."

Coddington lifted his bulk back to his feet. "Look, Barnie, this is a rotten business. Anything you need, you say the word. I'm going to ask for a meeting with the commissioner this afternoon. We're going to get to the bottom of this."

Onstott nodded soberly, turned toward the door. "Right now," Coddington said, "I want you to see about a guard being put on Barnie's room. If he's in danger—"

"It's all taken care of," Onstott said. He closed thumb and forefinger for Ellis to see. "Come on, Captain. He looks tired."

They left side by side, an incongruous Mutt and Jeff pair—the tall assistant DA and the short, fat fire captain.

Ellis smiled, feeling better after their visit despite his moment of anger. The wheels were turning.

Miss Birch came in as soon as they were gone. From somewhere—*Midair?* wondered Ellis—she produced a tiny, white paper cup.

"And now for your sleeping pill," she said.

"Not yet," Ellis said. "I have some thinking to do."

"Oh, you'll have weeks and weeks to think," said Miss Birch. She handed him the cup with the capsule. "Down the hatch!"

Ellis glared at her, put the cup on the table. "Put that phone where I can reach it."

"But it's three o'clock in the morning!"

"Tell the switchboard my wife will call. When she does, put her right through—no matter what time it is."

"I don't know—"

"Just put the phone where I can get it," Ellis snapped. *Goddamit!* His ribs ached when he barked like that. "If you really want me to get some rest, give the switchboard that message."

Reluctantly, she nodded, moved the phone closer.

"Now, please crank my bed up as far as you can," said Ellis. "And leave the door open when you go."

Miss Birch's voice was tightly disapproving. "You are not going to be cranked way up. Doctor's orders. And you should take your pill. You need rest and quiet."

He waited for her to leave. She fought it, but the habits of obedience were too strong, and Ellis was a man used to giving orders. Disapproval was apparent, though, in the stiff set of her shoulders as she marched out.

Ellis was more aware of his leg than he wanted to be. The sleeping pill was a temptation. But first he had to hear from Jane—and that would take at least an hour, probably nearer two.

He reached for the phone, managed to get through to Bill Torrance in Fairfield.

"I'll be there when Jane arrives," the burly deputy sheriff promised. "And I'll stick with them till I hear from you."

Ellis cradled the phone. He felt better with Torrance on the job—but he was still uneasy.

Now he understood McCoy's fear. Ellis shook his head angrily, thinking of the bruise Mrs. McCoy had seen on her husband's stomach. He could imagine those thugs threatening to do the same thing to McCoy's pregnant wife. A blow on the stomach—a message. Those low, crawly scum!

Ellis clutched the sheet in his fists, glared at the open doorway, picturing the tiny Mrs. Christian McCoy. So like a child—yet nine months pregnant.

Ellis muttered several of his favorite swear words, tried to shift position, and swore again at the jab of pain in his chest.

A light doze closed his eyes. He woke up sharply when the phone rang. Jane! He took a deep breath of relief as he heard her voice on the phone. He glanced at his watch as he talked to her. 4:00 AM. She'd made good time. The children were safely in bed.

Ellis reached for the sleeping pill, stopped at a familiar sound in the hall. He watched the open doorway, waiting.

In a moment, he saw what he'd waited for: a scrubwoman in a white uniform pushed a mop down the hall. He waited as she plodded back out of sight, then returned, pushing a low cart loaded with a bucket of steaming water and a rack of brooms and mops, stopped in front of his door, and dunked her mop.

A sharp tang of soap and disinfectant filled his nose.

Ellis stared at the mop bucket, thinking. It was almost twice the size of the one Mrs. McCoy had used. And hanging on its side was a heavy lid.

"Hey!" he called in a low voice. "Hey!"

The woman glanced through the door.

Ellis beckoned. "Come here a minute."

The woman glanced up and down the hospital hall, hesitating, mop in hand. She shook her head slowly. "If it's booze you want, mister, I'm temperance. You'll have to get someone else."

"No," said Ellis. "Nothing like that." He pointed at the cleaning cart with the bucket. "Could you wheel that a little closer?"

"You nuts?"

"What have you got to lose?" Ellis asked.

The woman shrugged, pushed the steaming cart half into the room.

Ellis took a long look at the cleaning bucket with its tight lid, nodded. "Okay," he said. "Thanks."

The woman shook her head. "Takes all kinds," she muttered as she wheeled the cart out the door, worked on down the hall.

Ellis leaned back in bed—feeling that there were a lot of pieces, but finally he was beginning to sense a shape. It had been a break, seeing that lid on the mop bucket. That answered a big question.

He began assembling his thoughts, lining up procedure in his methodical way, getting everything in order for when he saw Onstott in the morning.

In the middle of a thought, he dozed off.

He woke up suddenly at an odd noise in the hall—footsteps that didn't sound right. Someone had paused where he couldn't be seen, just beside the open door. If it had been a nurse or an aide, they'd have barged right in.

Ellis froze, watching the doorway. He reached under his pillow, shifted the .38 down beside him under the covers. *Come in,* he thought. *I've got a score to settle with you.*

With one quick motion, the young fireman, McCoy, darted into the room, closed the door behind him.

Ellis waited, all senses alert, hand on the .38. Was this it?

McCoy moved quietly toward the bed, spoke softly. "You awake, Lieutenant?"

Ellis took a deep breath. "I'm awake now. What're you doing here?"

McCoy smiled and it lit up his thin face. "Everything's okay now, Lieutenant. Marianne just gave birth to a nine-pound boy."

Ellis relaxed his grip on the gun at his side, permitted himself a slight smile. "Congratulations, McCoy. That's wonderful." Then he stiffened again. "How did you know where to find me?"

McCoy stared. "Is it a secret? Captain Coddington told me. I ran into him in the lobby, and he told me what had happened."

Some protection this room has, Ellis thought in disgust. "Is there a police guard in the hall?" he asked.

"Not right outside your room." McCoy swallowed. "But there's a cop talking to a nurse near the elevators."

"That figures," Ellis said. "You got any special reason for seeing me, McCoy?"

McCoy gulped, started to speak, then swallowed his words.

Ellis took a long, careful look at the man. So damned young and eager. Was McCoy the rotten apple in the barrel? He'd be a perfect one. Who'd suspect that ingenuous face—that open, puppy look?

McCoy cleared his throat nervously. "I'm sorry, Lieutenant, if you didn't want visitors. I—I feel responsible. I had to just let you walk into a mess without—"

"I'm over twenty-one," Ellis barked. "I walk into any mess I choose." He stared up at the ungainly traction apparatus over the bed, sorting out his thoughts. Who could you really trust when the syndicate was involved? Onstott? Maybe. McCoy? Probably not. Coddington? Ellis swore to himself. The whole damn fire department was suspect till they got this cleared up.

Ellis focused again on McCoy. The kid looked like he'd lost his last friend. Ellis nodded toward the straight chair. "Sit down," he said.

McCoy swung the chair into position with its back to the bed, sat down straddling it. "I'm really sorry. I—"

Ellis took a deep breath. "How'd they get to you?"

McCoy gripped the back of the chair, looked down at his hands. "It was Marianne," he said. "They threatened—"

"Who did?" Ellis asked sharply.

"A couple of guys in the hotel. They beat me up bad, said they'd do the same to Marianne if I didn't lay off. I've never been beaten up like that before." In the light from the table, Ellis noted

McCoy's face was flushed. "Christ, Lieutenant—the baby and all—I just—"

Ellis remembered his own fear for Jane. "I know," he said grimly. "Who were they?"

"I never saw them before," McCoy said. "There were two of them. I went down the hall to that pay phone, and a big guy grabbed me from behind and pulled me into a room. A big, blocky guy—he looked like an ex-fighter. There was another guy there—same type, but less of him. He held the gun while the big guy worked me over."

Ellis nodded, recognizing the description of the two men.

McCoy took a deep breath. "I didn't dare tell you yesterday. You don't know how glad I am to have Marianne safe in the hospital. With her here, I can ..." He broke off as the phone rang.

Ellis's glance darted to his watch. 4:45 AM. *What the hell?* He picked up the receiver. "Yes?"

The voice was muffled. "You were told to lay off—have you forgotten the message?"

Ellis stiffened, the phone suddenly heavy in his hand. "Who—"

"I said—have you forgotten the message?"

McCoy stared at Ellis's face, then stood up suddenly, made a futile snatch at the phone. "What is it?" he asked in a loud voice.

Ellis shook his head, but it was too late. "Is McCoy with you?" the muffled voice asked. "Too bad." The phone was hung up with a click.

Ellis returned it slowly to the cradle, then grabbed it up, dialed the operator. "This is Ellis in 330," he said. "Where'd that call come from?"

"There was no call through the board, Mr. Ellis. It must have been an inside call."

Ellis cradled the phone, stared at McCoy. So the young fireman thought his Marianne was safe in the hospital. That was a joke.

"What the hell was that call?" McCoy asked. "You looked sick."

"This hospital is about as safe as a gas truck in a forest fire," Ellis said. "It's wide open. Look how easy you got in here."

McCoy got to his feet. "Do they know I'm here with you? Those thugs said if I talked to you, they'd get Marianne."

"Better go to her," Ellis said. "They know you're here. That was one of their playmates on the phone. He knew your voice—or he saw you duck in here."

McCoy started for the door.

"Hold on," Ellis said. "You'd better know what I think they're doing."

McCoy paused, his hand on the doorknob.

"When a man dies in a fire," Ellis said, "the coroner can tell it from the amount of carbon monoxide in the body. He can tell if the man was already dead—or he could tell if he was drugged or drunk."

"So?" McCoy's voice was impatient.

"So in this case, they knocked their victims out with smoke—just as it would happen if it were a natural fire. Remember those rings you spotted on the floor?"

McCoy nodded.

"They're scorch marks. I think the killers are using empty cleaning buckets—the big commercial kind with a tight lid. They fill them with charcoal or something to produce a dense, heavy smoke. This bucket goes just inside the door of a victim's room. If he's asleep, and especially if he's drunk, the smoke knocks him out. When he's out, they cover the bucket—maybe douse it first with water—stage a fire in the mattress with a cigarette, pick up the bucket, and beat it."

"Sounds too tricky," McCoy said. "Someone would be sure to spot a guy carrying a big bucket."

Ellis shook his head. "Not if the guy was a cleaning woman. Or a man disguised as a cleaning woman. What would be a more natural thing to see late at night in a public building or a hotel than a cleaning woman with a bucket and mop?"

McCoy's eyes widened. "For Christ sakes!"

"I may even have found where they hid the bucket after using it in the Sander's Hotel," Ellis said. "There's a scorch ring on the floor of an old supply closet on the fourth floor."

"Yeah," McCoy said. "The bucket would have to be full of hot coals. It would leave a burned mark like the ones we found."

"Better get to your wife," Ellis said. "Call the local precinct and identify yourself. Ask for a guard. Tell them to call me if there's any question about it."

"What about you?" McCoy asked.

"I'll tell the nurse to send that pet cop of hers in here."

McCoy nodded, stepped away quickly as the door behind him opened.

His way out was blocked by a very angry Nurse Birch.

She glared at McCoy. "Visiting hours end at nine!" she snapped. She turned on Ellis. "Why haven't you taken your sleeping pill?"

With a quick motion, McCoy slipped around her, murmuring as he left, "I was just leaving."

Ellis pushed the gun against his thigh. The last thing he wanted tonight was a sleeping pill. "I'll take it right away," he lied.

She crossed to the bed, loomed over him. Her uniform stretched angrily across her superstructure. "I'll wait right here while you take it," she said.

Ellis knew her type. This was the sort of female who ran offices, marriages, and hospital wards—would allow nothing to thwart her. "I'm quite tired," he said in as calm a voice as he could manage. "I don't believe I'll need a pill tonight."

The nurse sniffed. "You didn't take your pill when you said you would, and it's almost dawn. Dr. Greenleaf left strict orders." She picked up the paper cup with its capsule, thrust it at Ellis. "Now!"

He sighed. Wasn't there enough trouble without having to fight this martinet? "I'm sorry," he said, "but I can't take your pill right now. It's important that I stay awake."

"It's more important you get your rest," she said.

He shook his head, feeling oddly like a recalcitrant child refusing his cod-liver oil. "Look, at least let me talk to that policeman in the hall first."

"No more visitors," she snapped. Then she turned on her heel and left the room.

Ellis suspected victory about the sleeping pill was not to be that easy; knew he was right when she returned almost immediately, followed by an orderly.

She stepped close to the bed, and with one swift motion, pulled Ellis's arm up, produced a hypodermic, and gave him a shot.

Ellis fought to sit up, found it impossible with his leg in traction. Fury filled him. "You stupid bitch! What did you shoot into me?"

The orderly moved closer. "There's no call—"

"I checked with the doctor," the nurse interrupted smoothly. "That was just a mild sedative to help you relax." She reached over, switched off the light.

"Wait a minute," said Ellis. "I gotta talk to that cop. It's vital."

"The patrolman has gone for a cup of coffee," she said. "I told him I'd keep an eye on you, and that's just what I'm doing." She wheeled table, light, and telephone beyond Ellis's reach. "Good night," she said and left, flanked by the orderly.

"Wait," Ellis called, but the door closed firmly behind them.

The only light in the room came from a tiny night-light near the bathroom door. By its dim glow, Ellis could barely see the closed white door to the hall. Beyond the window, there was the faintest suggestion of dawn to come.

Anger made him feel like yelling and fuming; he didn't dare fall asleep! He glared at the shadowy traction sling overhead that froze him in one position. He could ring; but all he would get would be that same martinet.

He still felt wide awake, but he didn't know how long the drug gave him.

The extension table with its unreachable light and telephone were silhouetted against the window.

No matter how he stretched, the phone was too far to reach.

Ellis forced himself to take several deep breaths to calm his anger. Just exactly where did he stand? The cop was no good to him—neither was the nurse.

And no use kidding himself that they couldn't find him. Whoever had rung this phone knew exactly where Ellis was—and would put his own construction on a council of war with McCoy at this predawn hour.

If only McCoy would come back before the drug took hold. Damn that nurse!

And yet—could he be sure of McCoy? Onstott said the gangsters were working with a fireman. But Christ! He couldn't suspect everyone!

But this whole arson scheme smelled of professional know-how. Smoke in the victim's lungs. Smoking in bed. The dirty old routine so common it seldom got a second look.

So goddam simple. The only flammable they added seemed to be lighter fluid—and that could be present in any room. Most arsonists got too complicated—and it was their complicated devices that revealed them.

This clever bastard hadn't made that error.

Ellis yawned.

He couldn't help it. Sleep moved across his mind like a cloud of grey feathers, fogged his thoughts.

Christ, he thought, how can I stay awake when I'm full of drugs and fastened in this one position? Damn that nurse!

He tensed his muscles, felt them relax against his will.

Why would a fireman help a bookie? The answer floated drowsily in his mind, just out of reach.

He shook his head, was overtaken by a yawn so deep it hurt his chest near the broken rib.

For a moment pain cleared his thoughts.

Coddington! he thought. *Captain Coddington!*

Ellis pushed the idea away, but it came back to his drowsy mind with the force of pure logic.

Coddington played the horses; could easily be involved with Tonelli.

Coddington had tried to call Ellis off the case.

Coddington had the know-how to plan the arson- homicides.

Coddington knew McCoy was in the hospital.

"Oh, Christ!" Ellis said aloud. His tongue felt thick. *Coddington.* He didn't want it to be true. He turned the thought around as carefully as if he had a year to think about it.

There was a loose piece—something that didn't fit.

Thoughts swirled by like dreams.

A fireman, he thought.

McCoy or Coddington—one or the other. They were the only ones close enough to all that had happened. Take your choice—

McCoy or Coddington. It was like a song.

It had to be a fireman. Onstott said so.

The thought turned over.

Why did it have to be a fireman? Because Onstott said so.

Was he the only one who said so?

Then Ellis remembered the missing piece—the piece that didn't fit. Coddington couldn't have ordered the attack because Coddington didn't know Ellis was in the old hotel. Coddington was out of the office at the race track.

But Onstott knew. And Onstott certainly had more than enough knowledge to plan the arsons.

Now I can go to sleep, thought Ellis drunkenly. *All solved. Now I can relax.*

He knew he shouldn't sleep, but he couldn't remember why. He forced his eyes half-open—

Had that door moved—or was it a trick of his doped mind?

No. It was definitely opening, a little at a time.

Panic flooded Ellis's brain, clearing away the drug haze. He fumbled for the gun beside him. It eluded his grasp. There, there it was! He held it, hidden by the blanket.

The door opened long enough for a white figure to slip in, closed again. Nurse? No, a doctor.

A tall doctor—much taller than Dr. Greenleaf.

Ellis' mind went torpid again. There was something he should do; he couldn't think what it was. Why did that doctor look so familiar—even in the half-light of the room? He clenched for the gun, but it slipped out of his fingers.

Horror filled his mind. He knew just what was happening, and he couldn't move a muscle.

The white figure crossed to the bed, reached for the bell-push, and placed it behind the bed, out of reach.

Ellis fought to move his hand and failed.

There was danger, his mind told him, terrible danger. But it was like playing with ideas of panic. His muscles would do nothing about it.

All he could see of the man was a white blur of face and uniform near his bed. Ellis tried to call out—no sound came.

The man crossed to the table, picked up something Ellis couldn't see. He heard a match strike and the sound of a cigarette being lit.

Ellis smelled cigarette smoke and something like gasoline. Lighter fluid?

The tall figure bent over the bed and said clearly, "You stupid jerk. I tried to warn you."

Ellis knew that voice. *Onstott!*

A quick glow from the cigarette lit Onstott's face, ridiculous yet evil over the white doctor's coat. Onstott bent down, placed the cigarette carefully just beyond the reach of Ellis' hand—as though the damn thing had rolled there—beside his suspended leg.

I've had it, Ellis thought. *He's setting fire to the bed—and there's nothing I can do!* He willed his hand to move toward the gun. Nothing happened.

Ellis wondered how close the glowing coal was to the lighter fluid he smelled.

Onstott expelled a contemptuous puff of smoke in one gulp. Ellis felt it sear his lungs. He heard Onstott move across the room toward the door.

With a racking, choking gasp, Ellis coughed. The pain of his broken rib scorched his mind.

Pain jerked him awake, drove back the drug for a precious instant.

Ellis's hand clutched at the gun, lifted it across his stomach. He fired toward the door. Once, twice. Then sank back—plummeted into unconsciousness by the drug.

A voice was saying, "Coddington." He heard the name distinctly, over and over. What did it mean? "Coddington. Coddington. Coddington."

Ellis laughed sleepily. It was his own voice. His eyes opened, and he saw McCoy standing beside his bed. God, that sunlight was bright, streaming through the window. His eyelids closed. Sunlight? Carefully, he opened his eyes again. "Where's Captain Coddington?" he asked.

"Right here, Barnie," Coddington said from the chair by the window.

Ellis smiled drowsily. He'd made it through the night. He came suddenly awake. "Is—is Onstott dead?"

"No, but he might as well be. He's in jail and singing like a bird. I understand he said enough to hang himself and get Tonelli, too. With a murder rap facing him, Onstott got real talkative."

Ellis pulled himself up as far as he could. "Jane? Where's Jane?"

"Safe at her mother's with your kids," said Coddington. He pulled his bulk out of the chair and crossed slowly to the bed. Ellis noted fatigue lines creasing the captain's face. "The police will keep an eye on them till Tonelli's trial—but there's no real danger. The whole mess is out in the open now."

Ellis took a deep breath, was sorry when the pain from his broken rib pierced him. "Did I hit Onstott when I shot?"

Coddington wheezed his short laugh. "All you hit was that traction device over the bed. It's a wonder you didn't shoot your own toe off."

"Then how—" Ellis began.

Codding waved a pudgy hand toward the young fireman. McCoy flushed. "You'll have to thank McCoy here. He spotted Onstott in his doctor getup."

"It took me too long to catch on," McCoy said. "I passed Onstott as I went down the back stairway to the maternity floor, but he was partly turned away, and I just got a glimpse of his face. I knew that doctor looked familiar, but I didn't think of Onstott right away. I expected trouble to look like a scrubwoman—not a doctor."

Ellis nodded. "Yet it's the same gimmick. A scrubwoman is a common sight in a public building late at night, but in a hospital, a doctor's even better. And with that shot in me, they didn't need a bucketful of smoke."

"After I made sure Marianne was okay," McCoy said, "I got to thinking about that doctor—wondering where I'd seen him before. It took me a long time to realize the last time I'd seen him was in your office, and that you'd introduced him as an assistant DA."

Coddington chuckled. "McCoy ran up from the second floor. He got here just as Onstott was leaving your room. Your shots blasted out. It caused quite a sensation when McCoy came sprinting down the hall and tackled a doctor."

McCoy grinned. "That bossy nurse was sure she was next on my list."

"I wish she had been," Ellis said, remembering the hypo.

McCoy nodded. "About that time, the cops I'd called came galloping up. Onstott almost managed to talk his way out of it until smoke started curling up from your bed!"

"That cop guarding me was as useful as a rubber crutch," Ellis said. "When I really needed him, the stupid jerk was on a coffee break."

McCoy said, "Onstott told him to play it cool. That you had demanded protection but there wasn't much danger in the hospital."

"Christ!" said Ellis. "Onstott sure had me going. What did the hoods have on the poor SOB? Gambling debts?"

"Hell, no," wheezed Coddington. "It was out-and-out greed. He was the syndicate's man from way back." He cleared his throat. "If gambling debts were all that scum needed ..." His voice trailed off.

McCoy noticed Coddington's embarrassment, broke in. "They owned Onstott lock, stock, and legal decree. He originated the arson trick, of course."

Ellis looked up at McCoy. "You were right from the beginning," he said. "You spotted arson when the rest of us might have missed it." Then Ellis remembered why McCoy had come to the hospital in the first place. "How's your wife—and the new baby?"

"A boy?" Coddington asked.

McCoy grinned. "A nine-pound, day-old fireman," he said.

Ellis faked a groan. "Will you do me a big favor, McCoy?"

"Sure. What?"

"Tell your kid never to phone me before ten in the morning," Ellis said.

THE LITTLE WINDOW

The sense of danger came over Angelo Serafim while he was levering his stiff old legs down the seven concrete steps from the sidewalk to his shoe repair shop. One moment he was savoring the spring day—still a taste of lunch on his tongue, a chill nip to the air, woodsmoke grey of concrete around him, grit underfoot—a distant door slam and hurrying feet.

Then ... this touch to the heart that he knew must come from something seen but not noticed.

He looked back up—past the impatient face of his nephew, Paul—saw that a black sedan had rolled to the curb beyond the iron rail. On the near side sat a fat man who stared at him across dumpling cheeks, eyes glaring like two spots of black lava.

"Come on, Uncle, unlock the door," said Paul. The young man moved down a step, one hand up, absently picking his teeth.

Angelo pulled himself around, but he still saw those eyes. He fumbled with the key in the lock. *Those eyes! Here or in the old country—the same: Killer! Why does killer look at me?*

All the fresh feeling of rebirth had gone out of the spring day.

Lock tumblers clicked. Creaking hinges echoed in the concrete stairwell. Angelo sniffed at the pungency of new leather stirred up by the door's motion.

Could it be thieves? he wondered. He wanted to look back, found his muscles unwilling. *Those eyes! Something is wrong ...*

Paul pushed past, shoving the door with a sullen hunch of shoulders. The young man skirted the front counter, and his sleeve brushed its dusty linoleum top. He went to the bench in the rear corner, beneath the shallow window that looked out at the feet of people passing on the side street.

Angelo clocked the switch beside the door. Yellow light from four metal-shaded bulbs filled the shop. He straightened a chair beside the window, still afraid to look outside. A bank of cubbyhole shelves extended along the left wall behind the counter. Angelo stared at them, saw the rows of paper-wrapped shoes as lumpy, brown creatures crouched in their lairs. The shop oozed menace. He sensed peril even in the way Paul walked—soft on the balls of the feet, holding something in like a cat stalking its prey.

"Did you finish those shoes for Mrs. Krantz?" asked Paul.

Angelo cleared his throat. He caught himself listening for a car door, for steps. "Yes," he said. "I finish. She say come today."

The old man's chest pained him—not the heart pain, but something more basic. He asked himself, *What if killer is here for Paul? What if Paul is in some trouble with that no-good Carlos? How do I know what Paul does when he says he goes to night school?*

Paul made a clattering noise at the bench. "We still have lots of work here," he called. "Better get started."

Angelo nodded, not answering, not consciously hearing, but concentrating on the way Paul walked. *You can tell much from how people walk,* he told himself. The young man's stride had been getting tighter and tighter these past few weeks. And Paul was only four months out of uniform. He still should move with that long pack-on-the-back swing.

Sounds of a car motor flared outside, faded. Angelo closed the door, darted a glance out the dusty front windows and up the stairwell. The car and its shark-eyed occupant were gone. *Maybe I am wrong,* he thought. But he still could feel tension. Automatically, he flipped the "Out to Lunch" sign on the door.

Paul dropped a hammer.

Angelo whirled, then: "You getting clumsy, Pavlos?"

The young man's face darkened. "Uncle, I've asked you not to call me that! Over here my name's Paul."

Angelo lapsed into Greek: *"What is wrong with the name Pavlos? It is a good Greek name."*

Paul thought, *Here we go again!* And he answered in English, "But we're in America now."

Angelo shrugged. "Hokay. But you speak Greek. You want to be lawyer. Fine. You be lawyer for Greek people in America."

Paul threw down an awl. "No! I'll be a lawyer for anyone who needs a lawyer!"

"Sometimes I don't understand you, Pavlos," said Angelo.

"Paul!"

"I'm sorry," said Angelo. "But I got big empty in head where I forget."

Paul ran a hand through his curly black hair, went back to work.

Seeing the gesture reminded Angelo of the way his own hair had looked before it had turned white and brittle. There was much of the Serafims in his sister's boy—the sharp nose, dark eyes under thick brows and high forehead. Even the clear wedge shape of the face spoke of endless Serafims descended from Serafims. It was the mouth that had come from the Heropolis boy, the father—full and firm, almost grim.

Angelo looked down, patted his paunch, and thought of his own youth gone to fat and a skin as leathery as the hides hanging from a side wall of the shop. He shook his head.

"Ah, well ..." he said.

"It's Wednesday," said Paul. "We have to finish this stuff early. I have extra classes tonight, you know." He snapped on the buffer, bent over it. The humming racket filled the shop.

Does he really go to classes? Angelo wondered. He raised his voice. "Every week it comes all over Wednesday for extra classes. Is that what you do? You really go to classes?"

The sound of the buffer stopped in midsentence, and the shouting of his own voice momentarily shocked Angelo.

Paul glared at him. "What do you mean by that?"

"I just wonder," said Angelo. "You in some kind of trouble?"

And Paul thought, *Uncle Angie all day! Prof Emory on contract law for half the night! It's too much!* He threw a boot at the bench. "Yeah! I'm in trouble! I've got to listen to your crazy yak all day! Then

I've got to study half the night! Isn't that trouble enough?"

"You don't like to hear what your own uncle say, hokay." Angelo wiped an eye.

"And you're sure taking a long time getting back to work," snapped Paul. "It's after one."

"That is right," said Angelo. He scratched his head, took off his coat, put on an apron. He saw that Paul was back at the bench, working on the half Wellingtons for Mr. Filmore. "First I grab middle of my day," Angelo called. "Don't get good grab on middle—back end get away." He advanced into the shop.

Footsteps could be heard coming along the sidewalk from the south—a familiar dragging hesitancy. That would be Mr. Mullhausen, Angelo knew. Everyone who passed here regularly, he knew them by the sound of their feet and the look of their shoes through the little window above the bench. For many, he knew names because they were customers. But they seldom became faces—just familiar feet.

A chipped yellow clock with a cracked crystal sat on the end of the bench. Angelo set the alarm, saw that Paul was attacking the work with concentrated fury.

"I ask you like they ask in this country," said Angelo. He brushed leather chips off the end of the bench. "What is bugging you, man?"

Paul shrugged without breaking the rhythm of his work. And he thought, *That damn accent! Why does he have to make everybody think he's just the ignorant foreigner? Wearing that pose like a mask! Over here more than thirty years and still talking like a fresh-off-the-boat vlakas! Not even a good Greek accent! I might accept that.*

"You know what wrong with you?" asked Angelo. "You need wife. Get good wife, two-three kids. Nice little apartment. Then you don't go reaching out all time for things too big for you."

"Nothing's too big for me!" snapped Paul.

"Lots of room for good Greek lawyer over here," said Angelo. "Fix contract. Write will. Sometimes somebody get in trouble ..." He nodded. "Be important man. People come to you. Lots friends."

Paul sniffed, thinking as he had many times since arriving in America six years before, that Angelo had no real friends—only acquaintances and customers. *Sure! Lots of friends! Won't even put in a telephone! Why? Who would call?*

Angelo took down the English-style brogans he had made two years before for Mr. Levy, the garment manufacturer. They needed new soles and heels, but the uppers still were in sound condition. He glanced at Paul, tried another approach. "Why does that Carlos hang around you all time?"

"How do I know?"

"He is no good," said Angelo. "Why all time he comes in here for see you?"

"Maybe he's lonesome!" snapped Paul. "My God! The guy lives in the same building with us!"

"I wish he moves," said Angelo. "No good! In jail two-three times."

"So he's a punk," said Paul. "I don't encourage him, but I'm not going to be nasty, either."

Angelo put a hand in one of the brogans, felt the stitching—no breaks.

Paul worked furiously, silent.

Angelo misinterpreted Paul's stillness. "You are twenty-two, time you stop acting like little boy," he snapped. "Why you think I bring you this country?" He rapped a knuckle on the bench. "Six years ago I bring! What you think? I want for cheap helper? You should inherit business when I am gone, hah?"

Paul said: "Look, Uncle, I appreciate every—"

"Appreciate! You think is what I want?"

"Oh, skip it!"

"Hah!" Angelo went back to the brogan in his hand. "You talk good English." Two strokes of his knife slashed away old stitching from a sole. He pulled back the worn leather. "Me, I just learn from school in old country and what I stuff in head here. But you study hard. Fine. Now you want be lawyer. Fine. Before my sister die, when she say you should come this country for—"

"What do you want me to say, Uncle?" Paul put down his work, glared at Angelo.

"Say anything you like—or don't say it. That's what it is in this country!" Angelo nodded. "Freedom from speech!"

"Oh, brother," breathed Paul. He went back to his work.

"I got forty-three more years from you," said Angelo. "Next June I got sixty-seven years. Old man—that's me."

"And when you're gone, you want me to have the money from the business," intoned Paul. "You've told me!"

Angelo glanced at his nephew, shrugged. "That is right. You take money, let rest die with me. Fine. I what they should say: 'They don't make shoes anymore like they make when old Angelo is alive.' But you should be lawyer. Fine. Lawyer is better from shoemaker."

Paul put down the boot, spoke without turning. "Please stop the lecture, Uncle."

"Lecture?"

Paul faced Angelo. "All I said last night was I'd like to ditch the school sometimes, get out with people my own age, have a good time. Make friends. That's all I said. It won't hurt to miss a few classes."

Angelo's hands trembled. "Does it hurt if you miss few nails or few stitches in boot?"

"It's not the same!"

"We got full life," said Angelo.

Paul's eyes opened wide. "You call your life full?"

"Sure. Got work, got nice apartment, got *tee*vee." He nodded. "Got good radio. Got good books."

"But no telephone," said Paul.

"Telephone?" Angelo frowned. "I tell you we don't need telephone. Costs money. Anyway, who calls us?"

"That's just it," said Paul. And for a moment, he had the sensation that he could feel his youth slipping away from him, that he was growing suddenly as old as Angelo. It was like awakening on a roller coaster to find the cold wind blowing in his face. He took a trembling breath, said, "It's not just that you don't have a telephone. It's what that means with you. You have no friends—nobody to call and ask you out for an evening."

Angelo's face darkened. He spoke through tight lips: "And who *you* want go out with? That no-good ... Carlos!"

Paul sighed, returned to the boot. "It isn't that I want to go out with Carlos. It's ... Oh, hell! It doesn't matter who it is. You always get just as mad."

"Ask little respect for your olders," muttered Angelo. And he thought: *Who need friend like that Carlos?* He lapsed into Greek, mumbling.

"Oh, speak English!" snapped Paul.

"Why don't I speak my own language?" demanded Angelo. "My own language I got born with?"

"You're an American citizen now," said Paul. "That's the whole idea."

"You got hole in your idea!" growled Angelo. He blinked, swallowed. Silence stretched between them—then, "Pavl ... Paul, let's don't fight, hah?"

Paul took a deep breath. "Okay, Uncle. Drop it."

"If you leave all this work to me," ventured Angelo. "Go school in day so you got more time for study your ..."

"Let's drop it!" snapped Paul.

Angelo frowned, sighed. *Such a stubborn, proud boy,* he thought. *Won't let me work for him. Proud, just like all Serafims.* Then, because he couldn't avoid it, he asked himself, *But does he go to night school? Is it classes, or does he run around with Carlos and young hoodlums?*

He studied Paul covertly while taking down a blank of hard-cured steer hide to cut new soles.

"Shoe get scuffed," said Angelo. "But if is good shoe inside, it lasts and lasts and ..."

"What's wrong with my going out, making friends?" asked Paul. "With Carlos or anyone else? So he's a little wild, okay. I can take care of myself. Work and study! What do I see of the world?"

"You already see army! You just home four months!"

"Yeah, the army. One barracks after another." Paul gestured with his hammer toward the shallow window at eye level above them. In contrast with the dusty glass at the stairwell, this window shone. "See the world from a barracks!" he barked. "The narrow view—like that!" He pounded a nail into the boot with extra vehemence.

A staccato of feminine heels went by on the walk outside. Through the window above the bench, Angelo caught a glimpse of slim ankles, brown alligator pumps. She went to the mailbox on the corner. It clanged. Presently, she returned. Angelo grinned as he saw Paul's gaze following the ankles.

The rhythm of her walk felt good to Angelo's ears—pert, alive. *That is a nice girl. Secretary in law offices down Seventh Street. No pushing, man-posing in her walk as it is with so many women nowadays. A feminine woman.*

Above the sound of Paul's hammering, Angelo said, "You think my little window's not much of world, hah? You be surprised ... what I know from my little window. Thirty-one years I watch from here. God give man senses. Man should use what God give wherever he is. I know everybody walks regular by my window. I know more about those people than they think. They look down here, see old man working, they think he doesn't know much. They be surprised."

"Sure," said Paul. "You read minds."

Angelo smiled, nodded. "You take young woman just now. She is secretary. With lawyer. Mr. Carter. Down street there." He gestured with his head. "Name is Miss Lovett. Jean. Nice name. She support mother, but mother die. Now she is very lonely girl. Work from when she is sixteen. Never have boyfriend time." He shrugged. "Now ... how does girl learn new tricks from old dogs?"

"If you've just seen her through your window, how do you know so much about her?" asked Paul. He put aside one of the boots, took up the other.

"Well ..." Again, Angelo smiled to himself. "I know name because she is customer. Yes. Got shoes right over there in work pile. I bring for her."

"Sure, but all that other ..."

"I tell you! Don't jump on gun." Angelo's smile became a grin. "When I fix my will at lawyer office. Before she is customer even. I hear walk. Same girl. Look at feet. Same girl. I ask Mr. Carter. A jewel he calls her, like she is diamond! He tells me. About mother. About work. And she got nice voice, too. And pretty. Like they say: a stacked dish."

It was too much. Paul grinned. "Uncle, what're you doing—running a marriage bureau like in the old country?"

"Good thing," said Angelo. His face suddenly sobered. "When I am young jerk in old country, no papa or mama to do for me. Only sister younger from me. Maybe things be different."

He sighed, shrugged. "But they could use in America fine honorable *proxenetes*. So many people lonely. Need *proxenetes* to fix marriage. Nice man people trust."

"Like you?" asked Paul.

"Why not?"

"And you've got the girl all picked out for me," said Paul.

"You need good woman," said Angelo. "And this girl—secretary! In law office! She know all about your work."

At the end of the bench, the ticking of the yellow clock was drowned abruptly by its alarm.

"So soon," said Angelo. He slipped off his apron, gestured toward the brogans. "I promise Mr. Levy he gets shoes tonight. When you finish boots, you work on these, hah? I be back one hour."

Paul turned a puzzled frown on Angelo. "Where do you go every Wednesday, Uncle? Before I went away in the army, you never ..."

"Don't ask! How many times I tell you don't ask?" Angelo scowled, put a hand to his chest, coughed. "I be back in one hour." He turned away, exchanged his apron for the coat on the hook, slipped into the coat with stiff movements, and left the shop.

As he labored up the steps, Angelo thought, *Why don't I tell Pavlos where I go? So I go to a doctor. Do I hide this from everyone? No ... I just try to hide it from myself. I tell Pavlos sometime.* Then he was in the street, and again he thought of the fat man with killer eyes. *Is it really a killer? Who could he want?* He shook his head. *I am an old fool. I see ghosts.*

Through the dusty front windows, Paul had watched his uncle's progress up the steps. Presently, Angelo's feet moved across the little window above the bench. He was wearing shoes he had made for himself: low oxfords in two tones of brown and with ornate floral patterns punched into the toes. They were a young man's shoes, but the shoes of a *European* young man. They shuffled out of view to the left.

Paul returned to his work, thinking, *Where does he go?*

And now he found his attention caught by the view through the shallow window. A fireplug stood at the curb across the sidewalk. Marks from wrench jaws scarred the square metal heads of the outlets. An old brownstone with outcurving front steps dominated the view across the street. As Paul watched, an armored car pulled up below the steps. Two uniformed men wearing sidearms emerged, took a pair of canvas bags up the steps, returned empty-handed, and drove off.

The wind blew a scrap of paper like a dancing white insect from left to right along the sidewalk. And people walked past just outside the window.

The look of the moving feet caught Paul's mind. Their rhythm ... or lack of it. There was something disquieting in this view of people: cut off (most of them) around the calf. They were like disembodied pieces of marionettes dancing past for his benefit alone. It was like an unguarded view into the soul. Here, down at ground level, lay a thin strip where human inhibitions did not extend.

Paul thought of his uncle—thirty-one years staring out at people as though they were nude! He felt sudden rage at the window, thinking, *Without this window, Uncle Angie would have been forced to go outside, see people face to face, make friends. How can you make friends with bodiless feet?*

A man's feet came from the left—dark blue pants with knife-edge creases, black shoes shined to a hard gloss. They sauntered slowly past, full of elaborate casualness compounded by something furtive: a hesitant pause on the balls of the feet.

Paul thought of a beast walking in its jungle. Imagination conjured up a swarthy face, glittering eyes. The feet paused, still in the frame of the window, turned back the way they had come, and passed out of view. Paul found himself feeling deeply uneasy, as though he had witnessed a crime that he had been powerless to prevent.

He shook his head to drive away the imagery. *Nonsense! It's just a game Uncle Angie plays. This is the kind of thinking that traps people in basements!*

"Damn Uncle Angie and his window game!" he muttered.

Feminine heel taps clattered along the walk—alligator pumps, slim ankles, and sleek silk stockings. It was the young woman his uncle said worked in the law offices. Same shoes. Same walk.

Uncle Angie, matchmaker! thought Paul.

She passed out of sight, headed for the corner. He expected to hear the mailbox clang, waited for it. But the staccato of her heels stopped at the head of the stairwell, clap-clap-clapped into the echoing concrete hole at the front of the shop.

Paul turned, saw through the grimed front windows as she descended: the alligator pumps, shapely legs, a tailored green skirt, then a matching suit jacket of reserved and classic cut that swelled *un*reservedly over a full figure.

What had his uncle said—*"A stacked dish!"* Paul grinned.

The front door creaked open. She was redheaded, her face spattered with freckles. It was an alive face—generous lips, stubborn chin, a nose that turned up ever so slightly, and level, grey-green eyes.

"You must be Paul Herro," she said. Her voice was a sparkling contralto. She swung the door closed, advanced to the counter, and plopped an alligator bag on the linoleum top.

Paul crossed to stand opposite her, the counter between them. What had Angelo said her name was? He found that the name was important. *Jean! Jean Lovett!* He smiled at a sudden urge, said: "What can I do for you, Miss Jean Lovett?"

The grey-green eyes opened wide—a level, examining stare followed immediately by a flickering of long lashes, a shy downward glance. "We've met?" Her gaze flicked up, down. "No ... I've never been in here be ..." She looked directly at him. "Your uncle told you my name!"

Laughter bubbled in Paul. He explained about the window. At his urging, she came around to see the view for herself. Four boys ran past playing stickball. An old man with a cane followed. The cane had a brass tip that glistened in the spring sunlight, catching the eye.

"It's like ... it's like those one-way mirrors," she said. "You know—where you can see the person on the other side, but he can't see you. Imagine that funny old man standing here every day, looking right through people from his little window!"

Paul's mouth went thin. A nerve twitched along his jaw. *Funny old man!* He had a sudden image of this girl and her lawyer-boss laughing at Angelo.

"I'm glad the *funny old man* amuses you," he grated. "His accent's hilarious and he uses all kinds of words wrong and he talks too much and he repeats him—"

"Just a minute!" She took a backward step. The freckles stood out like spattered brown paint against her suddenly pale face. "I was …"

"I know what you were doing." He closed the gap between them. "But that *funny old man* has been mother and father to me since I was sixteen. No smart-mouth dame is—"

"That's quite enough!" she flared. "I meant no disrespect." She whirled, strode back to the counter, retrieved her purse, and snapped it open. Sharp, jerking motions emphasized each word as she spoke. "And I'm only here now as a favor to *him*, to deliver *this!*" She threw an envelope onto the counter, started toward the door.

"Wait!" Paul ran to the counter. The anger was gone, leaving him feeling drained, foolish.

She paused, glared back at him. Moisture glistened in her eyes.

His lips quirked upward in a rueful smile. "The name's Pavlos Heropolis," he said. "Jerk. A Greek jerk with a short temper. I'm sorry."

As suddenly as it had come, the anger melted from her face. "Well … perhaps I should've chosen my words more carefully. I only meant that I like your uncle—that he amuses me because he tries to amuse me … to make me laugh." She matched his smile. "I'm always opening my mouth and putting my foot in it."

He looked down. "And a nice foot, too."

"And there's nothing wrong with *your* accent," she said.

Suddenly they were both laughing.

Paul shook his head. "And if you only knew some of the things I was thinking about Uncle Angie just a little while ago."

"That's the way it is," she said. "We say anything we like to people we love. But just let some outsider step in and be the least bit critical. When my mother …" She stopped, a sudden stillness coming over her features, then continued, "Sometimes I forget she's gone."

Into the silence, Paul said, "I was all primed to blow up this afternoon, too. Uncle Angie's been riding me because I …" He broke off, thinking, *Old Angie, matchmaker. He sent this girl down here so that ...*

"He's been picking on you?" she said. She smiled encouragement.

He continued rather lamely, "Because I've been getting kind of tired of nothing but work work work—school and here. You know how it is.

She spoke softly. "Yes."

And he thought, *She is a stacked dish. At least Uncle Angie has a good eye.*

"Your uncle told me you're studying law," she said.

"Yeah. I'm in night school. I just got out of the army a few months ago."

"My father was in the army," she said. "He died when I was sixteen." She looked down, long lashes flickering, a disconcertingly feminine motion accented by its complete unconsciousness. "I work in a law office now."

He nodded. "Uncle Angie told me."

She glanced around the shop, then at Paul's hands on the counter. "This must be hard work. Your Uncle's hands always look so ... rough."

"He's done this work all his life," said Paul.

She shook her head. "And he still works every day."

"Yeah." Paul took a deep breath. "And if I'd let him, he'd have me attending school during the day and not helping at all here in the shop."

"He's such a nice old man," she said. "Mr. Carter—that's my boss—he always says it brightens up his day whenever Mr. Serafim comes in."

Paul had a sudden image of his uncle as a succession of masks: one for the shop, one for the apartment, one for Mr. Carter's office—and he wondered if he actually knew what was beneath his uncle's masks, the real face they hid.

To fill the silence, he said, "Uncle Angie's worked hard all his life. That's all he knows—work."

"And you're the independent type," she said. "That's what he told me."

"Well, why should I sponge off him? The government pays my tuition. I earn my own keep." Her words had touched another small spark to his anger, and he thought, *Independent type! And he's working on that, too. A nice little wife, two-three kids!*

"He's told me a lot of things about you," she said.

"I'll bet! Like I'm always reaching too high. What a fine husband I'd make. He thinks he's a matchmaker just like they have in the old country."

Her eyes looked round and deep. "Old people are like that in every country. You have to ... well, discount it."

"It was kind of obvious, wasn't it?" he asked. "Giving me the big buildup with you? Then asking you to bring this ..." He touched the envelope. "When he could just as well bring it himself."

A dark flush spread from her neck up across her face. "But I ..."

"Not that I'm really objecting," said Paul.

She spoke shortly. "No. I can see that." She gestured toward the envelope. "So we've met, and there's your envelope."

"Look ..."

"I've *looked.*" She glared at him.

"Now who's got a foot in the mouth?" he asked.

She didn't rise to his banter. "I really must be going. I have my *own* keep to earn."

"I guess I'm not the only independent type," he said.

The grey-green eyes remained level and aloof. "Of that you can be sure."

"May I see you again?"

She shrugged. "Why don't you consult your uncle on it?"

"Oooof!" He ducked his head, started to reply, but she was already letting herself out. He watched her climb the stairs—a last flash of slim ankles and alligator pumps.

"So much for Uncle Angie, matchmaker," he muttered.

Presently, he turned back to the bench. It was lonely and empty in the shop. He saw how dirty the place was: cobwebs in the corners, leather dust in every crack, stains on the floor, decrepit chairs beside the front windows.

He kicked the buffer stand.

Footsteps sounded in the stairwell. He whirled, hoping she was coming back. But it was a man. The door opened. Paul recognized him: Carlos Besera, the Carlos whom Uncle Angie did not like. He was a pale-skinned young man with a sharp, beaked nose dominating a narrow face. His raven's wing of black pompadour always appeared too neat, and the close-set dark eyes carried a look of thinly veiled panic.

"Well, look who's watching the till," he said. He closed the door behind him with a curious sealing-off motion, darted a glance around the shop.

For no reason he could explain, Paul felt anger at the intrusion. He spoke curtly. "What do you want, Carlos?"

"Do I have to want something?" Carlos crossed to the counter, slipped around it, bending like a dancer. "Maybe I just come for friendly visit."

Paul shrugged. "I have lots of work to do. Besides, Uncle Angie'll be back pretty soon. He doesn't like you hanging around here all the time."

"Now, you're not being very friendly," said Carlos. "Nowhere near as friendly as I bet you were with that doll who just left."

"I don't feel friendly!" snapped Paul. The other man's tone rasped on him: the way he spoke, as though saying one thing but meaning something different.

"But man, the company you keep!" said Carlos. He moved past Paul in a soft, springy stride, headed for the workbench.

Paul turned. "Where're you going? Uncle Angie'll flip if he finds you behind the counter."

Afraid I'll dip into the till?" Carlos sneered. "Fat chance in this dump!" He stopped at the bench, peered out the shallow window. "I'm just admiring the view."

Involuntarily, Paul glanced down at Carlos's feet, saw dark blue pants with knife-edge creases, black shoes polished to a high gloss. He had seen those pants and shoes recently—walking past the little window. The same feeling of disquiet returned to Paul. He said, "Have you been hanging around outside there?"

Carlos whirled. For an instant, there was a savage cast to his face. Then he relaxed, smiled—feral and toothy. "What makes you ask that?"

Paul shrugged.

"You see something that interested you?" asked Carlos.

"Just your feet," said Paul.

"My ... feet?" Carlos exploded into laughter.

"What do you want?" demanded Paul. He felt uneasy, sensing an undercurrent in the other's actions and words.

Carlos assumed a confidential manner. "While you're away in the army, something interesting happens around here." He nodded toward the window over the bench. "That old rat trap across the street—a factory moves in. Real sweet kind of a factory. Makes jewelry. You know: ice, gold—all kinds of real nice goodies."

Abruptly, Paul recalled the armored car, the armed guards.

Carlos said, "Now, just to look at a place like that, you wouldn't think it was much. Old dump like that. Unless you happen to have a little inside leak, kind of, that says there's going to be half a million bucks in ice shipped in there this afternoon. Yes, sir. Half a million. About three thirty, four o'clock. Maybe a little earlier."

Paul swallowed past a lump in his throat. He felt sudden menace, thought, *A robbery? This small-time punk?* He said, "So what?"

"'So what?' he asks!" Carlos shook his head sadly. "Man, you just don't fit. Strictly a square."

Paul glanced at the yellow alarm clock on the bench—2:25. Uncle Angie would be coming back soon.

And again, he thought, *A robbery? But this punk's the car-thief type—shoplifting, snatch and grab.* Then: *But even punks dream of the big time. And if he's moved in with some gang ...*

Carlos glanced back out the window, then returned to his smirking observation of Paul. "They got guards on the truck," he said, "but they'll be easy to handle. No sweat. The real problem's an old character sits at an upstairs window with a shotgun every time there's a big shipment. You can see him real easy from down here. Every time."

Paul frowned. "You're planning on robbing ..."

"You don't get a business opportunity like this every day," said Carlos. "Uh-uh!"

"But ..."

"Strictly a square," said Carlos. Again, that flicking glance out the window, then back to Paul. "That guard in the window. Man stands down here with a rifle—*blowie*! And everything gets real simple."

Paul took a step forward. "Murder?"

"Business necessity, call it," said Carlos. "Like you got competition, maybe."

Paul shook his head as though to clear it. "You can't just ..."

"Is that right?" Carlos straightened, and his right hand dipped into his suitcoat pocket. "Why not?"

Paul pointed to the window. "You think we'd just let you shoot some ..."

"Aw, shut up!" rapped Carlos. He leaned forward. "You think because you're studying this law bit, that makes you a lawyer? You ain't arguing in no court, man. Besides ..." He displayed a wolfish grin. "... you ain't heard my whole case yet."

"I know what to ..."

"You don't know nothing! Look, little man—have you thought what could happen if your uncle gets too excited?" Left hand up, he snapped his fingers. "His ticker. Just like that!"

Paul stared at him. "His ticker?"

Carlos looked surprised. "Yeah. His ticker. His heart. The beat-beat-beat machine. You mean you ain't with it?"

"I ..."

"You mean like you don't know he goes to the sawbones up the street here every Wednesday? The heart fixer? Don't you know your dear old uncle had a couple attacks while you're off doing the army bit?"

Paul shook his head. "I didn't ..."

"Well, then!" said Carlos. "You see how it is. We got to keep Uncle Angie from getting too excited."

Paul glanced at the envelope on the counter. *From the lawyer's office. Uncle Angie's will?*

"We got this figured real close," said Carlos. "You got no phone here. You ain't going no place. And even if you thought about trying to get the word to somebody ... well, me and my friends could always get poor old Uncle Angie all excited ..."

Again, he snapped his fingers. "See how it goes?"

"You wouldn't ..."

"Like I tell you," said Carlos. "Business necessity." He lifted a small automatic from his pocket far enough for Paul to see it. "And like any good business, we got insurance. You learn about these in the army, don't you? Guns? They use 'em to kill people."

Paul's chest felt tight, breathing difficult. He thought, *My God! He's serious!* He said, "But what ..."

"Now, all you gotta do is stay out of the way and act natural," said Carlos. "Then, nothing happens to Uncle Angie."

Paul just stared at him.

"I told my friends you'd be sensible," said Carlos. "You wouldn't want to make me out a liar, would you?"

And Paul thought, *Just give me one customer I can get to call the cops!*

"You don't get many customers in the middle of the week," said Carlos.

Paul took a quick, short breath.

Carlos laughed. "You think we ain't got all the angles figured?" He hefted the gun in his pocket. "Don't make no mistakes, Pauly boy. I'm gonna be right here with you until it's all over. If you get any customers, you just act natural. All business, see?"

Paul nodded, thought, *But Uncle Angie's going to blow up when he sees this punk here again. And when they come in with the rifle!*

"Kinda makes you squirm, don't it?" asked Carlos. "You keep wondering what you can do. Just make up your mind, little man— you can't do nothing! Just take it!"

He's getting his kicks out of telling me all this! thought Paul. *The punk!* He said, "What if Uncle Angie objects to you being here?"

"Oh, we can handle Uncle Angie, can't we?" asked Carlos. "It'll just be for an hour or so."

And Paul thought, *I could take this punk right now, gun or no gun. What chance would a yuk like him have against someone trained in combat judo? Look at him! Wide open!* He inched forward, glanced out the window, hoping Carlos would turn to look.

"I mean, like we got to keep everything *real* natural in here," said Carlos. "We don't want nothing to happen to dear old Uncle Angie."

Talk away, punk! thought Paul. *Another two feet and I can rush you before you know what's happening!*

Abruptly, Carlos slid away along the bench, glanced up and out the window, back to Paul. It was done swiftly—no time to close the gap. Now he stared narrowly at Paul. "What you coming over here for?"

"I have to work." Paul gestured toward the bench.

Suspicious, tense, Carlos backed away to the left. "Yeah? So get to work then."

Paul hesitated. The ticking of the alarm clock beat loudly in his ears. He saw the feet of a small boy run past the little window, heard the gear clashing of a truck turning the corner.

"I mean like now!" snapped Carlos. "Natural! Remember?"

Footsteps echoed in the stairwell. Paul whirled.

Angelo was making his painful descent—slow, stiff-legged. He opened the door, shuffled into the shop, closed the door. "Got lots of business while I am gone?" He began removing his coat, saw Carlos, and froze.

Carlos moved out of the rear of the shop. "Hello, Mr. Serafim."

"What *you* want?" demanded Angelo. He finished removing his coat, glanced at Paul, back to Carlos, and thought, *The minute I get out of sight, this no good shows up!*

"Just having a friendly visit with your nephew," said Carlos. He crossed to the front windows, leaned over a chair to peer out and up, pushed back to stare at Angelo.

Paul raged to himself, *Why'd he have to come back just then? Another couple of minutes!*

"Visit is over now," said Angelo. "You go. Is time for work. Don't you got work?"

"I got a real good business going," said Carlos. He sank into one of the wooden chairs beside the front windows.

"I say you go!" snapped Angelo.

"Oh, now, Mr. Serafim. I thought I'd read one of your magazines." He picked up a magazine from the seat of the next chair.

Paul slipped around the end of the counter, stood behind and to one side of Angelo. He felt frustrated, impotent. *Uncle Angie's getting too excited!*

Angelo's face darkened. "You go now," he repeated.

Carlos gestured with the magazine. "But I was just ..."

Angelo snatched the magazine from his hand. "These for customer! You are not customer!"

Paul saw Carlos's hand slip into the gun pocket. He moved closer, wet his lips with his tongue. There was a pinched look of rage on Carlos's face.

Angelo stepped back, pointed toward the door. There were little flecks of spittle on his lips. "You get out! You no good! You stay away from my Pavlos!"

Uncle Angie's too worked up! thought Paul. He felt desperate, inched closer, ready to dart in at the first hint of a wrong move from Carlos.

Carlos stood up, spoke through tight lips. "What you jerks think? I'm just gonna ..." He broke off, stared at Angelo.

Paul turned to his uncle in an instant of white panic, thinking, *His heart?*

Angelo had stepped backward, gaze fixed on the stairwell. He looked terror-stricken, mouth working soundlessly—then a whisper escaped him: *"Dolofone!"*

Paul translated it unconsciously, thought, *Killer?* He looked through the front windows.

A short, round-faced fat man was coming down the stairs. The man let himself in the door, closed it. His actions were precise, steady—like the movements of a heavy machine. Then Paul focused on the eyes shaded under the brim of a brown hat: eyes of a dark, wash blue—empty and deadly. The man wore a lumpy brown overcoat buttoned to the neck. A dead cigar jutted from his thick, wet lips, and bits of dark cigar leaf—chewed and damp—trailed down the front of the coat.

The man rolled the cigar from one side of his mouth to the other, said, "Good afternoon, Carlos." Flat, empty voice—like the eyes.

"You come just in time, Finch," said Carlos.

"Oh?" The shark eyes seemed to see everything without looking at any single object. "They are not cooperating?" He shook his head. "Sad."

Paul heard his uncle muttering in Greek, realized that Angelo was praying. The sound grated on Paul's nerves as he tried to think. *Two of them. How can I handle two of them?*

"Be quiet, old man," said Finch.

"Please!" said Angelo. It was almost a shriek. "We not anything to you! Please!"

"Oh, this will never do," said Finch. He glanced at Carlos. "A customer comes in, sees him like that? Oh, no."

Carlos said, "Maybe we better ..." He shrugged. "Hang up the sign saying they're closed."

"Considered and rejected," said Finch. "The one across the street there, in the window—we know him to be very observant. It is possible he counts the number of persons who come and go from this shop. Especially on a day such as today. If the shop is closed with several people still inside, that could arouse his suspicions. We do not seek to arouse his suspicions."

Carlos nodded toward Angelo, who was backed against the counter, eyes closed, praying in Greek. "Sure, but ..."

Paul stepped forward. "Look, let me—"

"You will be quiet," said Finch in a flat, conversational tone.

"Let me take him somewhere out of this," urged Paul.

"Did I not ask for quiet?" said Finch. The shark eyes turned toward Paul, seemed to pin him without focusing. "You do not want trouble with me, lad. Really you don't."

The very casualness of the statement coupled to the cold stare chilled Paul. Now he began to see the thing that Angelo's more experienced eyes had detected immediately in this man.

Finch turned back to Carlos. "You will take the old man up to the truck. It is around the corner, out of sight of the one across the street. You will appear to be helping the old man. Put him in the back of the truck."

Carlos said, "How ..."

"Patience," said Finch. "There is a large roll of surgical tape in the back of the truck. Merely be certain that no one sees you taking the old man in there. Close and lock the doors when you come back out."

"He's an old man," said Paul. "He's sick."

"Patience," repeated Finch. "We will only detain him there for his own good. And if you behave, the old man may live to grow even older."

Paul looked at Carlos, at the way he was staring at Angelo. Paul had seen that expression on the faces of boys tormenting a cat. He trembled.

"Old man!" snapped Finch.

Angelo opened his eyes and mouth, stared mutely.

"You will go now with Carlos," said Finch. "Go quietly, attract no attention, and the young lad here will remain unharmed. It is only for a little while." He glanced at his wristwatch. "Less than an hour now."

"Don't hurt my Pavlos!" begged Angelo. He looked at Paul, eyes glazed. "Don't do something, Pavlos. They get mad! Don't do something."

Paul stared at his uncle, wanting desperately to help him but menaced now by two men. And he could hear Angelo's words ringing in his ears: *"Don't do something."*

"You must remain calm," said Finch. "Hear me, old man?"

Angelo gulped, nodded. He thought, *Killer stays here with Pavlos ...* He looked up. "What you do? Please!"

Carlos said, "What if we get up there on the sidewalk and he—"

"He's an old man," said Finch. "They know this around here. He's ill. You're helping him. Traffic is very light just now. You'll have no trouble once you get him around the corner."

"Please," mumbled Angelo.

Carlos took Angelo's coat from the hook, tossed it to him. "Gotta look natural. Put this on."

Finch produced a pistol with silencer from his coat pocket, held it on Paul, and opened the door. "No heroics, eh?"

Paul swung his gaze from the gun to his uncle, watched Angelo slip into the coat and shuffle out the door. Carlos held Angelo's arm. A cobweb smear marked Carlos's sleeve.

The door hid the smear as Finch closed it, gesturing with his pistol. "Now you have a reason to cooperate, eh?"

Paul tried to swallow a lump in his throat. "You won't let that punk hurt my uncle?"

"Punk?" Finch rolled the cigar to the opposite corner of his mouth, smiled. It transformed his face into a roly-poly image of good humor—all but the eyes. "You are correct—he is a punk." Finch nodded. "But as long as you remain reasonable, I will hold the punk in check. All right?"

Paul looked away, saw the clock on the bench—3:00 PM. *If delivery time is three thirty ...* He turned back to Finch with the abrupt certainty that the man meant to kill him and Angelo. *This kind won't leave anyone alive who can positively identify them. What are two more murders to men who'd plan the cold-blooded killing of that guard across the street?*

"You must have work to do," said Finch. He slipped the hand with the gun back into his pocket. "Everything must appear natural. We would not want to excite the suspicion of a chance customer, eh?"

Paul's mouth felt dry, his throat raw. He turned, headed for the bench, thinking, *Could I slip notes in some of the shoes that'll be picked up today? But we only have a half hour, maybe!*

Finch slipped past him, moving swiftly for such a fat man, glanced out the window above the bench, back to Paul, examined the area around the bench, again looked at Paul. "I will wait up front, young man. You will not try anything foolish, eh? You will remember the old uncle outside there with the punk?"

"Sure," grated Paul.

"Good." Again, Finch took on the image of roly-poly good humor. "Then I will assume the pose of the patient customer waiting for shoes." He returned to the front.

And Paul stood at the bench, thinking, *I just let Carlos walk out of here with Uncle Angie. How do I know what that punk will do to him?* He felt sudden desperation. *And all I can do is stand here thinking about notes in shoes!* He turned, glared at Finch, who stood by the front windows.

"Natural, remember?" said Finch. "Do your work." He glanced up the stairwell. "Ah-hah!"

Carlos came down the steps, let himself in, and closed the door. He appeared out of breath, perspiration dotting his forehead. The cobweb was gone from his sleeve.

"No problems?" asked Finch.

"He's all tucked away," said Carlos. He brushed a sleeve, straightened his tie, and shot a glance at Paul.

"And you did the old man no harm?" persisted Finch.

"Harm? Oh ... no. Of course not. Just taped him up like you said."

"Good!" Finch produced his smile. "You see, the young lad back there worries about his uncle. But as long as he remains reasonable, he has no cause to worry, eh?"

And Paul thought hysterically, *Yeah! No cause!*

"We have a few details to take care of," said Finch. He pulled something from his left pocket, handed it to Carlos. "The silencer for the rifle."

"Yeah." Carlos looked at Finch's coat. "You got the rifle under that?"

Finch glanced out the front, then back to Carlos. "Stand here and keep watch. We must be sure that no one sees this." He moved behind the counter, unbuttoning his overcoat.

Carlos stared up the stairwell. "All clear."

Finch turned his back on Paul, fumbled under the overcoat. Something clicked. He pulled a rifle from beneath the coat, pushed it back on the long shelf beneath the counter.

Paul looked at the rifle. *An M-1!*

"What about the ammo?" asked Carlos.

"You have a full clip," said Finch. He turned around, faced Paul. "Needless to say, young man, it is required that you stay away from this counter unless you are waiting on a customer. And then, you must remember: if you think of becoming heroic, Carlos—whose chief characteristic we both recognize—will be forced to shoot both the customer and yourself, using the small automatic he carries for such purpose. And then ..." Finch shook his head sadly. "... the nice old man, too. You understand?"

Paul found it difficult to control the trembling in his chest. He nodded.

"Good. Good!" Finch returned to Carlos, glanced at the stairwell, and shot his left cuff to look at a wristwatch. "It is now 3:05."

Carlos looked at his own wristwatch. "Yeah."

"The latest word on the delivery time is that it will be very close to ten minutes to four. That gives us forty-five minutes."

And Paul thought, *Maybe I could get a note into a shoe!*

Carlos said, "You going out now?"

"Yes." Again, Finch glanced up the stairwell. "I'll return as soon as I have everything set."

Carlos rubbed at his neck. "Okay."

"You know what to do?" asked Finch.

"You can trust me, Finch," said Carlos.

"I *am* trusting you," said Finch. "Now, take no chances. If you believe a customer is suspicious, detain him. I'll be back in plenty of time to help you get set. You're not nervous, now?"

Carlos swallowed, wet his lips with his tongue. "Me?"

"Yes," murmured Finch. "Well …" He patted Carlos's arm. "… just remember how nice it'll be in Mexico City this time of year, eh?"

"Sure, Finch."

"And take no chances with the lad back there. He *is* nervous." Finch let himself out, moved out of sight up the stairs.

Presently, Paul saw the feet go past the little window—comfortable brown shoes, the kind worn by a man who pampers his body, heels slightly run over. Then he looked up to the brownstone across the street, saw a curtain fluttering at an open window, a man standing there, just into the light. *Is that the one they mean to kill?* he wondered.

"Go on, get to work," said Carlos.

Paul glanced around, saw Carlos leaning on the counter. The look of panic that Paul had detected in Carlos's eyes lay close to the surface, and Paul thought, *He's scared! The punk's as scared as I am!*

"You heard Finch say you're to act natural," said Carlos.

"Okay," said Paul. He found himself suddenly heartened by the realization of Carlos's fear. He turned his back on Carlos, pulled one of Mr. Levy's brogans against his apron, and began rubbing the leather.

"I can't see what you're doing there," said Carlos. "What're you doing?"

Paul lifted the brogan. "You want me to work? I'm working."

"See that you do!" snapped Carlos.

Paul listened to Carlos's restless pacing at the front of the shop, thought, *The little punk's scared!* He palmed the pencil stub out of his apron pocket, leaned over a scrap of wrapping paper on the bench. His heart was suddenly pounding. *I mustn't look back,* he thought. *It might make him suspicious. I can hear him.* Quickly, he scribbled:

"Mr. Levy, call police. Man with me is criminal, dangerous. Name Carlos Besera. Other name Finch. Help."

He stuffed the note into the toe of the brogan, pushed the pencil back into his apron pocket.

"What a dump!" muttered Carlos.

Heel taps on the sidewalk. Paul thought he recognized them even before they came into view—the same alligator pumps. She stopped at the corner, clattered down the stairwell.

"It's your girlfriend!" hissed Carlos. "Get rid of her! And act natural, see?"

She came into the shop, flicked a glance across Carlos, advanced to the counter, and gave Paul a hesitant smile. There was an ink smudge along one freckled cheek. Her red hair was windblown.

Paul stood rooted at the bench, heart hammering. His mouth tasted dry, fuzzy.

"When I was here earlier ..." she said. She hesitated. "Well, I forgot something. Your uncle has a pair of my shoes. He brought them down himself about a week ago. They needed ..." She broke off. "Do you know if they're finished?"

Paul tried to still the trembling in his legs. He saw Carlos leering at Jean. Carlos nodded, dropped a broad wink at Paul. And suddenly Paul thought, *Mr. Levy's shoes! The note! If I give her the wrong shoes ... will she suspect something, look in them?*

"I'll have them for you in just a minute," said Paul.

"I'm just on my coffee break," she said. "Will it be long?"

"No." Paul shook his head. He turned his back on them, concealing his actions with his body. A length of used wrapping paper from under the bench ... Uncle Angie never threw away anything! He swathed Mr. Levy's brogans in brown paper, took them to the counter, reached down.

Carlos tensed, relaxed when Paul lifted a length of fresh paper.

"I'll just take them like that," said Jean.

"Paper's a little dirty," said Paul. "Liable to get it on your clothes."

"These old things?" she said.

But Paul already had the new paper around the package. He tied the bundle with string, broke the string.

"There you are." He pushed the package across the counter.

She said, "Lucky thing you didn't need the number. I forgot it. Your uncle didn't have a tag at the office, and he gave me a number."

"He told me which shoes were yours this morning," said Paul.

"About the bill," she said. "I don't know what your uncle was going to charge."

"You can catch it next time you're in," said Paul. And he thought, *Just get out of here! Please! Just get out!*

Behind Jean's back, Carlos was frowning, nodding toward the door.

Jean lifted the package, glanced back at Carlos, returned her attention to Paul. "About ... when I was here earlier ... I'm sorry I flew off the handle. I just ..." She stopped, lifted the package, balanced it in her hands. "Are you sure these are my shoes?" Again, she hefted the package. "They don't feel ... well, they're so heavy."

Paul felt a choking sensation.

Carlos moved up beside Jean, kept his right hand in the gun pocket, pushed the package down to the counter with his left hand. The arm in the gun pocket looked steel taut.

Jean released her hold on the package, stepped back, stared from Carlos to Paul.

"Maybe Paul's made a mistake," said Carlos. He kept his attention on Paul. "Let's open up and see." He smiled at Paul. "Anybody can make a mistake, eh?"

Now Jean sensed the tension in the room. "I really don't want to cause any trouble," she said.

Carlos used his left hand to tear the paper off the shoes, glanced down, back at Paul. "Imagine! Shoes like that for such dainty feet!"

Jean spoke to Paul. "It was just that the package felt so heavy. Maybe I'd better come back when your uncle's here."

"You just wait," said Carlos. He fumbled in one of the shoes then the other, pulled up the note, shook it out, glanced at it. "Notes yet!"

Jean's attention suddenly riveted on Carlos's right hand in the gun pocket. She lifted a wide-eyed stare to Paul—grey-green eyes full of question marks.

"Maybe you had better come back when Uncle Angie's here," said Paul.

"Well, I am just on my coffee break," she said. She turned as though to leave.

"I said wait!" snapped Carlos.

She turned slowly, looked down at Carlos's hand in his pocket.

"That's right, honey," said Carlos. "It's a gun."

Freckles stood out along her cheeks as she paled. She looked at Paul.

Carlos spoke to Paul. "Now, why did you have to complicate things by making her suspicious? You know what Finch said."

"You can't kill everybody who comes in the shop!" rasped Paul.

"Who said anything about killing?" asked Carlos. He leered at Jean. "My motto is you never throw away good merchandise."

She opened her mouth, closed it silently, and shot a frightened glance at Paul. And Paul felt an abrupt surge of anger at her. *Why couldn't you have just walked out with the package? Why make a fuss about it? Of all the ...* He realized suddenly that Carlos was speaking.

"I said everybody in the back of the shop," repeated Carlos. "Move!" He herded Jean ahead of him around the counter.

"What is this?" whispered Jean.

Paul backed toward the bench. "Look, Carlos, why can't you just let her go?"

"Now?" Carlos shook his head. "What a square!"

"Put her out in the truck with Uncle Angie, then."

"You know better than that," said Carlos. "Now, don't you? You called her attention to me. She got a good look. Tomorrow, the cops have her downtown looking at pictures, and she makes me." He shook his head. "And not at all the way I want." Carlos stopped halfway between counter and bench. Jean stood at his left, attention fixed on Carlos.

And Paul was thinking, *So I was right! They do intend to kill anyone who can positively identify them!*

"What *is* this?" repeated Jean.

"Just keep it quiet, honey," said Carlos. "Like you'll get the picture in time."

Paul pushed himself away from the bench, eyes on Carlos.

Instantly, Carlos was alert, menacing with the gun in his pocket. "Let's keep our distance, chum!"

Paul stopped, swallowed. *If I can only get within reach of him …*

Jean said, "What's all this talk of killing and … Please, won't someone tell me?"

Carlos looked at Jean. "Now, there's no real reason you *have* to get hurt, honey." He smiled. "This time tomorrow, I'm on my way to Mexico City with a bag full of hot ice. One hundred grand! My share. How'd you like to come down with me, help spend it?"

She said, "Spend …"

"Sure! Nice-looking doll like you, what do you see in a square like him?" He nodded toward Paul.

She stared at him, backed away along the counter. Carlos had to turn farther away from Paul to watch her. His eyes were focused hungrily on her body. "Now, me," he said, "I can show you a *real* good time."

Jean backed away another step.

"No need to be scared, honey," said Carlos.

"I'm …" She shook her head. "… not."

"Good!"

She took a deep, trembling breath, backed away another step, and turned to face the front of the shop. "Did you say you'd have one hundred thousand dollars?"

"Sure, honey. There's five of us. We split half a million five ways."

Jean looked down at the corner of the counter. "What if I say yes?"

And Paul, who had been watching her feet, thought, *My God! She's deliberately taking his attention off me!* That narrow little line where inhibitions did not extend, the marionette feet just as they were framed by the shallow window over the bench: cautious, controlled—stepping only far enough to keep Carlos from growing suspicious!

Carlos was grinning. "Why, then I buy *two* tickets on that plane!"

She turned, faced Carlos, seemed to be looking for something in his expression.

Carlos swallowed. "I'm leveling, honey."

She nodded. "Okay."

Again the grin stretched Carlos's mouth.

Paul acted. One quick step forward, his left hand grabbed Carlos's gun arm just above the wrist, his right hand swung in a vicious chop that caught Carlos full on the throat. All the pent-up desperation of this day went into the blow.

The gun exploded as Carlos dragged his arm upward. Paul ducked a wild, gouging, left-handed clutch at his eyes, broke the gun arm with a single motion of knee and downward pressure of hands. The gun clattered against concrete, skidded across the floor.

Gurgling sounds came from Carlos's mouth.

Paul swung him around, sent a knee to the groin, another chop to the side of the neck, and yet another to the back of the neck.

Carlos pitched forward.

From the corner of his eye, Paul saw a glint of metal outside the shallow window. He acted without thinking, dove across Carlos as glass exploded inward. There was a whining ricochet against the concrete floor.

Jean shouted something, but the words were lost to him. He scrambled for the wall at the end of the counter, yelling at her, "Get behind the counter!"

A popping sound—like a cork being pulled from a bottle. Another bullet screamed off the floor.

Finch! Thought Paul. *He's back early! Why?* Frantically, Paul groped under the counter for the rifle, kept his attention on the window above him. His fingers closed on the M-1 as though it were an old friend. He slid it out, levered a cartridge into the chamber, saw Jean scramble around the end of the counter toward him.

"He's coming down the front!" she hissed.

"Keep your head down," he said.

Glass shattered at the front of the shop. A bullet splatted into the face of the counter.

"Is somebody shooting?" whispered Jean. "I can't hear the gun."

"Silencer," said Paul. He reached under the bench for a shoe to throw, hoping Finch would shoot at it, leaving an opening for counterfire.

Finch's voice echoed from the stairwell. "All right! I told you what'd happen! The old man gets it!"

Paul threw the shoe, leaped up and sideways, snapping off a shot that thundered in the narrow length of the shop.

But Finch was gone.

Running feet pounded along the sidewalk at the corner. Paul whirled, swept the rifle muzzle against the window. Glass showered onto the bench, on the sidewalk.

Finch was slanting across the street toward a large green-and-white van parked to the left of the brownstone. He ran bent over, fat legs pumping, the overcoat billowing out behind. He had lost hat and cigar. A woman with a shopping basket stopped on the sidewalk to the right, stared.

Paul slapped the rifle against his shoulder, elbow out, the forestock smooth and familiar under his left hand. He could almost hear the sergeant at the Fort Ord infiltration range hissing in his ear, *"Lead him a little! Lead him!"*

The rifle bucked—a roaring explosion that reverberated in the shop. Finch slammed forward onto his face, rolled over, and lay without moving. His right hand clutched a long, bulge-snouted revolver.

The cab door of the truck banged open. A skinny, hard-faced man in white coveralls leaped out, lifted a sawed-off shotgun toward the shop window.

Paul aimed low, slammed a bullet into the man's legs, and saw him pitch sideways, the shotgun skidding from his hands and under the truck.

The woman on the sidewalk had dropped her shopping basket, and was screaming, hands up to her face. Paul heard brakes screech to the right, saw the armored car lurch to a stop against the curb. He thought, *The delivery! It's early! That's why Finch came back so soon!*

An abrupt roaring explosion filled the street. Paul jerked his gaze upward, saw a man standing at a second-floor window of the brownstone, holding an automatic shotgun pointed down toward the far side of the truck. *The guard they were going to kill!* thought Paul. *He got somebody getting out the other side of the truck!*

"What's happening?" demanded Jean. She arose from behind the counter, her red hair disarrayed, and stared at him.

But Paul was thinking, *Uncle Angie's in that truck!*

He almost knocked Jean over rushing past her, out of the shop, and up the stairs.

"Where're you going?" she shouted after him.

He ignored her, raced for the corner. Part of his mind registered faces framed in windows above him, querulous voices, distant wailing of a siren. Then he was at the corner, skidding to a stop as the guard in the second-floor window of the brownstone shouted, "You down there! Drop that rifle!"

Paul looked up, saw the shotgun centered on him. "My uncle!" he called. "They've got him in that truck!"

"You the one shot that guy in the street?" shouted the guard.

"Yes! I tell you they've got my uncle in that truck!"

"Then relax, son! That truck's not going anywhere! I just ..."

Sirens filled the street, drowning his voice. Police cars roared down the street from both ends, skidded to stops. Uniformed men leaped from them, pistols ready. The banshee wailing droned away to silence.

Paul's gaze went to Finch's body in the street near the rear wheels of the truck. A dark stain spread along the overcoat beneath one arm, and a rivulet wandered off toward the gutter. One of Finch's run-over brown shoes had slipped off, exposing a hole in the heel of his sock.

Abrupt reaction hit Paul. He felt that if he moved, his muscles would collapse. He saw the frightened eyes of the woman with the shopping basket peering from behind steps down the street, police hurrying toward him, the guard still staring down from the upper window of the brownstone.

Revulsion swept over Paul. He thought, *I've killed a man!* The rifle dragged at his arm. He wanted to drop it but could not will his fingers to release their grip.

A policeman with sharp features stepped warily up beside him, slipped the weapon from his hand. "All right, mister," said the policeman. "You mind telling us what's going on here?"

In a dry, shallow voice, Paul told him, beginning with Carlos's visit. Presently, it seemed that he drew back from his own voice, listened to it droning on and on and on and on ...

There was a brief interruption when the ambulance came to take away a pale but still breathing Uncle Angie and the wounded bandit from the street. A police car drove away with an ashen, stumbling Carlos Besera after the ambulance attendant immobilized the broken arm and gave him a shot.

And later—after all the questions, the avid faces, the flaring flashbulbs—Paul stood at the corner in the gathering dusk. Police technicians still worked around the big truck across the street, but the only reminder of Finch was a chalked outline on the pavement and a dark, irregular stain growing dim in the twilight.

Small boys crowded around the barricades blocking off the street. Uniformed officers with nightsticks patrolled in front of them.

One boy pointed at Paul, spoke shrilly to a newcomer: "That's the guy shot 'im."

Paul looked away, shivered.

A plainclothes lieutenant came up beside Paul, touched lighter flame to a cigarette. The man had a craggy, rocklike face under a grey hat brim. He studied Paul with hard, cynical eyes. "Thought you'd like to know," he said. "Carlos talked. We got the fifth member of this mob while he was waiting in the getaway car." He shook his head. "When I think how close this one was ..."

"When can I go over to the hospital to see my uncle?" asked Paul. "I've told you everything I know."

"Soon as I can spare a car and driver," said the lieutenant. "But you heard what the ambulance doc said—your uncle will probably outlive all of us. Those old guys surprise you sometimes."

"I know, but ..."

"Now, don't you worry," said the lieutenant. "Last we heard, your uncle was resting easy. They'll tell us if there's a change."

Paul took a deep breath, turned away. He felt restless, uncertain.

The lieutenant inhaled a deep drag of the cigarette, blew smoke across the darkening air. "I saw that Carlos," he said. "Man, you really worked him over. Took guts to go up against a guy with a gun like that."

Paul shook his head. "I just knew I had to do it."

"You ever want a job on the force, let me know," said the lieutenant. He glanced back at the stairwell. "Don't worry about boarding up your shop tonight. We'll have two men patrolling."

"They can come and cart the place away for all I care," said Paul.

The lieutenant flicked his cigarette into the gutter. "Well ... we'll be through here pretty soon. We just have to make sure we got all the prints off that van across there. Could have been some others in this that Carlos didn't know about."

Paul nodded, his mind veering to a memory of Angelo waiting on the stretcher here in the street while the ambulance doctor prepared a hypodermic. The old man's face had looked pale, strained, with raw red marks where the tape had covered his mouth. Paul had been forced to bend close to hear his uncle's low voice.

Angelo spoke in Greek: *"When that Carlos took me outside, I looked down through my little window. It was as though I had never looked through there before. Such a little place. So dirty. It was like looking inside myself."*

Paul slipped into his mother tongue. *"Uncle, please save your strength."*

It was as though Angelo had not heard. The dark old lips moved slowly, fumbling for words. *"Pavlos ... I keep thinking— thirty-one years! Is that what thirty-one years is like ... inside? No wife. No kids. No friends. Just a dirty little shop with one window ... squinting at me!"*

Paul glanced at the ambulance doctor, wishing he would hurry. *"Uncle, we can talk later."*

The doctor bent over, pulled Angelo's coat off one arm, ripped away the shirt. He nodded to Paul. "Could you hold his arm like this, please?"

Angelo ignored the intrusion. *"I have seen your letters from friends in the army. I thought they were taking you away from me. I wanted to keep you all to myself. Instead, I drove you toward someone like Carlos."*

"No, Uncle!"

"I have been an old fool, Pavlos." He winced at the bite of the needle. *"Don't be like me. Don't crouch in a little dirty place ... inside ... afraid of everything."*

The doctor tucked a blanket around Angelo's neck. "We'll leave him just a minute until that takes effect."

Angelo gulped, took a trembling breath. *"In that truck ... in the dark ... I thought many things. How smart I believed I was—watching people through my window, learning things about them. But—you know, Pavlos—never once did I do a good thing with what I learned."*

Angelo blinked, stared up into the anxious young face, the features so much like his own had been. His vision blurred, faded. Muddiness washed across his mind. He brought up a last reserve of consciousness. *"Maybe one good thing that I did, Pavlos. That nice girl—she is the right girl for you."* He closed his eyes.

Paul stood up as the ambulance attendants lifted the stretcher. *"Yes, Uncle."*

He watched them slide the stretcher into the ambulance, drive away.

And now it was full dark on the corner. The lieutenant had joined the technicians across the street. The officers at the barricades paced through yellow patches from streetlights. Only a few children remained.

Abruptly, someone started the motor of the van.

Paul sensed rather than saw a figure come up beside him. He smelled perfume, looked down. Jean Lovett stared up at him, the grey-green eyes reflecting specks of light. He saw that she had straightened her hair, removed the ink smudge from her cheek.

She turned away, spoke without looking at him. "I haven't had a chance to thank you."

"Well, I got you into that trouble," said Paul. He shrugged. "Besides, if you hadn't taken Carlos's attention off me ..."

"I knew you'd do something. I don't know how I knew it, but I did." She turned back, facing him. "When you go to the hospital to see your uncle ... may I go with you?"

"You don't owe us anything," he said.

She glanced down, long lashes flickering. "There's something you should know that ..." She hesitated.

And Paul noted how the yellow streetlight almost faded out her freckles. He decided that he liked her better with freckles.

"I *asked* your uncle to let me deliver that envelope," she said. Her glance came up, down. "Wasn't that brazen of me? I wanted to meet this paragon he described. But I was afraid ..." She stopped, looked up at him. "You won't get mad?"

"I'm through getting mad."

"I was afraid you'd be like him ..." She plunged ahead. "... I mean, bent over, afraid ... just like my mother." She smiled—shy, tentative. "But you weren't."

Paul matched her smile. He felt suddenly lighthearted.

Jean stepped closer.

It felt natural to put his arms around her—she stepped so easily into them. He rested his cheek against her hair, smelled the wonderful, soft pungency of it. There was a kind of weary humor in the thought that flitted through his mind: *Uncle Angie— matchmaker!* And then the bitter aftertaste: *Imagine building a whole life around "Don't do something!"*

Jean stirred, pushed away, patted his cheek. It was an intimate, possessive gesture that made him feel warm and sure of the future.

"I called my boss," she said. "Mr. Carter. He and his wife want me to bring you to their home ... later. They want us to spend the night. I think maybe it's a good idea. I don't want to be alone tonight."

"Never again," said Paul.

He heard the van driving away, saw the lieutenant approaching. The lieutenant looked breezy, happy—his cragginess broken by a smile.

"Well, let's go, kids," he said. "Guess I'll have to take you over to the hospital myself. Then, whatsay we get all the routine business out of the way and let me buy you a dinner on the expense account? I guess the city owes you that much, anyway." He took Jean's arm, pulled them into motion.

They rounded the corner three abreast.

As they passed the little window, Paul felt glass grind under his feet. He glanced down into the dark eye of the shop, kicked at the pieces of the shattered window. *God!* he thought. *Thirty-one years!*

THE WATERS OF KAN-E

T he voice of the old woman drifted up to us on the veranda. She was seated cross-legged at the bole of a fara tree on Makatea's north shore, the fattest woman I have ever seen. She was a round hillock of flesh heaped upon the sand, a faded *lavaru* only half covering her. Five dark-skinned children danced and laughed around her as she clapped and sang for them.

The woman's skin was what attracted my particular attention. It was a pattern of the conventional dark brown broken by blotches of dead gray. And yet she didn't appear to be ill or in any discomfort.

Off and on, all morning, I had been watching the old woman and the children, wanting to ask Paul Sargeant beside me about the peculiar skin but afraid to show my ignorance.

As I watched, the woman gestured with her right hand. The children stopped their dancing and sank to the sand around her, looking up expectantly. The woman bent forward, and her voice seemed to lift out of the background of hissing surf, a tone plaintive, low, and so sad it crept into my breast and cried.

> "*A harres ta fow,*
> "*A toro ta farraro,*
> "*A now ta tararta.*"

Paul looked up from the six-week-old copy of the *Melbourne Times* he was reading. "Right out of Melville," he said.

"The palm tree shall grow,
"The coral shall spread,
"But man shall cease."

He put aside the paper and took his pipe from the table before us. "That's Grandma Pu-pu," he said. "She doesn't believe that herself about man going the way of the dinosaur." He put a match to his pipe. "Although that old chant may be closer to home than we think, what with atom bombs and hydrogen bombs." He took the pipe from his mouth and gestured toward the paper on the table. "Grandma Pu-pu could teach them a lesson."

"How's that?" I asked.

"Take a good look at that old woman," Paul said. "Look at her skin. There is a real, honest-to-God living legend. She's famous from here to Hawaii. There are chants about her. Not as good chants as the old ones, I'll grant you, because the old manner seems to have been lost, but those chants about Grandma will live long after she's gone."

I turned back toward the beach. The children were still watching, and the old woman was half talking, half chanting to them. Her arms moved in a graceful rhythm, which shrugged off the heavy flesh and said that here was still a woman. It was only a caricature of a woman, though. A ridiculous wattle of fat beneath her chin swayed and undulated with her chant.

Now she swayed back and again forward. I caught the word "mo-o-o-o-o," long and drawn-out.

"She's telling them about Au-ke-le, the seeker," Paul said. "It's the legend of the Polynesian hero who sought the waters of Kan-e, the source of everlasting life."

Paul's wide-set eyes stared fixedly at the beach, and his brows drew down in mirrored *T* crosses above his thin nose. "I dare say Grandma Pu-pu knows more about that particular legend than any other living human," he said. "You see, she found the waters of Kan-e."

"Oh, come now," I said. "I know the Polynesian fountain of youth story. That nice old grandmother down there doesn't look like any Ponce de Leon."

Paul's wide mouth split in a grin. "No," he said. "But where the Spaniard failed, she succeeded."

I leaned back. "Spill it," I said.

"Spill it?" Paul looked at me questioningly. "Oh, you mean tell you the story." He chuckled. "Spill it. I thought you meant the sacred waters."

He paused to get his pipe going. The tobacco glowed red. Then he looked down at Grandma Pu-pu on the beach with eyes that peered through her and beyond into the distant years.

"It was 1924," he said. "Grandma is a Raratonga woman. She was married to Pete Mahi, a quarter-breed French and Polynesian shell buyer. Pete traded the lower archipelago in his schooner, the *Auroheva*. They'd been married seventeen years and had four sons, the oldest, Pete Junior, being eighteen."

Paul's voice began to blend with the more remote chanting of Grandma Pu-pu and took on some of her rhythm.

"It was the end of the pearling season. They were Papeete-bound from Fakarova with a full load of shell and some fair pearls. The *Auroheva* was an old schooner, twenty-two tons and with the long, sour smell in her hold of the shell there. There was a holiday feeling aboard her, though.

"Grandma Pu-pu was just as fat then as you see her now. She always went with Pete on the trade tour, and her boys with her. It was a queer custom to the Polynesians, who leave their women at home, but then Pete was one-fourth 'Papaa.' The whites were notoriously strange in the head. In addition to young Pete, the boys were Paalo, Wim, and Joe. They had seven natives in the crew and two divers with their families.

"They were twenty-nine souls on the *Auroheva*, the old schooner standing west of Faaite, course west-southwest. Every person aboard was urging the ship to a few more knots; they were that anxious to start the holiday. Then it happened."

Paul knocked out his pipe on the veranda rail.

"Hurricane?" I asked.

Paul smiled distantly.

"We live with hurricanes down here," he said. "You have to understand that completely to know what the people on the *Auroheva* were thinking and what they did. Not only had they lived with hurricanes, but so had their ancestors back to the earliest legends. Hurricane is a god, a capricious god, who comes to smite the evil in men to stillness. I do not know if those aboard the schooner completely believed this, but certainly it was so close to their lives that they could not entirely disbelieve it.

"Yes, it was a hurricane.

"First, the glass began to drop. It went down from 29.90 to 29.80 in the first hour and then plummeted as though the mercury was being siphoned out. They knew what it meant, but they had both ancient and modern lore with which to meet it. They were seafaring people with confidence in themselves and their ship, which had ridden out a full six such storms before.

"Pete tried running for it on the port tack, the standard move here below the equator. When he saw he wouldn't make it, he still wasn't afraid. He ordered all sail off, and they lashed down every movable object. Then they put over the beg kedge anchor with one hundred fathoms of line as a drag. It's an old hurricane trick.

"The full weight of the storm struck about midmorning. The wind swept across the water like a black wall, actually flattening the seas before it.

"Then came the hurricane waves—'Long Wave and Short Wave,' the Polynesians call them. You must see them to believe them. They advance like mountains until even an ocean liner is a puny mite before them. They are accompanied by the sting of driven water, which you cannot face and breathe, and the banshee of the wind, which seems to still the voice of life within you.

"The *Auroheva* was a fluff of gull down on those waves. Her rigging whined in protest. Strange music was strummed from the stays. The masts waved barren against the steel sky.

"Pete and the eldest were on deck with the seven crewmen. The others were below, with the hatches battened above them. What happened on that deck isn't clear. Some think the line to the drogue parted. Others believe the old *Auroheva* just gave up after twenty-five years of deep-water passages and hurricanes—the proverbial last straw.

"The way Grandma Pu-pu tells it, she was wedged in a corner of the galley, slicing bread for sandwiches with the shark knife she wore on a line around her neck. Suddenly the schooner lurched and heeled over. There was a roar like a thousand surfs. Grandma found herself sitting in the water, still clutching the knife, and the schooner was nowhere to be seen. That isn't remarkable because she couldn't see six feet in any direction through the spume. Her dress had been torn off, and she floundered there, stark naked, with the knife in one hand.

"There is a clue to the nature of these people in the fact that this scene provokes laughter when Grandma tells it now.

"For a time, she wasn't certain which was the sea and which the air. But she was a born swimmer, and, too, she was padded with buoyant fat. In the midst of this melee of spray and wind, she thrashed around, and her hands encountered a rope. It was a line to a cargo sling full of coconuts, which had been on the *Auroheva*'s deck. And on such a chance hangs this legend.

"Grandma had no idea how long the storm lasted. She missed the center, so it probably was six or eight hours. The wind passed, though, and it was night. She clung to the net all through those dark hours. The sea shook her. It bruised her against the coconuts. It offered forgetfulness and tore at her grip on the line. She held fast to the rope and prayed to Kau-hu-hu, the shark god, for protection from his people."

"Shark god?" I asked. "I know you didn't say so, but somehow, I got the impression she was a Christian."

"Oh, she is," Paul said. "But who would deny her a shark god in the middle of the ocean?

"The sun came up hot that first morning. When Grandma tells it, she says she called out Ma-ui to shield her from A-hele-a-ka-la, the rays of the sun. And her listeners nod. They know of Ma-ui. He is part of another legend. It is right that legends intertwine.

"The seas had become long, rolling swells by that time. They moved in from the southwest. Once it was full daylight, she tried to climb upon the net of coconuts. The net shifted each time, and the coconuts rolled, tumbling her back into the ocean. She gave it up at last and worried out a nut, cracked it with her shark knife, drank the milk, and ate some of the meat.

"About noon, she noticed a flock of seabirds to the east, screaming and diving down onto the water. Some circled her but flew back to their companions without alighting. Grandma pushed herself out of the water as far as she could. The crest of a wave lifted her. She glimpsed something dark on the water beneath the birds. It wasn't far. She pushed away from the net and swam toward the birds. She was almost upon them before she realized they were at a body. She swam up, scattered the birds with a fistful of water, and rolled the body over. It was Pete Junior. He was tangled up in a line and a broken spar.

"I think many people would have given up to grief right there—probably drowned. But Grandma Pu-pu came to a decision. She knew there was nothing she could do for her firstborn, so she turned away and swam back to the net.

"She was about halfway back when she saw the fin. It was like a knifeblade in the seas, circling her. She paddled slower, pausing to put her face in the water and watch for the attack. The shark is a coward, and this one took a long time to make its first rush. Grandma saw it and met the shark with the flat of her hand on its snout. The force of the rush pushed her half out of the water.

"She had no thought of using her knife. Blood would have brought other sharks. Besides, she was still praying to Kau-hu-hu, the shark god, and didn't want to offend him.

"She swam on, keeping an eye on the shark as it circled her.

"She says this was Kai-ale-ale, the king of the sharks. Her listeners know Kai-ale-ale. He is part of another legend.

"This king of sharks waited longer before making the second rush. Again she met it with a hand on its snout. Twice more she met the attacks with the flat of her hand. Kai-ale-ale gave up and went back to his palace in the bottom of the sea. There were no more sharks that day. Grandma gained the net and prepared for another night. The pull of the waves swayed her body and made the coconuts knock against each other. She could still hear the gulls. Salt needles stabbed at a score of scratches she had suffered in the breakup of the *Auroheva*. And in her heart, Grandma Pu-pu was certain that all of the others had met death, but she had no time for grief.

"Survival came first."

"What about the waters of Kan-e?" I asked.

"In due time," Paul said. He smiled toward the beach, where Grandma Pu-pu was chanting a new story for the children.

"Before the dark came on that day, she broke out another nut and drank the milk," he said. "The pain of grief hovered about her like a man-o'-war bird. She clung tightly to a small thought given her by Noana, the sea, and held away the grief.

"Grandma catnapped that night, her arms laced through the netting, never dozing for more than a few seconds at a time. The water was warm and caressing. It comforted her.

"The next day, the birds began to bother her. They were ha-lu-lu, she thought—birds of evil. She felt that she was near death, and she didn't want the birds to have her. When they alighted on the netting, she shooed them away. When they circled overhead, she screamed at them. At last the circling birds made it impossible for her to forget her loss. She opened her mouth and let the death chant pour out, shouting it to the ha-lu-lu and the lapping sea. In the middle of the chant, she improvised new verses to tell of her husband and her sons and their friends.

"For the better part of that day, she wailed her chant of grief. I have heard it just once, and I will never be the same again. 'The breath of my life has gone out beneath the shroud—the black shroud—of the sea,' she chants. 'Bones of my ancestors, gather up softly these I love. Carry them up the rainbow, oh Hina-in-the-sky.' When she chants them, all the listening people are still. They hear in Grandma Pu-pu's chant a part of their past, and they mourn as much for the loss of that as for Grandma's loss.

"Again the following night she dozed, and again the sharks did not come. 'Kau-hu-hu answered my prayers,' she says. Well, who is to say to her, 'nay'?

"On the third morning, she began to take more careful stock of her situation. A land bird rested for a while on her net. She knew she wasn't more than fifty miles from Faaite, but the current set away from the island, toward Rangiros and Makates there. Both were more than sixty miles distant. She drank the milk from two more coconuts. They gave her strength, and she thought. She knew the current, unaided, would set her south of these islands into the interisland channel. That would not do.

"Alternating with a period of rest and a period of work, she began swimming northward, towing the net of coconuts with a line across her shoulder. All that day she struggled, pausing only to eat of a nut when she found the need. That night, she wedged her face between a stack of nuts and the netting and slept until the shifting cargo made her change position. She had gained perhaps four knots the whole day.

"Again the next day she took up her work.

"On her seventh day in the water, she saw a steamer's smoke in the south, but not the steamer. It was the *President Cleveland* limping into Papeete, taking more water into her holds than her pumps could handle. The storm had caught the ship near Flint Island, and it had been all that time coming south. Grandma watched the steamer's smoke disappear below the horizon. It was like a last touch with the world of humans.

"Another day passed, and another. She was still a mountain of a woman, floating high, but her skin had begun to loosen, and there was a chafing sore on her shoulder where she swam against the line of the cargo net. Around her was nothing but the ocean, the sky, and an occasional seabird. She says that her skin began to get numb and she couldn't feel the water or any pain.

"She already had been alive in the water longer than doctors say is possible for a human.

"On the fourteenth day, Kau-hu-hu sent another shark—or perhaps it was Kai-ale-ale again come to test this woman and her prayers. Grandma, a woman whose flesh was puckered and ridged from the long immersion, swam out to meet the attack. She caught the first rush with the flat of her hand on the shark's snout. Seven passes that shark made before abandoning the fight. Grandma swam back to the net and clung to it. Her left arm had been torn from wrist to elbow by the shark's sandpaper side as it brushed against her, but she swears her wound did not bleed.

"'It was a sign from Kau-hu-hu,' she says.

"From that point on, Grandma isn't too clear as to how many days passed between incidents. Somewhere in that period, her strength ebbed to the point where she could no longer tow the cargo net and its coconuts. The nut supply had gone down to less than half of the original load. She no longer felt as much like eating, though. And as her strength diminished, so did her flesh.

"We know the date the *Auroheva* broke up, and we know the day Grandma was found. Therefore, we know it was the night before her twenty-third day in the water when she heard the surf on the barrier here at Makatea. She said another prayer to Kau-hu-hu.

"In the first dawn light, she saw the reef and beyond it, in the lagoon, a canoe with two fishermen. They were too far away, she knew, to hear a shout. She saved her strength. The coconut net floated nearer and nearer the reef. With her last strength, Grandma maneuvered the net between herself and the sharp coral of the barrier. She was so intent on the task that she failed to see the final shark Kau-hu-hu sent against her. The shark was a big fellow, a mala-ke-nas that had feasted on human flesh before. It circled behind her and dived down deep, deep—a milky-gray shadow beside the rainbow colors of the reef.

"As the wave which Grandma hoped would carry her over the reef lifted under her, the shark made its run. She sensed her peril—'Kau-hu-hu warned me,' she chants—and put her head in the water in time to see the monster rushing up at her. She rolled sideways, and the shark came up alongside her. Its hide rasped the skin from her stomach, the inside of her left arm, which held the cargo net, and the left side of her face. It was that close. Then the wave deposited both of them on the reef.

"Coral spines gouged into her. The flailing shark struck her a glancing blow, which broke her leg. And the following sea came onto the reef and washed both into the lagoon. The shark was gone in the instant, but Grandma was bleeding now in a dozen places, and she knew others would come. The coconuts had become lodged on the reef, and she no longer had a float. Her buoyant flesh was gone. But Grandma wasn't finished. Nursing the broken leg, she set out toward the canoe, shouting on every other stroke.

"There were two fishermen in the canoe. They saw her when she had covered about a third of the distance from the reef.

"'Save me!' she cried.

"But she wasn't fooling those fishermen. They knew a sea demon when they saw one. They were certain it was a demon because the creature came from the sea and not from the land. 'Mo-o!' one shouted. And they fled, beating the water to foam with their paddles.

"Grandma Pu-pu almost gave up when she saw that there would be no help from the fishermen. She floated for a minute in the water and then, she said, there came a last strength. Slowly, she began the long swim to the island two miles away. Her leg was broken, she was bleeding over half of her body, she had been a full twenty-three days in the water, and she had lost more than one hundred pounds of her fat. But she still had the will to survive.

"Look at her!" Paul gestured with his right hand, his finger pointing. "I say she is magnificent!"

The group was still beneath the fara tree, and now the children were laughing as Grandma Pu-pu recounted a humorous part of the story she was telling them.

I could see it too. It was a calmness that mantled every gesture she made. There was no mystery in life for her. She knew. She knew!

"The two fishermen reached the island here," Paul said. "They ran up the beach, shouting, 'Mo-o! A Mo-o comes from the sea!' People scattered before them.

"They ran past the hut of Tiki, the one-legged diver, and Tiki, who could not run, came out to watch their retreating backs. 'A Mo-o,' he sniffed, rubbing the shark-chewed stump of his left leg. 'It is more likely someone from the storm.'

"He took his crutch from beside the doorpost and made his way down to the canoe the fishermen had abandoned. Out in the lagoon, he saw the swimmer. Hidden behind him, the people watched. He picked up the paddle and shoved off. The gap between swimmer and canoe closed rapidly. Then the canoe swerved in front of the swimmer.

"Even Tiki's courage wavered when he saw Grandma's bloody face and torn body. He took two deep breaths and thought back to his own time in a sea turned red by the blood pouring from the stump of his leg. Then he reached down and pulled Grandma into the canoe. He marveled at the way her skin hung loosely on her thin body.

"At the beach again, Tiki shouted and reviled his neighbors before they ventured down to the canoe. 'It is a poor sufferer from the storm!' he screamed. 'Would you leave her to die and bring down a curse upon us?'

"At last they came, with Chief Kauo-la-oe, the father of the present chief, leading the way."

Paul chuckled. "I imagine Grandma was quite a sight. For that matter, she still is. As you see, her skin, which was bleached a dirty gray, never quite regained its original pigment. She says it took two months before people were wholly convinced she was a human being. Tiki's mother doctored her with herbs for almost four months before she really regained her strength. And in five months, when the mission schooner *Faith of Jesus* put in here, she was well enough to board and make passage for Papeete. She was still quite a sight, skin loose, the left side of her face scarred into a grimace. Most people shunned her.

"At Papeete, she was greeted as one returned from the dead. The wreckage of the *Auroheva*'s longboat had been picked up by a trader from Tahanea and its story pieced out. Along with the others aboard, Grandma's name had been added to the rolls for the Easter Mass.

"She chanted her story there at the spring feast, and her fame began to spread. In about three months, an insurance agent came around with a check for the schooner and Pete's life insurance. Grandma was suddenly a very rich woman by any standard. She was thirty-six years old, which is aged for Polynesian women, but she found herself very popular, surrounded by suitors—all with some scheme or other they wanted her to finance. She thumbed her nose at the lot of them. When the *Faith of Jesus* made its fall run back here to Makatea, Grandma was aboard. She was just Mrs. Pupuamahele Mahi, a widow, though.

"She stepped out of the schooner's boat onto the beach here and went right up to Tiki's hut. Did I tell you about Tiki? You'll see him around. He's as ugly as original sin and a born clown. The shark that took his leg also got part of his face, and he has a perpetual grin. It's pretty horrible until you get to know him. Grandma went up to the village and stopped there, where Tiki sat in the sun outside his door. She was acting as shy as a schoolgirl and ignoring all greetings.

"'Mea maitai?' she asked. 'You are well?'"

"'Tauhere, you have come back to me,' he said.

"And that's the way it was settled. Captain Arahab Nobles of the schooner read the ceremony that afternoon. Grandma Pu-pu was a bride again at thirty-six.

"Old as she was by Polynesian standards, Grandma Pu-pu bore three more sons—Tiki Junior, Pete, and Joe.

Paul pointed toward the old woman who was getting to her feet stiffly at the fara tree. "That toddler is Joe's youngest, Wim."

"Where did she get that tremendous will to survive?" I asked.

Paul watched the group on the beach. "She told me once that it came over her when she realized all of her sons were dead. Out there in the ocean, she knew that if she died, the lines of her family died, and so did part of her race."

"What about the waters of Kan-e?" I asked.

"Isn't it plain to see?" Paul countered. Again he pointed at the old woman.

Grandma Pu-pu had picked up the toddler, taken another youngster's hand, and was leading the procession away down the beach. "Where do you think they're going?" he asked.

"Where?"

"Down to the lagoon," Paul said, "for their daily swimming lesson. In Polynesia, it is the sea that buoys up life, feeds it, carries it on its bosom, makes life possible at all. The sea—it is the source of life. They swim in the waters of Kan-e."

PAUL'S FRIEND

"That's Paul's Friend."

Charlie Jens waved a whiskey glass toward the fire, a demon of red-and-yellow light on the hot beach below the veranda. At the fireside squatted a black man, part of the darkness around him, taking of the world only in mahogany reflection from the blaze. The light showed a broad, dull face with brow and cheeks a plowed field of scars. His flanks were thin and dim in the shadows; his heels were drawn back beneath him in the aboriginal way, and he stretched scar-laced arms toward the flames.

It was the fire which had prompted me to ask, "Who is that?"

A beach fire in July on the equator is a thing of fiction. And this night had drunk too freely of the sun's heat on the day just past. It was hot beyond caring, and the only escapes were in getting sodden drunk or flirting with the sharks beyond the drumming reef. Charlie Jens and I were choosing the former. In the tropics, it is a white man's privilege.

"Paul's Friend?" I asked. "Doesn't he have a name? Who's Paul?"

"That's his name, Paul's Friend," Charlie said.

There was silence broken by the gurgling of the bottle as Charlie poured. From up in the village beyond the palm-guarded beach there came a high-pitched, giggling laugh. Someone began playing a harmonica on the schooner in the lagoon. And the heat closed in, carrying the scent of night blooms like a dark weight that oppressed the senses.

I waited. The signs revealed that Charlie Jens was about to tell a story.

Instead, he slammed down his glass, spilling the liquor in a dark blot across the rattan table.

"Damn your nosy, stinking prying to hell!" he shouted. "Don't think I don't know why you come up here, filling me full of your good liquor! I don't know why I put up with it."

Again there was silence interlaced with the dim harmonica music. With a shaking hand, Charlie picked up the bottle, looked at it, and filled his glass to the brim.

"Yes, I know. This is why." He held up the bottle and slammed it down. "You'll take my stories, and you'll write 'em up like I always intended and never did. And you'll get rich while I stay here, selling trade goods to heathens."

"They're Christians, Charlie," I said.

He snorted and gulped the drink, throwing back his head to show a thin neck with a bobbing Adam's apple. The light from a hissing gas lantern that hung from a porch rafter sent a black shadow across his left cheek, reproducing a thin caricature of his bulging nose. His hair, totally white, hung unkempt down to the collar of a faded blue navy dungaree shirt. On top, it rimmed a bare pink spot in the center of his head—like an island surrounded by surf.

"Christians!" Again he snorted. "Fat lot you know about it!"

I leaned back, watching the play of Charlie's wide mouth as he spoke.

"Take Paul's Friend there," he said, spilling a bit of his drink on his arm as he gestured with it. "He was an orphan, raised by a missionary on the mission grounds like one of their own. Speaks almost as good English as you; better than me. Many's the time he's come here to borrow my books to read. Don't look it, does he?"

The black man by the fire stirred slightly and lowered his arms. I became embarrassed. The man wasn't sixty feet from us, just below the palm line. On the still air, sounds carry far. I knew he could hear us talking. Before, when I had considered him just another *bêche-de-mer* native, it had made no difference. When I realized he could understand us, it touched a chord the white man does not enjoy. It vibrated at the wall of our security.

"His parents were kinky-haired cannibals," Charlie Jens said. "How far away from them you think he is? Feh!" He spat over the veranda rail. "People don't live forever on the equator, especially black people. He's forty years removed from cannibalism. Christianity's a thin skin on him."

"How'd he get his name?" I asked.

Charlie reached over to the veranda rail with his whiskey glass and very carefully squashed a red crawler almost hidden in the shadow of a pillar. Then he sat back. The flesh of his stomach, showing fish belly white through the spread front of his shirt, began to quiver. The laugh rose within him like a shark swimming to the surface, and it broke coldly on the fetid air.

"Aani Paul," he said, making the *Paul* come out *Pol*. The laughter died slowly, struggling on the hook of his curved lips. "Paul's Friend!" He bit it off.

"She was gorgeous ..." His voice had suddenly grown dim, almost hidden under the soft hiss of surf on the shingle of beach, blending with it. "She had hair like golden feathers, eyes like the blue-green of the lagoon on a spring afternoon. And she was proud of her figure and her long legs. She carried her breasts high."

"In Heaven's name, who?" I asked.

"Paul's wife," he said. "Waa ..."

It was an involuntary exclamation and revealed much of this man who had spent a lifetime resisting the easy languor of native ways.

"So you fell in love with this Paul's wife, whoever he is," I said.

"Was," Charlie corrected me. "She'd have taken me, too, if it hadn't been for what he did." He gestured again toward the black figure on the beach, whose arms were once more outstretched toward the flames as though in some mystic ritual. "In time, she'd have taken me."

Charlie picked up the bottle and held it toward the gas lantern, sloshing the amber fluid and watching the play of color. The diffused portion of light through the bottle made a yellow bar on his face. "Ever hear of Paul Rejoc?" he asked.

I extended my glass for a refill. "It seems I've heard the name," I said.

As he poured, Charlie mimicked me. "It seems I've heard the name." He carried it a half tone higher. The glass full, he replaced the bottle on the table and studiously avoided his own glass.

"He was a *paianayo*," he said. "A man's man. And a woman's man, too. There wasn't another white man in the whole of the South Pacific knew these waters like he did. He was one of the first blackbirders into New Guinea and New Ireland, on one of his old man's boats. I seen him take natives off the beach at Nukumanu with the wreck of the *Tamana* sitting right there in the lagoon, her dead—what was left of 'em—rotting on her decks.

"His head boat boy was an Eromangan who boasted of having eaten a piece of the Rev. John Williams. And no doubt was telling the truth.

"Paul was twenty then and a first mate. He stood six feet six in his peou sandals, with shoulders like a Lingayen ox. His great-grandfather had been a French duke who escaped the revolution. His mother was Irish and Polynesian. He took the best of all of them and made it better.

"He had an Atafu woman then, back in the Union group. She died the following year in a hurricane.

"Remember the stories about the Japs keeping us out of the Marshalls. Hah!" Charlie snorted and brought out a crumpled red bandana, into which he bugled noisily. "Hell," he said, replacing the bandana, "Paul Rejoc spent a year on Jeluit livin' like a native with a native wife, and they never even knew it. That was later, of course. He'd've been a fine one to've had in the last little blowup.

"Oh, he helled around aplenty in his youth. He ran a pearl raider clean to Mytho and down to Condore Island and then down to the Straits Settlement. That was the last we heard of him for three or four years until he turned up at Bougainville with an eighty-foot schooner, fourteen kanakas, and a white wife. Paul's Friend there was one of the kanakas. Fair worshipped Paul, they did. It seems Rejoc scooped 'em off the little island at Mapia, where they were being fattened for the table, so to speak. They owed their lives to him, and they damn well knew it.

"The wife was named Sheila. She was White Russian from Singapore, and he found her at Puerto Princessa. That's Palawan, and enough said—bugs and heat. She'd been with a touring company of actors that got stranded, and she was about to take the easy way out when he showed up. She worshipped him too.

"Everybody worshipped him."

"Even you?" I asked.

Charlie slammed his glass onto the tabletop. The veins stood out on the back of his hand where he clenched his fist. "Yes, damn you! Even me! He took me off Malekula when I didn't have a thing but the borrowed clothes on my back and a place scooped out in the sand for a bed. He set me up in business, showed me how to handle the natives. I wouldn't even be alive today if it hadn't been for him, and he'd be alive today if it hadn't been for me."

His hand slowly relaxed from around the whiskey glass, fingers outstretched limply against the golden tan of the tabletop. The glass rolled free on its side.

"Nature plays the rough game down here," he said, voice flat. "She may make a couple of passes at you, a hurricane or two, only playing—but you can always tell when the real number is up. There's no fooling and no use running. She's played with you long enough, and that's the time and place. You might just as well face it."

He grimaced and swiveled abruptly, pouring himself a drink with trembling hands. The drink disappeared down his throat in one convulsive gulp. The heat around us pressed even closer.

"It was 1927," he said, rolling the glass under his hand on the table. "You maybe read about the blow. It cleaned off half the islands through here. I was running the trading station at Tongareva then. It was coming on for the hurricane season when we heard about the strike at Nuku Hiva; all clean shell and, if you'd believe half the stories, pearls big as marbles in every third one.

"We were making big plans then, Paul and me. We were partners by then. We were going to start up a fleet of schooners trading through the Marquesas, the Tuamotus, and down to the Society group. We were going to set up an empire, and a strike like that one set our blood on fire. It was just the beginning we needed."

Charlie closed his eyes and went on speaking, his voice lower. "Paul had grown more cautious, though. He said he could feel a big wind in the air. He wasn't afraid; it was just that he had responsibilities by then—little Sheila and Paul Jr., who had just turned ten.

"The kid was a small copy of his dad—big for his age. He used to go swimming in the lagoon with the native kids and, just like his old man, he was the boss. He was better'n they were, and they knew it and so did he. He had a Polynesian amah he drove nuts keeping up with him and, of course, Paul's Friend there. That man was like his dog."

Charlie looked at his hands, which were trembling violently, and made a visible effort to quiet them. They became still like something dying.

"I couldn't make the run," he said, looking at his hands. "Things were set up at the station then so I could handle it best. That's a lie, of course, but it's what I tell myself. Besides, Paul was the sailor half of the partnership, and we both knew it.

"I kept after him. 'A quick run and we'll be millionaires,' I kept telling him. 'We're the only outfit in the area with a diving suit.' That's what I told him, and lots more: 'Sure, there's a risk this time of year, but not a great one with you running the show.'

"Finally he agreed. He picked ten kanakas, Paul's Friend among 'em, and Riki, a half-French, half-Polynesian first mate who worked for us. And he took the boy. It was her idea—his wife's. She knew he'd run no big risks with the boy along. He took the big schooner, the *Hiva Oa* she was called, after the island in the Marquesas.

"We got some of the story from the boy afterwards and a damn little of it from Paul's Friend there.

"They had good winds all the way up past Caroline Island, and then headwinds slowed 'em ten days into Eiao. They'd no more than anchored in the lagoon behind the big island when the wind dropped and the air became muggy. Paul ducked into the doghouse. When he came out, his face was grim. 'The barometer's at 29.80,' he said. 'It's fallen fourteen-hundredths of an inch in the past hour.'

"'Let's get outta here,' Riki urged.

"But there they were, easterly of Eiao, with a chance of getting the latest word on the big strike. Paul made a quick decision and ordered the whaleboat over. He took Paul's Friend and the boy, and they went ashore, the boy at the tiller, the two men at the oars.

"There was a French civil agent on the island then—M. Clemenceau, a little man with a goatee and a handlebar mustache. He met 'em on the beach and asked to be taken off in the schooner along with the natives. There were some twenty souls on the island, the rest being down at Nuku Hiva. There was a plenty bad wind coming, he said. He had it on the wireless. He thought they'd have a better chance at sea than on that inverted dish of an island with the highest point six feet above sea level. Paul told him all right and to hurry it. M. Clemenceau began rounding up his charges.

"Meanwhile, Paul signaled Riki on the *Hiva Oa* to up anchor and make sail. The schooner got under way, tacking back and forth in the lagoon like a chicken looking for a hawk.

"Paul took the boy and went up to the village to hurry things. The natives were Polynesians and slow as a matter of principle. By the time they were all rounded up with their belongings, they could hear the surf breaking clean over the reef, and there was a long swell onto the island beach. They ran for the whaleboat. When they reached it, they all just stood clustered around it for a minute, looking seaward. The *Hiva Oa* was running free through the reef channel, shortening sail fast. One look to the southeast showed why: there was a black line out there in the distance, rushing down on the island like an express train. Those on the island had to take their chances there; Riki was trying to save the schooner.

"Paul went into action. With the natives helping, he picked up the whaleboat and ran it over the island to the lee side. There he took the axe from under the thwart and lopped off a palm tree about four feet up. From this he ran a long mooring line to the whaleboat and launched it into the lagoon, calling for as many to join him as would.

"But the natives and M. Clemenceau were already picking out their palm trees and lopping off the tops and lashing themselves down. They were none too soon, either. The hurricane struck them like all the winds of the worlds rolled into one.

"Little Paul crouched with his dad and Paul's Friend under the whaleboat's gunwale. He said they could see palm fronds whipping past overhead like bullets. Once there was a shouting voice that went by them, out of reach. Seas were breaking clear over the island by then, sweeping everything before them.

"The kid said you couldn't put your head above the gunwale and face the wind without it puffing out your cheeks and almost blowing your head loose. The air seemed to become filled with flying water, and there was an increasing howl of wind.

"The whaleboat took it well. She was built to stay afloat, and she did, with the long line to the palm stump humming taut as a guitar string. The noise and the surge of the seas seemed to go on until they imagined it would never end, and right at the point where they figured they couldn't take any more ... well, it ended. They were in the heart of the storm. Outside the reef, the seas rose straight up like Chinese mountains, crashing down on the coral barrier and sending their uneven turbulence toward the island.

"There were blots of wreckage and palm trees scattered clear out to the reef. When they looked at the island, they counted only five people still lashed to the stripped palms.

"Then the wind struck them again, flattening everything, driving down the seas, and the waves came back, sweeping over the reef and on over the island. For more than an hour, the whaleboat must've taken this new beating and then, just like that, with no extra sound or excitement, their palm stump gave way and let 'em go out into the lagoon toward the reef.

"The stump and the weight of the wet line to it acted as a sea anchor and kept their nose into the wind, or they would've capsized and swamped in the first minute. They were heading for the reef fast. Paul ordered the kid to lay low and told the kanaka to take a steering oar; then he went over the side at the stern, holding onto the grab lines.

"The kid knew what Paul was trying to do—the seas were breaking clean over the reef, and they had maybe a fifty-fifty chance to ride one safely over the top. Paul was going to try to boost that chance by picking the wave. He had a knife in his teeth, ready to cut the line to the stump.

"There weren't many sounds that could survive in that wind, but the surf on the reef was one of 'em. It kept getting louder and louder until even the wind took second place. Then there was a lurch, and the wind and water seemed to pick up the whaleboat and sweep it over the reef. The kanaka managed to keep her bow on while the kid rigged a new sea anchor out of the boat's kedge and two oars. He was a sailor's kid, little Paul was, and he did it up smart, got it over the side himself, and snugged it down.

"Where was Big Paul? He was hanging onto the side, and there was a gray look on his face. The kanaka hauled him aboard, and the kid seen what the coral had done to his dad's left arm and back—right down to the bone and deep into the ribs. A big spike of it must've caught him. Little Paul was a brave kid, though, and he helped the kanaka make bandages out of a shirt and got his dad comfortable. And he even took his trick with the steering oar.

"The storm left them sometime the next morning. They kept a sharp eye out for the *Hiva Oa*, but she was never seen again—by them or anybody else.

"First thing the kanaka did was take stock. They had the axe, four tins of bully, six tins of pork and beans, and six tins of pineapple, a fifteen-gallon water breaker about three-quarters full, a mast and sail, a boat compass, a small tarpaulin, a tablet, a pencil, and a protractor.

"Paul was conscious most of that day, but he'd lost so much blood he could barely move. They rigged the tarp over him as soon as the sun got hot. Toward noon, Paul shared a tin of pineapple and cup of water with the kid and the kanaka. He was rational enough to help make the decision not to head back toward Eiao against the wind. The big blow left 'em somewhere to the northwest of the island. He told Paul's Friend to set course for Caroline Island and showed 'em how to use the protractor on a meridian sight for latitude.

"Toward sunset he got delirious, and he raved and tossed all night so bad the kanaka had to sit on him sometimes to keep him from throwing himself overboard. The kid was at the steering oar most of the night. At daylight, Paul quieted down and slept some. He woke up about noon. He told 'em he felt a little light-headed but otherwise all right. And he got Paul's Friend down under the tarp with him and made the native promise by the white man's God that he'd get the boy home safe to his mother no matter what happened. And Paul's Friend promised.

"That was the second day.

"More than a week passed. They were through the pineapple and well into the beans. Paul was so weak by then that even the kid could hold him down when he got delirious. The whaleboat had developed a nasty leak, too, so it had to be bailed every four or five hours, the kid and the native taking turns about.

"Paul's Friend whiled away the time telling the kid stories, some he'd learned at the mission school and some he'd learned other places. He knew all the stories about his own people and those of the Polynesians. He told the kid about Vitu Tapani, the fire god whose son stole the secret of fire and traded it to a mortal in exchange for a bride.

"He told him about the demigod Sagsag, who had a hut with a center pole that was really a stairway to the underworld, and how Sagsag's sons, Niku and Keaki, battled for possession of the stairway when the old man was away.

"These stories were told in the native way, which takes a great deal of time. The kanaka knew Big Paul was dying and he wanted to distract the kid. Sometimes Big Paul was awake enough to listen, and sometimes he raved so loudly the kanaka had to be silent.

"On the eighteenth day, they hit a line squall and caught some rain—about three gallons—with the tarpaulin and the sail. Paul was unconscious most of the time by then. The storm passed and left a wicked cross chop on the ground swell. As they were making sail, the boat shifting and heaving, the kid fell over the center thwart and hit his head on the water keg that was lashed amidships. He just lay there, with blood running from his scalp into the bilge. The kanaka cleated the sheet line, lashed the steering oar, and rushed to the kid. He felt the boy's head, and there was a soft spot where the kid had cracked into the keg. Paul's Friend rigged a place for Little Paul beside Big Paul and went back to the steering oar—course south-southeast, bailing every five hours.

"With his own knowledge of the sea, the native had already realized they'd missed Caroline, what with leeway and the easterly current through there. He was trying for Vostok by that time.

"Three more days he sailed and tended his sick, spoon-feeding Little Paul, trying to get some water down Big Paul with no success.

On the third day after Little Paul was injured, three things happened: the kid regained consciousness for a few minutes, Big Paul died, and the kanaka realized they'd missed Vostok too. There he was, a mission savage, son of a cannibal, grandson of a cannibal, in the middle of an ocean in ten degrees south latitude with an injured kid, a dead man, and a promise. He changed course due east for Rakahanga and prepared his master for burial at sea."

A grim laugh from Charlie brought me back to the present.

"There's a scene for you to put into a book," he said. "A black savage mumbling Christian words over his friend with an ocean for a backdrop. Hah! Rakahanga was four hundred miles away, and he was about out of food, water half gone, and no charts. The whaleboat could do three knots top speed, and it made two knots leeway for every five ahead. But he made it—that determined kanaka made it, and he delivered the kid to the Australian doctor at Rakahanga. Then he went away by himself and made his own grief over the death of his master.

"See those scars!" Charlie Jens pointed again at the dark man by the fire. "He made 'em himself in his grief. Christian? Pfah! And that fire! What do you think he's doing there? He says he can see Paul in the flames. See Paul, mind you. And him blinded by his own hands!"

I found that I was sitting on the edge of my chair and I consciously forced myself back. Charlie Jens became silent. There was a little sea breeze now, flickering the flames of the fire on the beach, shifting the shadows on the scarred face and arms. It dried the perspiration on our faces and gave us a momentary illusion of coolness.

From out of the shadows to the left of the kanaka came a tall man, wide shouldered, with a free and easy stride. For a moment I had the feeling that here was Paul Rejoc, brought to life by Charlie's story. And then, as the figure paused by Paul's Friend, I realized that this must be the son.

Charlie began to speak, almost in a whisper. "She had her son, and he became her whole life. She didn't need me. If he hadn't come back, she'd've needed me ... like I needed her."

The tall white man by the fire put a hand on the kanaka's shoulder. "Come, Aani Paul. It's time to go home." The kanaka arose, and they walked away down the beach, the black man hobbling on a twisted leg, supported by the white man.

"How did he make that four hundred miles without food?" I asked when the last sound of their footsteps had disappeared. "I would have said it was impossible."

Charlie's voice had lost all expression when he spoke. It came out like a dead, flat calm. "And so it would have been for most people," he said. "If you knew the language, though, you would see it: he is Aani Paul—literally, the man who is closest to Paul." The voice became grim. "He buried his master at sea back there, south of the Line Islands ... all except the legs!"

SCIENCE
FICTION

PUBLIC HEARING

With an increasing sense of unease, Alan Wallace studied his client as they neared the public hearing room on the second floor of the old Senate Office Building. The guy was too relaxed.

"Bill, I'm worried about this," Wallace said. "You could damn well lose your grazing rights here in this room today."

They were almost into the gauntlet of guards, reporters, and TV cameramen before Wallace got his answer. "Who the hell cares?" Custer asked.

Wallace, who prided himself on being the Washington-type lawyer—above contamination by complaints and briefs, immune to all shock—found himself tongue-tied with surprise.

They were into the ruck then, and Wallace had to pull on his bold face, smiling at the press, trying to soften the sharpness of that necessary phrase: "No comment. Sorry, no comment."

"See us after the hearing if you have any questions, gentlemen," Custer said.

The man's voice was level and confident. *He has himself overcontrolled,* Wallace thought. *Maybe he was just joking ... a graveyard joke.*

The marble-walled hearing room blazed with lights. Camera platforms had been raised above the seats at the rear. Some of the small UHF stations had their cameramen standing on the window ledges.

The reporters noted, then picked up tempo as William R. Custer—"The Baron of Oregon," they called him—entered with his attorney, passed the press tables, and crossed to the seats reserved for them in the witness section.

Ahead and to their right, the empty chair at the long table stood waiting with its aura of complete exposure.

"Who the hell cares?"

That wasn't a Custer-type joke, Wallace reminded himself.

For all his cattle-baron pose, Custer held a doctorate in agriculture and degrees in philosophy, math, and electronics. His western neighbors called him "The Brain." It was no accident the cattlemen had chosen him to represent them here.

Wallace glanced covertly at the man, studying him. The cowboy boots and string tie added to a neat, dark business suit would have been affectation on most men. They merely accented Custer's craggy good looks—the sunburned, windblown outdoorsman. He was a little darker of hair and skin than his father had been, still light enough to be called blond but not as ruddy and without the late father's drink-tumescent veins.

But then, young Custer wasn't quite thirty.

Custer turned, met the attorney's eyes. He smiled.

"Those were good patent attorneys you recommended, Al," Custer said. He lifted his briefcase to his lap, patted it. "No mincing around or mealymouthed excuses. Already got this thing on the way." Again he tapped the briefcase.

He brought that damn light gadget here with him? Wallace wondered. *Why?* He glanced at the briefcase. *Didn't know it was that small ... but maybe he's just talking about the plans for the crazy device.*

"This is the only thing that's important."

Into a sudden lull in the room's high noise level, the voice of someone in the press section carried across them: "... greatest political show on earth."

"I brought this as an exhibit," Custer said. Again he tapped the briefcase. (It *did* bulge oddly.)

Exhibit? Wallace asked himself.

It was the second time in ten minutes that Custer had shocked him. This was to be a hearing of a subcommittee of the Senate Interior and Insular Affairs Committee. The issue was Taylor grazing lands. What the devil could that … *gadget* have to do with the battle of words and laws to be fought here?

"You're supposed to talk overall strategy with your attorney," Wallace whispered. "What the devil do you…?"

He broke off as the room fell suddenly silent.

Wallace looked up to see the subcommittee chairman, Senator Haycourt Tiborough, stride through the wide double doors followed by his coterie of investigators and attorneys. The senator was a tall man who had once been fat. But he had dieted with such savage abruptness that his skin had never recovered. His jowls and the flesh on the back of his hands sagged oddly. The top of his head was shiny bald and ringed by a three-quarter tonsure that had purposely been allowed to grow long and straggly so that it fanned back over his ears.

The senator was followed in close lockstep by syndicated columnist Anthony Poxman, who was speaking fiercely into Tiborough's left ear. TV cameras tracked the pair.

If Poxman's covering this one himself instead of sending a flunky, it's going to be bad, Wallace told himself.

Tiborough took his chair at the center of the committee, noting how many other members were present. Senator Spealance was absent, Wallace noted, but he had party organization difficulties at home, and the senior senator from Oregon was, significantly, not present.

Illness, it was reported.

A sudden attack of caution, that common Washington malady, no doubt. He knew where his campaign money came from … but he also knew where the votes were.

They had a quorum, though.

Tiborough cleared his throat, said, "The committee will please come to order."

The senator's voice and manner gave Wallace a cold chill. *We were nuts trying to fight this one in the open,* he thought. *Why'd I let Custer and his friends talk me into this? You can't butt heads with a United States senator who's out to get you. The only way's to fight him on the inside.*

And now Custer suddenly turning screwball.

Exhibit!

"Gentlemen," said Tiborough, "I think we can ... that is, today we can dispense with preliminaries ... unless my colleagues ... if any of them have objections?"

Again he glanced at the other senators—five of them. Wallace swept his gaze down the line behind that table—Plowers of Nebraska (a horse trader), Johnstone of Ohio (a parliamentarian—devious), Lane of South Carolina (a Republican in Democrat disguise), Emery of Minnesota (new and eager— dangerous because he lacked the old inhibitions), and Meltzer of New York (poker player, fine old family with traditions).

None of them had objections.

They've had a private meeting—both sides of the aisle. It was another ominous sign.

"This is a subcommittee of the United States Senate Committee on Interior and Insular Affairs," Tiborough said, his tone formal. "We are charged with obtaining expert opinion on proposed amendments to the Taylor Grazing Act of 1934. Today's hearing will begin with testimony and ... ah, questioning of a man whose family has been in the business of raising beef cattle in Oregon for three generations."

Tiborough smiled at the TV cameras.

The son of a bitch is playing to the galleries, Wallace thought. He glanced at Custer. The cattleman sat relaxed against the back of his chair, eyes half-lidded, staring at the senator.

"We call, as our first witness today, Mr. William R. Custer of Bend, Oregon," Tiborough said. "Will the clerk please swear in Mr. Custer?"

Custer moved forward to the "hot seat," placed his briefcase on the table. Wallace took a chair beside his client, noting how the cameras turned as the clerk stepped forward, put the Bible on the table, and administered the oath.

Tiborough ruffled through some papers in front of him, waited for full attention to return to him, then said, "This subcommittee ... we have before us a bill, this is a United States Senate bill entitled SB-1024 of the current session, an act amending the Taylor Grazing Act of 1934 and ... the intent is, as many have noted ... we would broaden the base of the advisory committees to the act and include a wider public representation."

Custer was fiddling with the clasp of his briefcase.

How the hell could that light gadget be an exhibit here? Wallace asked himself. He glanced at the set of Custer's jaw, noted again the determined confidence he'd seen in Custer's eyes. The sight failed to settle Wallace's own nerves.

"Ah, Mr. Custer," Tiborough said. "Do you ... did you bring a preliminary statement? Your counsel ..."

"I have a statement," Custer said. His big voice rumbled through the room, requiring instant attention and the shift of cameras that had been holding tardily on Tiborough, expecting an addition to the question.

Tiborough smiled, waited, then said, "Your attorney ... is your statement the one your counsel supplied the committee?"

"With some slight additions of my own," Custer said.

Wallace felt a sudden qualm. They were too willing to accept Custer's statement. He leaned close to his client's ear, whispered, "They know what your stand is. Skip the preliminaries."

Custer ignored him, said, "I intend to speak plainly and simply. I oppose the amendment. 'Broaden the base' and 'wider public representation' are phrases of political double-talk. The intent is to pack the committees, to put control of them into the hands of people who don't know the first thing about the cattle business and whose private intent is to destroy the Taylor Grazing Act itself."

"Plain, simple talk," Tiborough said. "This committee ... we welcome such directness. Strong words. A majority of this committee ... we have taken the position that the public range lands have been too long subjected to the tender mercies of the stockmen advisors, that the lands ... stockmen have exploited them to their own advantage."

The gloves are off, Wallace thought. *I hope Custer knows what he's doing. He's sure as hell not accepting advice.* Wallace glimpsed shiny metal in the case before the flap was closed.

Christ! That looked like a gun or something!

Then Wallace recognized the papers—the brief he and his staff had labored over ... and the preliminary statement. He noted with alarm the penciled markings and marginal notations. How could Custer have done that much to it in just twenty-four hours?

Again, Wallace whispered in Custer's ear, "Take it easy, Bill. The bastard's out for blood."

Custer nodded to show he had heard, glanced at the papers, and looked up directly at Tiborough.

A hush settled on the room, broken only by the scraping of a chair somewhere in the rear and the whirr of cameras.

"First, the nature of these lands we're talking about," Custer said. "In my state ..." He cleared his throat, a mannerism that would have indicated anger in the old man, his father. There was no break in Custer's expression, though, and his voice remained level. "... in my state, these were mostly Indian lands. This nation took them by brute force—right of conquest. That's about the oldest right in the world, I guess. I don't want to argue with it at this point."

"Mr. Custer." It was Nebraska's Senator Plowers, his amiable farmer's face set in a tight grin. "Mr. Custer, I hope ..."

"Is this a point of order?" Tiborough asked.

"Mr. Chairman," Plowers said, "I merely wished to make sure we weren't going to bring up that old suggestion about giving these lands back to the Indians."

Laughter shot across the hearing room. Tiborough chuckled.

Custer looked at Plowers, said, "No, Senator, I don't want to give these lands back to the Indians. When they had these lands, they only got about three hundred pounds of meat a year off eighty acres. We get five hundred pounds of the highest-grade protein—premium beef—from only ten acres."

"No one doubts the efficiency of your factorylike methods," Tiborough said. "You can ... we know your methods wring the largest amount of meat from a minimum acreage."

Ugh! Wallace thought. *That was a low blow—implying Bill's overgrazing and destroying the land value.*

"My neighbors, the Warm Springs Indians, use the same methods I do," Custer said. "They are happy to adopt our methods because we use the land while maintaining it and increasing its value. We don't permit the land to fall prey to natural disasters such as fire and erosion. We don't ..."

"No doubt your methods are meticulously correct," Tiborough said. "But I fail to see where ..."

"Has he ... has Mr. Custer finished his preliminary statement yet?" Senator Plowers asked.

Wallace shot a startled look at the Nebraskan. That was help from an unexpected quarter.

"Thank you, Senator," Custer said. "I'm quite willing to adapt to the Chairman's methods and explain the meticulous correctness of my operation. Our lowliest cowhands are college men, highly paid. We travel ten times as many jeep miles as we do horse miles. Every outlying division of the ranch—every holding pen and grazing supervisor's cabin—is linked to the central ranch by radio. We use the ..."

"I concede that your methods must be the most modern in—"

He broke off at a disturbance by the door. An Army colonel was talking to the guard there. He wore Special Services fourragere—Pentagon.

Wallace noted with an odd feeling of disquiet that the man was armed—a .45 at the hip. The weapon was out of place on him, as though he had added it suddenly in an emergency.

More guards were coming up outside the door now—Marines and Army. They carried rifles.

The colonel said something sharp to the guard, turned away from him, and entered the committee room. All the cameras were tracking him now. He ignored them, crossed swiftly to the Senator, and spoke swiftly into Tiborough's ear.

The senator shot a startled glance at Custer, accepted a sheaf of papers the colonel thrust at him. He forced his attention off Custer and studied the papers, leafing through them. Presently, he looked up, stared at Custer.

A hush fell over the room.

"I find myself at a loss, Mr. Custer," Tiborough said. "I have here a copy of a report ... it's from the Special Services branch of the Army ... through the Pentagon, you understand. It was just handed to me by, ah ... the colonel here."

He looked up at the colonel who was standing, one hand resting lightly on the holstered .45. Tiborough looked back at Custer, and it was obvious the senator was trying to marshal his thoughts.

"It is," Tiborough said, "that is ... this report supposedly ... and I have every confidence it is what it is represented to be ... here in my hands ... they say that ... uh, within the last few weeks there have been certain demonstrations on your lands. A new kind of weapon. According to the report ..." He glanced at the papers, back to Custer, who was staring at him steadily. "... this, uh, weapon, is a thing that ... it is extremely dangerous."

"It is," Custer said.

"I ... ah, see." Tiborough cleared his throat, glancing up at the colonel, who was staring fixedly at Custer. The senator brought his attention back to Custer.

"Do you, in fact, have such a weapon with you, Mr. Custer?" Tiborough asked.

"I have brought it as an exhibit, sir."

"Exhibit?"

"Yes, sir."

Wallace rubbed his lips, found them dry. He wet them with his tongue, wishing for the water glass, but it was on the other side of Custer. *Christ! That stupid cowpuncher!* He wondered if he dared whisper to Custer. Would the senators and that Pentagon lackey interpret such an action as meaning *he* was part of Custer's crazy antics, too?

"Are you threatening this committee with your weapon, Mr. Custer?" Tiborough asked. "If you are, I may say special precautions have been taken—extra guards on this room, and we ... that is, we will not allow ourselves to worry too much about any action you may take, but ordinary precautions are in force."

Wallace could no longer sit quietly. He tugged Custer's sleeve, got an abrupt shake of the head. He leaned close, whispered, "We could ask for a recess, Bill. Maybe we—"

"Don't interrupt me," Custer said. He looked at Tiborough. "Senator, I would not threaten you or any other man. Threats in the way you mean them are a thing we can no longer tolerate."

"You ... I believe you said this device is an exhibit," Tiborough said. He cast a worried frown at the report in his hands. "I fail ... it does not appear germane."

Senator Plowers cleared his throat. "Mr. Chairman," he said.

"The chair recognizes the Senator from Nebraska," Tiborough said, and the relief in his voice was obvious. He wanted time to think.

"Mr. Custer," Plowers said, "I have not seen the report, the report my distinguished colleague alludes to; however, if I may ... is it your wish to use this committee as some kind of publicity device?"

"By no means, Senator," Custer said. "I don't wish to profit by my presence here—not at all."

Tiborough had apparently come to a decision. He leaned back and whispered to the colonel, who nodded and returned to the outer hall.

"You strike me as an eminently reasonable man, Mr. Custer," Tiborough said. "If I may ..."

"May I?" Senator Plowers said. "May I—just permit me to conclude this one point. May we have the Special Services report in the record?"

"Certainly," Tiborough said. "But I was about to suggest ..."

"May I?" Plowers said. "May I—would you permit me, please, Mr. Chairman, to make this point clear for the record?"

Tiborough scowled, but the heavy dignity of the Senate overcame his irritation. "Please continue, Senator. I had thought you were finished."

"I respect ... there is no doubt in my mind of Mr. Custer's sincerity and integrity." His tone and expression made him look grandfatherly, a kindly elder statesman. "I would like, therefore, to have him explain how this ... ah, weapon, can be an exhibit in the matter before our committee."

Wallace glanced at Custer, saw the hard set to the man's jaw, and realized the cattleman had gotten to Plowers somehow. This was a set piece.

Tiborough was glancing at the other senators, weighing the advisability of high-handed dismissal ... perhaps a star-chamber session. No ... they were all too curious about Custer's device, his purpose here.

The thoughts were plain on the senator's face.

"Very well," Tiborough said. He nodded to Custer. "You may proceed, Mr. Custer."

"During last winter's slack season," Custer said, "two of my men and I worked on a project we've had in the works for three years—to develop a sustained-emission laser device."

Custer opened his briefcase, slid out a fat aluminum tube mounted on a pistol grip with a conventional-looking trigger.

"This is quite harmless," he said. "I didn't bring the power pack."

"That is ... this is your weapon?" Tiborough asked.

"Calling this a weapon is misleading," Custer said. "The term limits and oversimplifies. This is also a brush cutter, a substitute for a logger's saw and axe, a diamond cutter, a milling machine ... and a weapon. It is also a turning point in history."

"Come now, isn't that a bit pretentious?" Tiborough asked.

"We tend to think of history as something old and slow," Custer said. "But history is, as a matter of fact, extremely swift. Think of the sudden turning points: an atomic bomb explodes over a city, a dam breaks, or a revolutionary device is announced."

"Lasers have been known for quite a few years," Tiborough said. He looked at the papers the colonel had given him. "The principle dates from 1956 or thereabouts."

"I don't wish it to appear that I'm taking credit for inventing this device," Custer said. "Nor am I claiming sole credit for developing the sustained-emission laser. I was merely one of a team. But I do hold the device here in my hand, gentlemen."

"Exhibit, Mr. Custer," Plowers reminded him. "How is this an exhibit?"

"May I explain first how it works?" Custer asked. "That will make the rest of my statement much easier."

Tiborough looked at Plowers, then back to Custer. "If you will tie this all together, Mr. Custer," Tiborough said. "I want to ... the bearing of this device on our—we are hearing a particular bill in this room."

"Certainly, Senator," Custer said. "A ninety-volt radio battery drives this particular model. We have some that require less voltage, some that use more. We aimed for a construction of simple parts. Our crystals are common quartz. We shattered them by bringing them to a boil in water and then plunging them into ice water ... repeatedly. We chose twenty pieces of very close to the same size—about one gram, slightly more than fifteen grains each."

Custer unscrewed the back of the tube, slid out a round length of plastic trailing lengths of red, green, brown, blue, and yellow wire.

Wallace noted how the cameras of the TV men centered on the inner workings of the device.

We're gadget-crazy people, Wallace thought.

"The crystals were dipped in thinned household cement and then into iron filings," Custer said. "We made a little jig out of a fly-tying vise and opened a passage in the filings at opposite ends of the crystals. We then made some common celluloid—nitrocellulose, acetic acid, gelatin, and alcohol—all very common products, and formed it in a length of garden hose just long enough to take the crystals end to end. The crystals were inserted in the hose, the celluloid poured over them, and the whole thing was seated in a magnetic waveguide while the celluloid was cooling. This centered and aligned the crystals. The waveguide was constructed from wire salvaged from an old TV set and built following the directions in the Radio Amateur's Handbook."

Custer re-inserted the length of plastic into the tube, adjusted the wires. There was an unearthly silence in the room with only the cameras whirring. It was as though everyone were holding his breath.

"A laser requires a resonant cavity, but that's complicated," Custer said. "Instead, we wound two layers of fine copper wire around our tube, immersed it in the celluloid solution to coat it, and then filed one end flat. This end took a piece of mirror cut to fit. We then pressed a number eight embroidery needle at right angles into the mirror end of the tube until it touched the side of the number one crystal."

Custer cleared his throat.

Two of the senators leaned back. Plowers coughed. Tiborough looked at the banks of TV cameras, and there was a questioning look in his eyes.

"We then calibrated the system using a standard oscilloscope, but any radio amateur could do it without the oscilloscope. We constructed an oscillator of that master frequency, attached it at the needle and a bare spot scraped in the opposite edge of the waveguide."

"And this ... ah ... worked?" Tiborough asked.

"No." Custer shook his head. "When we fed power through a voltage multiplier into the system, we produced an estimated four hundred–joule emission and melted half the tube. So we started all over again."

"You are going to tie this in?" Tiborough asked. He frowned at the papers in his hands, glanced toward the door where the colonel had gone.

"I am, sir, believe me," Custer said.

"Very well, then," Tiborough said.

"So we started all over," Custer said. "But for the second celluloid dip we added bismuth—a saturated solution, actually. It stayed gummy, and we had to paint over it with a sealing coat of the straight celluloid. We then coupled this bismuth layer through a pulse circuit so that it was bathed in a counter wave—180 degrees out of phase with the master frequency. We had, in effect, immersed the unit in a thermoelectric cooler that exactly countered the heat production. A thin beam issued from the unmirrored end when we powered it. We have yet to find something that thin beam cannot cut."

"Diamonds?" Tiborough asked.

"Powered by less than two hundred volts, this device could cut our planet in half like a ripe tomato," Custer said. "One man could destroy an aerial armada with it, knock down ICBMs before they touched the atmosphere, sink a fleet, pulverize tanks. One has to boggle at the enormous power focused in ..."

"Shut down those TV cameras!"

It was Tiborough shouting, leaping to his feet and making a sweeping gesture to include the banks of cameras. The abrupt violence of his voice and gesture fell on the room like an explosion. "Guards!" he called. "You there, at the door. Cordon off that door and don't let anyone out of here! Where's that damn colonel? Oh, there you are! Clear those halls, but don't let anyone out who heard this fool!" He whirled back to face Custer. "You irresponsible idiot!"

"I'm afraid, Senator," Custer said, "that you're locking the barn door many weeks too late."

For a long minute of silence, Tiborough glared at Custer. Then: "You did this deliberately, eh?"

"Senator, if I'd waited any longer, there might have been no hope for us at all."

Tiborough sank back into his chair, still keeping his attention fastened on Custer. Plowers and Johnstone on his right had their heads close together, whispering fiercely. The other senators were dividing their attention between Custer and Tiborough, their eyes wide and with no attempt to conceal their astonishment.

Wallace, growing conscious of the implications in what Custer had said, tried to wet his lips with his tongue. *Christ!* he thought. *This stupid cowpoke has sold us all down the river!*

Tiborough signaled an aide, spoke briefly with him, then beckoned the colonel from the door. There was a buzzing of excited conversation in the room. Several of the press and TV crew were huddled near the windows on Custer's left, arguing. One tried to leave, but he was stopped by a committee aide. They began a low-voiced argument with violent gestures.

A loud curse sounded from the door. Paxman, the syndicated columnist, was trying to push past the guards there.

"Paxman!" Tiborough called. The columnist turned. "My orders are that no one leaves," Tiborough said. "You are not an exception." He turned back to face Custer.

The room had fallen into a semblance of quiet, although there were still pockets of muttering, and there was the sound of running feet and a hurrying about in the hall outside.

"Two channels went out of here live," Tiborough said. "Nothing much we can do about them, although we will trace down as many of their viewers as we can. Every bit of film in this room and every sound tape will be confiscated, however." His voice rose as protests sounded from the press section. "Our national security is at stake. The president has been notified. Such measures as are necessary will be taken."

The colonel came hurrying into the room, crossed to Tiborough, said something in a low voice.

"You should've warned me!" Tiborough snapped. "I had no idea that—" The colonel interrupted with a whispered comment.

"These papers—your damned report is *not* clear!" Tiborough said. He looked around at Custer. "I see you're smiling, Mr. Custer. I don't think you'll find much to smile about before long."

"Senator, this is not a happy smile," Custer said. "But I told myself several days ago that you'd fail to see the implications of this thing." He tapped the pistol-shaped device he had brought as an exhibit. "I knew you'd fall into the old, useless pattern."

"Is that what you told yourself? Really?" Tiborough said.

Wallace, hearing the venom in the Senator's voice, moved his chair a few inches farther away from Custer.

Tiborough looked at the laser projector. "Is that thing really disarmed?"

"Yes, sir."

"If I order one of my men to take it from you, you will not resist?"

"Which of your men will you trust with it, Senator?" Custer asked.

In the long silence that followed, someone in the press section emitted a nervous guffaw.

"Virtually every man on my ranch has one of these things," Custer said. "We fell trees with them, cut firewood, and make fence posts. Every letter written to me as a result of my patent application has been answered candidly. More than a thousand sets of schematics and instructions on how to build this device have been sent out to various places in the world."

"You vicious traitor!" Tiborough rasped.

"You're certainly entitled to your opinion, Senator," Custer said. "But I warn you, I've had time for considerably more and considerably more painful thought than you've applied to this problem. In my estimation, I had no choice. Every week I waited to make this thing public—every day, every minute—merely raised the odds that humanity would be destroyed by—"

"You said this thing applied to the hearings on the grazing act," Plowers protested, and there was a plaintive note in his voice, as if he hoped to get back to normal business.

"Senator, I told you the truth," Custer said. "There's no real reason to change the act now. We intend to go on operating under it—with the agreement of our neighbors and others concerned. People are still going to need food."

Tiborough glared at him. "You're saying we can't force you to …" He broke off at a disturbance in the doorway. A rope barrier had been stretched there, and a line of Marines stood with their backs to it, facing the hall. A mob of people was trying to press through. Press cards were being waved.

"Colonel, I told you to clear that hall!" Tiborough barked.

The colonel ran to the barrier. "Use your bayonets if you have to!" he shouted.

The disturbance subsided at the sound of his voice. More uniformed men could be seen moving in along the barrier. Presently, the noise receded.

Tiborough turned back to Custer. "You make Benedict Arnold look like the greatest friend the United States ever had," he said.

"Cursing me isn't going to help you," Custer said. "You are going to have to live with this thing, so you'd better try understanding it."

"That appears to be simple," Tiborough said. "All I have to do is send twenty-five cents to the patent office for the schematics and then write you a letter."

"The world already was headed toward suicide," Custer said. "Only fools failed to realize—"

"So you decided to give us a little push," Tiborough said.

"H.G. Wells warned us," Custer said. "That's how far back it goes, but nobody listened. It's a simple and obvious graph. The growth curve on the amount of raw energy becoming available to humans—and the diminishing curve on the number of persons required to use that energy. For a long time now, more and more violent power was being made available to fewer and fewer people. It was only a matter of time until total destruction was put into the hands of single individuals."

"And you didn't think you could take your government into your confidence," Tiborough said. "You thought you were some kind of god, eh?"

There's the question that'll hang him, Wallace thought.

"The government was already committed to a political course diametrically opposite the one this device requires," Custer said. "Virtually every man in the government has a vested interest in not reversing that course. It was obvious from the few people in government that I did query that they couldn't distinguish between truth and personal advantage."

"So you set yourself above the government?" Tiborough demanded.

"I'm probably wasting my time," Custer said, "but I'll try to explain it. Virtually every government in the world is dedicated to manipulating something called the 'mass man.' That's how governments have stayed in power. But there is no such man. When you elevate the non-existent 'mass man,' you degrade the individual. And obviously, it was only a matter of time until all of us were at the mercy of the individual."

"You talk like a goddamn commie!" Tiborough snapped.

"They'll say I'm a goddamn capitalist pawn," Custer said. "Let me ask you, Senator, to visualize a poor radio technician in a South American country. Brazil, for example. He lives an imaginative, essentially unseen existence. What is he going to do when this device comes into his hands?"

"Murder, robbery, and anarchy," Tiborough growled.

"You could be right," Custer said. "But we might reach an understanding out of ultimate necessity—that each of us must cooperate in maintaining the dignity of all."

Tiborough stared at him, began to speak musingly. "We'll have to control the essential materials for constructing this thing ... and there may be trouble for awhile, but—"

"You're a vicious fool," Custer said.

In the cold silence that followed, Custer said, "It was too late to try that ten years ago. I'm telling you that this thing can be patchworked out of a wide variety of materials that are already scattered over the earth. It can be made in basements and mud huts, in palaces and shacks. The key item is the crystal, but other crystals will work, too. That's obvious. A patient man can grow crystals ... and this world is full of patient men, Senator."

"I'm going to place you under arrest," Tiborough said. "You have outraged every rule of decency and—"

"You're living in a dream world," Custer said. "I refuse to threaten you, but I'll defend myself from any attempt to oppress or degrade me. If I cannot defend myself, my friends will defend me. No man who understands what this device means will permit his dignity to be taken from him. In other words, Senator, you can no longer threaten anyone with impunity."

Custer allowed a moment for his words to sink in, then added, "And don't twist these words to imply a threat. Refusal to threaten a fellow human is an absolute requirement in the day that has just dawned on us."

"A single man is powerful with this thing. A hundred are ..."

"All previous insults aside," Custer said, "I think you are a highly intelligent man, Senator. I ask you to think long and hard about this device. Use of power is no longer the deciding factor because one man is as powerful as a million. Restraint—*self*-restraint—is now the key to survival. Each of us is at the mercy of his neighbor's good will. Each of us, Senator—the man in the palace and the man in the shack. We'd better do all we can to increase that goodwill—not attempting to buy it, but simply recognizing that individual dignity is the one inalienable right of—"

"Don't you preach at me, you commie traitor!" Tiborough rasped. "You're a living example of—"

"Senator!"

It was one of the TV cameramen in the left rear of the room. Wallace turned, stared at the man—a tall, blond man standing on a ledge beside his silenced camera.

"Let's stop insulting Mr. Custer and hear him out," the cameraman said.

"Get that man's name," Tiborough told an aide. "If he—"

"I'm an expert electronics technician, Senator," the man said. "You can't threaten me anymore."

Custer smiled, turned to face Tiborough.

"The revolution begins," Custer said. He waved a hand as the Senator started to whirl away. "Sit down, Senator."

Wallace, watching the Senator obey, saw how the balance of control had changed in the room.

"Ideas are in the wind," Custer said. "There comes a time for a thing to develop. It comes into being. The spinning jenny came into being because it was its time. There are many other examples in history. This is just the next step."

"What have you done?"

Tiborough's voice was subdued, and Wallace noted that the Senator had his full attention focused on Custer.

"It was bound to come," Custer said. "But the number of people in our world who're filled with hate and frustration and violence has been growing with terrible speed. You add to that the enormous danger that this might fall into the hands of just one group or nation or ..." Custer shrugged. "This is too much power to be confined to one man or group with the hope they'll administer it wisely. I didn't dare delay. That's why I spread this thing now and announced it as broadly as I could."

Tiborough leaned back in his chair, his hands in his lap. His face was pale, and beads of perspiration stood out on his forehead.

"We won't make it," he muttered.

"I hope you're wrong, Senator," Custer said. "But the only thing I know for sure is that we'd have had less chance of making it tomorrow than we have today."

THE DADDY BOX

[This story recently appeared in The Collected Stories of Frank Herbert, *Tor Books, 2014.]*

To understand what happened to Henry Alexander when his son, Billy, came home with the ferosslk, you're going to be asked to make several mind-stretching mental adjustments. These mental gymnastics are certain to leave your mind permanently changed.

You've been warned.

In the first place, just to get a loose idea of a ferosslk's original purpose, you must think of it as a toy designed primarily for educating the young. But your concept of *toy* should be modified to think of a device which, under special circumstances, will play with its owner.

You'll also have to modify your concept of education to include the idea of occasionally altering the universe to fit a new interesting idea; that is, fitting the universe to the concept, rather than fitting the concept to the universe.

The ferosslk originates with seventh-order multidimensional beings. You can think of them as *Sevens*. Their other labels would be more or less incomprehensible. The Sevens are not now aware and never have been aware that the universe contains any such thing as a Henry Alexander or his human male offspring.

This oversight was rather unfortunate for Henry. His mind had never been stretched to contain the concept of a ferosslk. He could conceive of fission bombs, nerve gas, napalm, and germ warfare. But these things might be thought of as silly putty when compared with a ferosslk.

Which is a rather neat analogy because the shape of a ferosslk is profoundly dependent upon external pressures. That is to say, although a ferosslk can be conceived of as an artifact, it is safer to think of it as alive.

To begin at one of the beginnings, Billy Alexander, age eight, human male, found the ferosslk in tall weeds beside a path across an empty lot adjoining his urban home.

Saying he "found" it described the circumstances from Billy's superficial point of view. It would be just as accurate to say the ferosslk found Billy.

As far as Billy was concerned, the ferosslk was a box. You may as well think of it that way, too. No sense stretching your mind completely out of shape. You wouldn't be able to read the rest of this account.

A box, then. It appeared to be about nine inches long, three inches wide, and four inches deep. It looked like dark green stone except for what was obviously the top, because that's where the writing appeared.

You can call it writing because Billy was just beginning to shift from print to cursive and that's the way he saw it.

Words flowed across the box top: "This is a daddy box."

Billy picked it up. The surface was cold under his hands. He thought perhaps this was some kind of toy television, its words projected from inside.

(Some of the words actually were coming out of Billy's own mind.)

Daddy box? he wondered.

Daddy was a symbol-identifier more than five years old for him. His *daddy* had been killed in a war. Now Billy had a stepfather with the same name as his real father's. The two had been cousins.

New information flowed across the top: "This box may be opened only by the young."

(That was a game the ferosslk had played and enjoyed many times before. Don't try to imagine how a ferosslk enjoys. The attempt could injure your frontal lobes.)

Now the box top provided Billy with precise instructions on how it could be opened.

Billy went through the indicated steps, which included urinating on an anthill, and the box dutifully opened.

For almost an hour, Billy sat in the empty lot, enraptured by the educational/creative tableau thus unveiled. For his edification, human shapes in the box fought wars, manufactured artifacts, made love, wrote books, created paintings and sculpture … and changed the universe. The human shapes debated, formed governments, nurtured the earth, and destroyed it.

In that relative time of little less than an hour, Billy aged mentally some five hundred and sixteen human years. On the outside, Billy remained a male child about forty-nine inches tall, weight approximately fifty-six pounds, skin white but grimy from play, hair blond and mussed.

His eyes were still blue, but they had acquired a hard and penetrating stare. The motor cells in his medulla and his spinal cord had begun increasing dramatically in number with an increased myelinization of the anterior roots and peripheral nerves.

Every normal sense he possessed had been increased in potency, and he was embarked on a growth pattern that would further heighten this effect.

The whole thing made him sad, but he knew what he had to do, having come very close to understanding what a ferosslk was all about.

It was now about 6:18 PM on a Friday evening. Billy took the box in both hands and trudged across the lot toward his back door.

His mother, whose left arm still bore bruises from a blow struck by her husband, was peeling potatoes at the kitchen sink. She was a small blonde woman, once doll-like, fast turning to mouse.

At Billy's entrance, she shook tears out of her eyes, smiled at him, glanced toward the living room, and shook her head—all in one continuous movement. She appeared not to notice the box in Billy's hands, but she did note the boy appeared very much like his real father tonight.

This thought brought more tears to her eyes, and she turned away, thus failing to see Billy go on into the living room despite her silent warning that his stepfather was there and in a bad mood.

The ferosslk, having shared Billy's emotional reaction to this moment, created a new order of expletives, which it introduced into another dimension.

Henry Alexander sensed Billy's presence in the room, lowered the evening newspaper, and stared over it into the boy's newly aged eyes. Henry was a pale-skinned, flabby man, going to fat after a youth spent as a semiprofessional athlete. He interpreted the look in Billy's eyes as a reflection of their mutual hate.

"What's that box?" Henry demanded.

Billy shrugged. "It's a daddy box."

"A what?"

Billy remained silent, placed the box to his ear. The ferosslk had converted to faint audio mode, and the voices coming from the box for Billy's ears alone carried a certain suggestive educational quality.

"Why're you holding the damn thing against your ear?" Henry demanded. He had already decided to take the box away from the boy but was drawing the pleasure-moment out.

"I'm listening," Billy said. He sensed the precise pacing of these moments, observed minute nuances in the set of his stepfather's jaw, the content of the man's perspiration.

"Is it a music box?"

Henry studied the thing in Billy's hand. It looked old ... ancient, even. He couldn't quite say why he felt this.

Again, Billy shrugged.

"Where'd you get it?" Henry asked.

"I found it."

"Where could you find a thing like that? It looks like a real antique. Might even be jade."

"I found it in the lot." Billy hesitated on the point of adding a precise location to where he'd found the box but held back. That would be out of character.

"Are you sure you didn't steal it?"

"I found it."

"Don't you sass me!" Henry threw his newspaper to the floor.

Having heard the loud voices, Billy's mother hurried into the living room, hovered behind her son.

"What's ... what's the matter?" she ventured.

"You stay out of this, Helen!" Henry barked. "That brat of yours has stolen a valuable antique, and he—"

"China? He wouldn't!"

"I told you to stay out of this!" Henry glared at her. The box had assumed for him now exactly the quality he had just given it: valuable antique. Theft was as good as certain—although that might complicate his present plans for confiscation and profit.

Billy suppressed a smile. His mother's interruption, which he assumed to be fortuitous since he did not completely understand the functioning of a ferosslk, had provided just the delay required here. The situation had entered the timing system for which he had maneuvered.

"Bring that box here," Henry ordered.

"It's mine," Billy said. As he said it, he experienced a flash of insight that told him he belonged as much to the box as it belonged to him.

"Look here, you disrespectful brat—if you don't give me that box immediately, we're going to have another session in the woodshed!"

Billy's mother touched his arm, said, "Son ... you'd better ..."

"Okay," Billy said. "But it's just a trick box—like those Chinese things."

"I said bring it here, dammit!"

Clutching the box to his chest now, Billy crossed the room, timing his movements with careful precision. Just a few more seconds ... now!

He extended the box to his stepfather.

Henry snatched the ferosslk, was surprised at how cold it felt. Obviously stone. Cold stone. He turned the thing over and over in his hands. There were strange markings on the top—wedges, curves, twisting designs. He put it to his ear, listened.

Silence.

Billy smiled.

Henry jerked the box away from his ear. Trick, eh? The kid was playing a trick on him, trying to make him look like a fool.

"So it's a box," Henry said. "Have you opened it?"

"Yes. It's got lots of things inside."

"Things? What things?"

"Just things."

Henry had an immediate vision of valuable jewels. This thing could be a jewel box.

"How does it open?" he demanded.

"You just do things," Billy said.

"Don't you play smart with me! I gave you an order: tell me how you open this thing."

"I can't."

"You mean you won't!"

"I can't."

"Why?" It was as much an accusation as a question.

Again, Billy shrugged. "The box ... well, it can only be opened by kids."

"Oh, for Chrissakes!" Henry examined the ends of the box. Damn kid was lying about having opened it. Henry shook the box. It rattled suggestively, one of the ferosslk's better effects.

Helen said, "Perhaps if you let Billy ..."

Henry looked up long enough to stare her down, then asked, "Is dinner ready?"

"Henry, he's just a child!"

"Woman, I've worked all day to support you and your brat. Is this the appreciation I get?"

She backed toward the kitchen door, hesitated there.

Henry returned his attention to the box. He pushed at the end panels. Nothing happened. He tried various pressures on the top, the sides, and the bottom.

"So you opened it, eh?" Henry asked, staring across the box at Billy.

"Yes."

"You're lying."

"I opened it."

Having achieved the effect he wanted, Henry thrust the box toward Billy. "Then open it."

Having achieved one of the moments he wanted, and right on time, Billy went for the effect. He turned the box over, slid an end panel aside, whipped the top open and closed it, then restored the end panel and presented the closed box to Henry.

"See? It's easy."

The ferosslk, having achieved an education node, convinced Henry that he'd seen gold and jewels during the brief moment when the box had been opened.

Henry grabbed the box, wet his lips with his tongue. He pushed at the end panel. It refused to move.

"Grown-ups can't open it," Billy said. "It says so right on the top."

Henry brought a claspknife from his hip pocket, opened it, and tried to find an opening around the top of the box.

Billy stared at him.

Billy's mother still hovered fearfully in the kitchen doorway.

Henry had the sudden realization that they both hoped he'd cut himself. He closed the knife, returned it to his pocket, and extended the box toward Billy. "Open it for me."

"I can't."

Ominously, Henry asked, "And ... why ... not?"

"I can't let go of it when it's open."

The ferosslk inserted a sense of doubt into the situation here without Billy suspecting. Henry nodded. That just might be true. The box might have a spring lock that closed when you let go of it.

"Then open it and let me look inside while you hold it," Henry said.

"I can't now without doing all the other things."

"What?"

"I can open it twice without the other things, but ..."

"What other things?"

"Oh ... like finding a grass seed and breaking a twig ... and I'd have to find another anthill. The one I—"

"Of all the damn fool nonsense!" Henry thrust the box towards Billy. "Open this!"

"I can't!"

Billy's mother said, "Henry, why don't you—"

"Helen, you get the hell out of here and let me handle this!"

She backed farther into the kitchen.

Henry said, "Billy, either you open this box for me, or I'll open it the hard way with an axe."

Billy shook his head from side to side, dragging out the moment for its proper curve.

"Very well." Henry heaved himself from the chair, the box clutched in his right hand, angry elation filling him. They'd done it again—goaded him beyond endurance.

He brushed past Billy, who turned and followed him. He thrust Helen aside when she put out a pleading hand. He strode out the back door, slamming it behind him, then heard it open, the patter of Billy's footsteps following.

Let the brat make one protest! Just one!

Henry set his jaw, headed across the backyard toward the woodshed—that anachronism that set the tone and marked the age of this house—"modest older home in quiet residential area."

Now Billy called from behind him, "What're you going to do?"

Henry stifled an angry retort, caught by an odd note in Billy's voice ... an imperative.

"Daddy?" Billy called.

Henry stopped at the woodshed door, glanced back. Billy never called him *daddy*. The boy stood in the path from the house; his mother waited on the back porch.

Now, why was I angry with them? Henry wondered.

He felt the box in his hand, looked at it. Jewels? In this dirty green little piece of stoneware? He was filled with the sense of his own foolishness, an effect achieved by a sophisticated refinement of ferosslk educational processing. Given a possible lesson to impart, the instructor could not resist the opportunity.

Once more, Henry looked at the two who watched him.

They'd done this deliberately to make him appear foolish! Damn them!

"Daddy, don't break the box," Billy said.

It was a nicely timed protest, and it demonstrated how well he had learned from the ferosslk.

His anger restored, Henry whirled away, slammed the box onto the woodshed's chopping block, and grabbed up the axe.

Don't break the box!

"Wait!" Billy called.

Henry barely hesitated, a lapse which put him in the precise phasing Billy wanted.

Taking careful aim, Henry brought the axe hissing down. He still felt foolish because it's difficult to shake off a ferosslk lesson, but anger carried him through.

At the instant of contact between blade and box, an electric glimmer leaped into existence around the axe head.

To Billy, watching from the yard, the blade appeared to slice into the box, shrinking, shining, drawing inward at an impossible angle. There came an abrupt, juicy vacuum-popping noise—a cow pulling its foot out of the mud. The axe handle whipped into the box after the blade, vanished with a diminishing glimmer.

Still clutching the axe handle, Henry Alexander was jerked into the box—down, down ... shrinking ...

Whoosh!

The pearl glimmering winked out. The box remained on the chopping block where Henry had placed it.

Billy darted into the woodshed, grabbed up the box, and pressed it to his left ear. From far away came a leaf-whispering babble of many angry and pleading voices. He could distinguish some of the names being called by those voices—

"Abdul!"

"Terrik!"

"Churudish!"

"Pablo!"

"James!"

"Sremani!"

"Harold!"

And, on a low and diminishing wail, "Bill-eeeeeeeeeee ..."

Having taught part of a lesson, the ferosslk recognized that the toy-plus-play element remained incomplete. By attaching a label at the proper moment, Billy had achieved a daddy-linkage, but no daddy existed now for all practical purposes. There were voices, of course, and certain essences—an available gene pattern from which to reconstruct the original. Something with the proper daddyness loomed as a distinct possibility, and the ferosslk observed an attractive learning pattern in the idea.

A golden glow began to emerge from one end of the box. Billy dropped it and backed away as the glow grew and grew and grew. Abruptly, the glow coalesced, and Henry Alexander emerged.

Billy felt a hand clutch his shoulder, looked up at his mother. The box lay on the ground near the chopping block. She looked from it to the figure that had emerged from it.

"Billy," she demanded, "what ... what happened?"

Henry stooped, recovered the box.

"Henry," she said, "you hit that box with the axe, but it's not broken."

"Huh?" Henry Alexander stared at her. "What're you talking about? I brought the damn thing out here to make sure it was safe for Billy to play with."

He thrust the box at Billy, who took it and almost dropped it. "Here—take it, son."

"But Billy was pestering you," she said. "You said you'd ..."

"Helen, you nag the boy too much," Henry said. "He's just a boy, and boys will be boys." Henry winked at Billy. "Eh, son?" Henry reached over and mussed Billy's hair.

Helen backed up, releasing Billy's shoulder. She said, "But you ... it looked like you went into the box!"

Henry looked at the box, then at Helen. He began to laugh. "Girl, it's a good thing you got a man who loves you, because you are weird. You are really weird." He stepped around Billy, took Helen gently by the arm. "C'mon, I'll help you with dinner."

She allowed herself to be guided toward the house, her attention fixed on Henry.

Billy heard him say, "Y'know, honey, I think Billy could use a brother or a sister. What do you say?"

"Henry!"

Henry's laughter came rich and happy. He stopped, turned around to look at Billy, who stood in the woodshed doorway, holding the box.

"Stay where you can hear me call, Bill. Maybe we'll go to a movie after dinner, eh?"

Billy nodded.

"Hey," Henry called, "what're y' going to do with that funny box?"

Billy stared across the empty lot to the home of his friend Jimmy Carter. He took a deep breath, said, "Jimmy's got a catcher's mitt he's been trying to trade me. Maybe he'd trade for the box."

"Hey!" Henry said. "Maybe he would at that. But look out Jimmy's old man doesn't catch you at it. You know what a temper he has."

"I sure do," Billy said. "I sure do … Dad."

Henry put his arm around Helen's shoulder and headed once more for the house. "Hear that?" he asked. "Hear him call me *Dad*? Y'know, Helen, nothing makes a man happier than to have a boy call him *Dad*."

If You Liked ...

If you liked *Unpublished Short Stories*, you might also enjoy:

Man of Two Worlds
Brian Herbert & Frank Herbert

Four Unpublished Novels
by Frank Herbert

ABOUT THE AUTHOR

Frank Herbert (1920–1986) created the most beloved novel in the annals of science fiction, *Dune*. He was a man of many facets, of countless passageways that ran through an intricate mind. His magnum opus is a reflection of this—a classic work that stands as one of the most complex, multilayered novels ever written in any genre. Today the novel is more popular than ever, with new readers continually discovering it and telling their friends to pick up a copy. It has been translated into dozens of languages and has sold almost twenty million copies.

His major novels included *The Dragon in the Sea*, *Soul Catcher* (his only non–science fiction novel), *Destination: Void*, *The Santaroga Barrier*, *The Green Brain*, *Hellstrom's Hive*, *Whipping Star*, *The Eyes of Heisenberg*, *The Godmakers*, *Direct Descent*, and *The Heaven Makers*. He also collaborated with Bill Ransom to write *The Jesus Incident*, *The Lazarus Effect*, and *The Ascension Factor*. Frank Herbert's last published novel, *Man of Two Worlds*, was a collaboration with his son, Brian.

OTHER WORDFIRE PRESS TITLES BY FRANK HERBERT

Destination: Void
Direct Descent
Four Unpublished Novels
A Game of Authors
The Godmakers
The Heaven Makers
Pandora Sequence 1: The Jesus Incident
Pandora Sequence 2: The Lazarus Effect
Pandora Sequence 3: The Ascension Factor

Frank Herbert & Brian Herbert

Man of Two Worlds

Frank Herbert & Bill Ransom

Soul Catcher

Our list of other WordFire Press authors and titles is always growing.
To find out more and to see our selection of titles, visit us at:

wordfirepress.com

Made in the USA
Middletown, DE
11 July 2022

68995127R00177